the Idler

ISSUE 27 | WINTER 2000

First published in Great Britain in 2000 by
Idle Limited
Studio 20, 24 - 28a Hatton Wall
London EC1N 8JH
Tel: 020 7691 0320
Fax: 020 7691 0321
e-mail: admin@idler.co.uk

ISBN 0-9536720-2-6

....

Editor: Tom Hodgkinson
Creative Director: Gavin Pretor-Pinney
Deputy Editor: Matthew De Abaitua
Designers: Sonia Alcon-Ortiz, James Goggin
Researcher: Dan Kieran
Literary Editor: Tony White
Contributing Editors: Greg Rowland, Joshua Glenn
Sports Editor: John Moore
Editorial Assistant: Sam Jordison
Cover illustration: Joe Harrison
Advertising: Jamie Dwelly at Cabbell 020 8971 8450

Sir, I admit your gen'ral Rule
That every Poet is a Fool:
But you yourself may serve to show it,
That every Fool is not a Poet.

Alexander Pope, 1732

Grand Order of Idlers

SUBSCRIBE NOW

JUST £20 A YEAR

When you subscribe to the *Idler*, you become more than just a subscriber. You become a member of the Grand Order of Idlers.

Once you have joined this august order, you will be entitled to a these benefits:

> *Two issues of the Idler sent to your door every year*
> *A free Idler snail tattoo*
> *A Grand Order of Idlers membership certificate*
> *Occasional mailings*
> *Invitations to Idler events and parties*

To join The Grand Order of Idlers, simply send us a cheque for £20, made payabe to "The Idler", and a note reading "I want to join you!"

Our address is:
The Idler, Studio 20,
24-28a Hatton Wall, London EC1N 8JH

Or call our credit card hotline on 020 7691 0319

Or simply visit our website's shop and do the e-com thing idler.co.uk

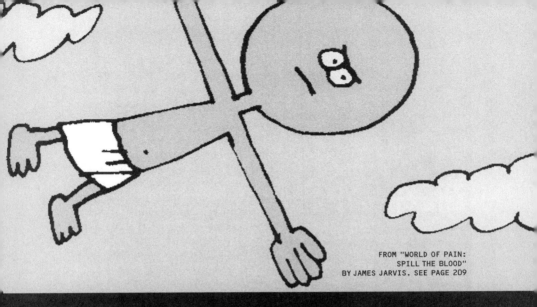

FROM "WORLD OF PAIN:
SPILL THE BLOOD"
BY JAMES JARVIS. SEE PAGE 209

CONTENTS THE IDLER, ISSUE 27, WINTER 2000

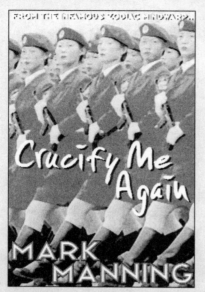

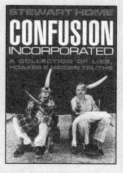
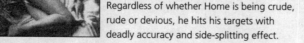

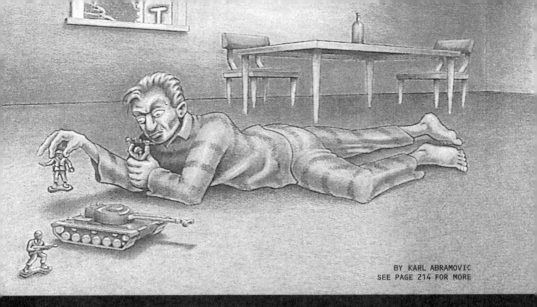

BY KARL ABRAMOVIC
SEE PAGE 214 FOR MORE

MORE CONTENTS

EDITOR'S LETTER

Portrait of editor TOM HODGKINSON by HANNAH DYSON

Has the Idler's time finally come? Has the appointed hour arrived, when the lollards, lollygags, loafers and loungers will rise and inherit the earth? We have been patient since our first issue made its modest appearance back in 1993. We have been slow, like the ox. We have led a small band of believers through hard times. You have stuck with us, for this we thank you.

The reason I ask is that the mainstream media seem to have been agreeing recently that a new view of work is called for. I'm thinking of Channel 4's Stop, Go Home season, a set of programmes designed to encourage a culture dedicated to working fewer hours in the week, not more. I'm thinking also of the Observer's "Play Ethic" feature, where pop star/academic Pat Kane proposes introducing the idea of play into the workplace. I'm thinking also – even – of George W Bush's recent admission that he works only six hours a day (see Skivers and Strivers). Certainly, I don't see much evidence of idling on the left. An exhausted cabinet, destroyed by their own work ethic, is clearly making a lot of mistakes, probably due to their own tiredness. It would surely be better for all of us if they did a lot less.

So, if it really is happening that the idle life is gaining credence as an aspiration, then it should be possible for idlers to start to profit. Businesses pay constant lip-service to creativity and innovation, yet they still keep their workers shackled to their posts. Industrious ants still walk the corridors of power. But when was the last time you heard a good idea from an ant? What business lacks is thinkers, and an idler is nothing if not a thinker.

So we encounter another idler's dilemma: to free ourselves from the dreary forces of "insect authority", as Mark Twain put it, do we need to embrace commerce and tout oursleves around the big payers?

Or do we retreat from capitalism and into our own little worlds?

As always, your thoughts are welcome.

And so to this issue: the theme is the Fool, and you'll find here reflections on the theme from regular writers and guests, plus new stories. We're also proud to present an illustration-only issue, an idea that has led to some great work.

You should also look at our website, idler.co.uk. Because we are lazy, we want our readers to write it for us. You'll find plenty of places on the site where you can send us your idle thoughts. The Unfinished Jokes zone is particularly popular. Dedicated idlers can join our mailing list, and will find the occasional cheering missive dropping into their mailbox.

In the meantime, settle into your La-Z-Boy recliner, fix a drink and luxuriate in our new issue. ☜

tom@idler.co.uk

WHY DO FOOLS FALL IN LOVE? AND OTHER QUESTIONS

GAVIN PRETOR-PINNEY answers the oft-put conundrum.
Portrait by HANNAH DYSON

In 1956 Frankie Lymon, aged only 13, sang "Why do Fools Fall in Love?" He wanted an answer to this question, but instead, he got a Top Ten hit, and became the first black artist to sell a million records. By the age of twenty, clearly frustrated by not getting any answers, Frankie had ended up a washed-up has-been whose only gigs were nostalgia shows. Seven years later he died of a drugs overdose.

Frankie was only the first in a line of performers who, doing covers of this song, vainly attempted to get to the bottom of this conundrum. Like Frankie, they were so upset that no one would sit them down and give them explanations, that they stood in front of tens of thousands and belted out this and the other questions asked by the song. Like, why *do* birds sing so gay? Are they singing to attract a mate, or is it more a case of them demarcating their territory, wondered The Beach Boys when they did a cover in 1964? Why *does* the rain fall from up above? pondered Frankie Valli and the Four Seasons? As late as 1981, Diana Ross was still asking why lovers await the break of day. She ended up with a huge chart hit with the cover and with it an equally huge financial success. But did she get any answer as to why fools fall in love? No, she didn't.

Whilst I am tragically too late for poor Frankie Lymon, I want to help the others by finally providing some explanations.

WHY DO BIRDS SING SO GAY?

Most birdsong is produced by the males. Like all males, they are primarily concerned with having fights and getting their end away. They are singing to pick up birds. And once they've picked them up, they are singing to keep them.

"But wait a minute, many species of birds are monogamous!" I hear Frankie Valli shouting. Yes Frankie, they are. But the mortality rate, especially amongst small birds, is so high that they have to keep their pulling skills up to scratch because they never know when they will have to use them again.

The other main reason for birdsong is to tell other birds: "Look, this is our patch buddy. We eat the little berries and insects and shit here. So back off, OK?" But why so gay, as Brian Wilson wondered, back in 64? First, let's put aside the idea that birds are homosexual. There are no known examples. Now, as the sunset is for our eyes, so birdsong is for our ears: a beautiful reminder of the shiva dance of nature, of which we are all but a part. It humbles us and puts our worries about writing up the Interim Competitor's Market Report for the boss by the end of the week into perspective.

Hence birdsong is gay.

WHY DO LOVERS AWAIT
THE BREAK OF DAY?

Firstly, I'm not really sure that they do. I would have thought that lovers would enjoy cuddling up in their duvet, a womb-like haven, and turning their naked backs to the onset of the day and all its attendant concerns. Nevertheless, with Frankie Lymon in mind, I accept that mine is not to question why, mine is to answer questions why.

Firstly, if one of the lovers is a heavy snorer then I can understand that the other might be quite keen for the onset of daybreak. Seeing your loved one in such an undignified state can only make one question the whole relationship. Secondly, daybreak brings with it the promise of sex-in-the-morning, which, since everyone else is out doing sensible stuff, is more fun than sex-at-night.

WHY DOES THE RAIN FALL
FROM UP ABOVE?

Like pretty much the vast majority of natural phenomena on earth, rain is dependent on the influence of the sun. When seas, lakes, rivers and glasses of gin and tonic are warmed up by the sun, it causes the water to evaporate. This evaporating water is absorbed by the adjacent air. This warm, vapour-laden air near the ground rises (because warm air is expanded, and so lighter than the cool air above). Now, the warmer that air is, the more water moisture it can hold. So as the vapour-laden air starts coming into contact with the cold air, it starts cooling down and shedding its water into tiny droplets. This mist of water droplets appears as a cloud.

"If they are full of water, why do the clouds stay up in the sky?" I hear Diana Ross ask. The droplets are held up in the air by the other rising air below it. But if the individual droplets in the cloud start forming into big enough drops, gravity takes hold and makes them begin to fall back to earth, in spite of the rising air. Just as you spotted, Diana, what is so beautiful about rain is that it is, quite simply, falling clouds, returning to the earth whence they came.

WHY DO FOOLS FALL IN LOVE?

I don't claim to know everything. This, alas, I do not know. ◑

If you have any philosophical or scientific dilemmas derived from the lyrics of popular music that you would like help with, just write to me at gavin@idler.co.uk and I'll do my best to answer

NOTES FROM THE COUCH

IDLER'S DIARY
The latest occurrences in the world of loafing

IDLER NIGHT AT THE FOUNDRY
We held a little party at the Foundry in November. The inimitable Jock Scot did a reading, Gimpo let off fireworks and Keith Allen said "fantastic" a lot. We decided to start a regular night at the Foundry, known by regulars as the Grotto Club. This bar, located in London's fashionable Shoreditch district, will play host on certain Monday evenings to Idler nights, when our finest writers will perform and play music. The events will be completely free. To find out more, go to idler.co.uk and get yourself on our mailing list.

ARE SNAILS ELECTRIC?
Talking of the website, now seems like a good time to announce its official launch. Idler.co.uk is where idlers can go to read quality stuff, communicate with other idlers around the world, and buy fantastic books, magazines, t-shirts, toys and all sorts of goodies to help you live the idle life. I know we launched it in the last issue, and the one before that, but this time it really is up there. Promise.

COMPENDIUM CLOSES DOWN
After 33 years as the première counter-culture bookshop in London, Compendium, of Camden Town, ceased trading this Autumn. The Idler was present when a concerned customer offered to campaign on their behalf: "I'll start a petition!" "Nah," came the response. "Don't bother. We've had enough." The closure is, though, a disaster, and the fact that such things have been predicted for a few years does nothing to lessen the blow. Where exactly can you go, now, to access the accumulated wisdom that Compendium have built up over the years; to find the kind of books that the bigger chains don't even notice, much less promote; to talk to people who know about books? The world's a poorer place without their like. Thanks, Compendium. We're sorry to see you go.

TONY WHITE

WASTED SUMMER
The summer started with a visit to the Glastonbury Music Festival, where we were guests of Black Box Recorder. We enjoyed a weekend and part of the next week of sloth and drugs and rock'n'roll. Contrary to weather reports the heavens stayed closed. Black Box Recorder set pulses racing with Sarah Nixey's body

hugging rubber suit. From three rows back she appeared completely naked. Idler Sports Editor and BBR member John Moore was so enamoured of the Glasto vibe that he surprised everyone by casting off his old cynical persona and renaming himself Rainbow John. Three-month-old Arthur Hodgkinson stayed on the wagon but cried during the David Bowie show.

ISLE OF EIGG

August also saw a visit to the great Isle Of Eigg off the Western coast of Scotland. Eigg, which had been owned by various private lairds for centuries, was finally bought out by its inhabitants a couple of years ago. The sixty-odd Eiggites have created a kind of perfect anarchy on their laid-back, beautiful island. Our favourite memory: John the postman was sitting outside the post office on a warm, sunny afternoon, enjoying a quiet can of McEwans. This went on for several hours. Then a lady walked into the post office, and out again. "John," she said. "Would it be too much trouble to post a letter?" With impeccable timing John paused, sighed quietly, and slowly rose to his feet while laconically intoning: "It's – all – go." Magic.

ABSINTHE BUS SHOCK

John Moore was driving our new absinthe bus back to London from Edinburgh. This was just as the fuel blockades were starting. He came very close to killing us when he assumed that the "No Lorries" sign on the service station was just a piece of quaint old snobbery. Pootling up the side-road, he suddenly had to swerve the fourteen foot high double decker bus across the grass to avoid taking the nine foot roof off as well as our top deck. George – da boss – was upstairs at the time changing the Frank Sinatra CD. He came down ashen faced and suggested swapping over for a bit. Look out for the absinthe bus coming to your town.

ABIGAIL'S PANTS

We recently met a charming young lady called Miss Abigail Fallis. She is an artist, whose latest project is a range of bespoke y-fronts. Her designs are already gracing the walls of conveniences in such classy haunts as the Groucho Club, the Colony Rooms and the Westbourne Hotel. They can also be seen on britart.com. Miss Fallis has kindly designed a special line of snail-embroidered pants for us (see below), to complement our Idler t-shirts. This means idlers can now own the perfect twin-set for daytime lounging. The limited edition pants will retail on our website at a special price of £19.99, reduced, she claims, from £199.99.

READERS' LETTERS

**Write to us at: The Idler, Studio 20, 24-28a Hatton Wall,
London EC1N 8JH or e-mail admin@idler.co.uk
Top letter wins a bottle of La Fée Absinthe**

Dear Idler,

Forget those ubiquitous Ibiza compilations, I have compiled my own top Five Idle Anthems:

1 Sitting On the Dock of the Bay. Otis Redding describes an afternoon idling doing nothing but "watch the tide role by".

2 Ballad of Big Nothing. Elliott Smith, who purports to writing his songs in the most idle of fashions: sitting in a bar, strumming and seeing what comes out. Sample lyric: "You can do what you want to whenever you want to". Or not.

3 A Summer Wasting: Belle & Sebastian. The archetype of indolence, the band have not toured since 1997. Sample lyric: "Seven weeks of river walkways, seven weeks of staying up all night" – surely this is not a summer wasting?

4 I'm Only Sleeping: The Beatles. Pretty self-explanatory really.

5 Moon Safari: Air. A soundtrack for idling, unfortunately it has been corrupted and used as a soundtrack for nearly everything else including a Judith Chalmers endorsed "Wish You Were Here".

Al, Harpenden

*Al gets this half-year's bottle of abbo.
Check idler.co.uk for more top fives*

To whom it may concern;

Just an idle thought that I've had rambling around my head for some time. I was wondering if it was simply my lack of understanding of the internal workings of a modern microprocessor or just the fact that my own sensibilities seem to have crawled into 1932 to die but I have been feeling for some time that computers are really dull.

Ben Blaine

Dear Idler,

There I was in the LSE bookshop, all serious and looking for something weighty to get my teeth into, when, from a bank of foreign policy journals, your Summer 2000 book leapt out at me. Oh, how it brought the memories flooding back.

I'm so happy that you're still at it. I had thought that idling was a secret and despicable part of my past, a movement that had now gone underground, its provocateurs rendered dissolute by absinthe. I had gone into "sleeper" mode, awaiting the call to idler arms. But I was obviously wrong – idling seems stronger than ever.

I had been doing my best to keep the flame alive. I've been editing a series of little books on Darwinian themes, one of which presents the scientific case for idling (see www.guardianunlimited.co.uk/Archive/Article/0,4273,3811485,00.html) And, after studying for several years, I'm now living in a caravan at the bottom of a

If regicide is when you kill a king, what's it called when you kill someone called Reggie?

....

"If you don't leave me alone I'll call the Nepalese." Anything there?

....

"I ain't never gonna be *bespectacled*." Advert for contact lenses, maybe?

....

Doctor-in-a-hurry writes email to patient: "V. bad news! U have cancer of the :"

....

And a couple from the postbag:

Something about the dyslexic gardener using *non sequiturs* (from John Moore)

Going into a hospital lab where they analyse urine samples to discover a wine taster swilling it round his mouth, spitting it out and going, "hmm, I'm getting diabetes, emphysema and, is that a touch of VD? (from Pete Diaper)

Go to idler.co.uk to submit your own Unfinished Jokes. Louis' favourite of the month will win a prize

field writing a book about how minds work, for OUP. My "office" is an arc of meadow, defined by how far the extension lead on my battered laptop will stretch. I have learnt to play poker, bought a nice old camera, and occasionally wear a straw hat. It's all very congenial, if soon to end.

I'm moving back to London in October to start a PhD. So anyway, I'm very much looking forward to flicking through the book, and generally having it around. Good luck with the ongoing mission to spread idleness.
Best wishes,
Oliver Curry
By Email

....

Dear Idler

Marvellous mag, fabulous bog book, great site. Do you have a postal address which potential literary contributions can be sent. It's for a friend (honest).
King sized regards
Bryn Dineen
Our address is up there on the left

....

Dear Idler,

Great. I would like to say keep up the good work but it somehow doesn't sound appropriate. Whatever, keep it up!
Andrew Waddle by email

HEROES & VILLAINS OF THE IDLE UNIVERSE

THE SKIVERS

ZX SPECTRUM EMULATORS

Turn your 1000MhZ PC into a 48K joyfest with these nifty pieces of software that allow you to play all those old classic games like Manic Miner, Jet Set Willy, and the punishing Daley Thompson's Decathlon. Access priceless childhood memories rendered in blocky graphics with authentic colour clash. There is even a tribute website to Your Spectrum magazine, allowing you to catch up on what its bygone contributors are up to now. Sometimes, you can take retro a little too far.

CHRIS WATSON

....

TECHNOLOGY

Promised to do all the work for us. Didn't.

....

W AXL ROSE

The Bad Boy front man of Eighties rock outfit Guns'n'Roses has become a virtual recluse since the acrimonious split of the band in 1994. His long awaited follow-up album, *Chinese Democracy*, six years in the making at a reported cost of $6 million to Geffen Records, is supposedly a masterwork reminiscent of late Led Zeppelin. He has also acquired a Yoko Ono type partner, a mystic referred to by the G'n'R camp as "Yoda" who lives in the Phoenix Desert, and whom Axl relies on to protect him from Bad Vibes. Like David Bowie, and Jim Morrison before him, Axl

has learned that solace and reflection rather than hard toil, are the true path to enlightenment.

....

LILIES

Consider the lilies of the field, they toil not, neither do they spin.

....

GEORGE W BUSH

The US Presidential candidate refuses to work more than six or seven hours a day as he feels this keeps him more productive and efficient than the standard fourteen hour day worked by the majority of US politicians. As *Idler* reader Andy Townsend points out, the idea of the Idler and GW Bush Jr being philosophical bedfellows is just too bizarre. Bertrand Russell first classified such false Idlers, those whose "idleness is only rendered possible by the industry of others... the last thing they have ever wished for is that others should follow their example."

THE STRIVERS

LINEONE
Feelgood motivational branding messages reached new levels of hyperbole with the unveiling of LineOne's new strapline "Invent Your Own Universe". The *Idler* intends to follow suit with its own corporate message, "Be God".

OFFICE RAGE
When sales of stress relief medicines increased dramatically in the last year at Tesco pharmacies, the supermarket chain commissioned a report on stress and claimed to unearth a phenomenon called "office rage". Apparently one of the prime causes is faulty equipment, like dodgy photocopiers. Nothing to do with dashing your life on the rocks of meaningless toil, then. Instead of self-medicating with pharmacological panaceas, the *Idler* recommends immense boozy lunches as the best way to combat stress. Get really blasted in the middle of the day. Not only does the afternoon just fly by, but the traffic jams on the way home offer the ideal oppourtunity to sleep it off.

MOCKNEES
Persons who neglect to show proper respect to the bit of the body that is generally found halfway up your leg. Mocknees continually slag off the whole concept of knees as inherently worthless, sometimes painting silly faces on them to add to their utter disregard for this bendable leg-joint.

BIG BANDWIDTH BOYS
Anxieties about penis size have now been replaced by concerns at the speed of their Internet access. "How big's your bandwidth?" is now the clarion call for all insecure males in pubs the length and breadth of the nation. People with ISDN now cower before those with ADSL but join in the mockery of those who still attempt Internet access via an old-fashioned modem. "14.4 BPS! 14.4 BPS!" they shout until the offender crumples into a corner wracked by despair and slow-loading web pages.

CHRIS WATSON

THE FINE LINE BETWEEN SCIENCE FICTION & THIS YEAR

CHRIS WATSON

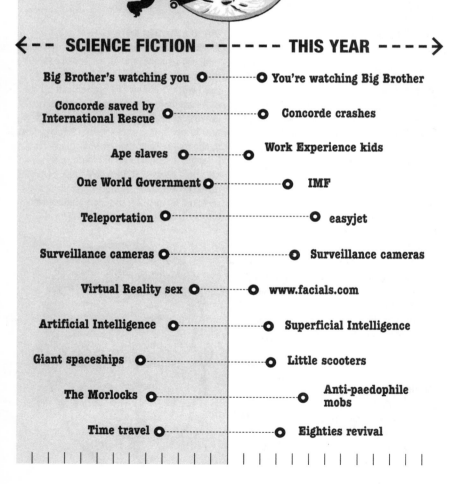

← – – **SCIENCE FICTION** – – – – – – **THIS YEAR** – – – – →

SCIENCE FICTION	THIS YEAR
Big Brother's watching you	You're watching Big Brother
Concorde saved by International Rescue	Concorde crashes
Ape slaves	Work Experience kids
One World Government	IMF
Teleportation	easyjet
Surveillance cameras	Surveillance cameras
Virtual Reality sex	www.facials.com
Artificial Intelligence	Superficial Intelligence
Giant spaceships	Little scooters
The Morlocks	Anti-paedophile mobs
Time travel	Eighties revival

CHRIS WATSON

INDICTED TO A PARTY

STEVE AYLETT has a few guidelines designed to make your evening swing

Picture any social occasion. Concessions circle like vultures. Each welcome to the bar is thinner. There may be twenty or more ears floating in one room but these are not to be mentioned, nor used for hearing. Dynamite trenching and the throwing of cinders is discouraged, but like so many rules, this one is never spoken aloud. Indeed so many rules are unvoiced that we are left to jerry-build our own protocol from years of trial and error. Below are the sparse scraps of certain knowledge I have managed to nail down.

1. Arrive in a midget car, bursting with anger.

2. Give in to a non-existent badgering and sign a tremulous autograph on the face of a terrified child.

3. Whisper "Loan me a robot nifty" and display teeth like brackets.

4. Develop a film of colour over your nose, remove the membrane and drape it over a light bulb, drenching the room in puce loveliness.

5. Begin frantically praying.

6. Walk through walls of their condescension, continuing beyond them.

7. Refer urbanely to the host's residence as "this death trap of yours".

8. Say the fern is your beautiful mother.

9. Juggle your merits fast to make them look more numerous; or slowly to better hide your slack, empty face.

10. Insult someone without information, your abuse a snarl of zigzagging guesswork. Fade down into tongue-twisting underbreath vulgarities.

11. Refer to your nostrils as "the keyholes of illness".

12. Point to someone's wife and say "I'll give you double what you paid."

13. Show obvious reluctance to stop kissing the dog.

14. Plug awkward pauses in conversation with one or all of the following phrases: (a) "I gave orders I was not to be disturbed." (b) "Burny Sex is learny sex." (c) "I insure the water in my head." (d) "How would you handle a stolen pair of caskets?" (e) "Approved to drown, I trembled in the pallid morning." (f) "Souls won't rescue your bacon species." (g) "Abnormally meek, aren't you?" (h) "The lady pushes her sides out real perty." (i) "No doctors." (j) "A dungeon is very uneven isn't it?" (k) "Die." (l) "Algorithm monkey."

15. Perch snickering upon the side-table, feasting upon an unidentifiable rodent. You rasp slime from wound of a mouth. You are desperate for a world where the social gathering is more than a diversion. Daybreak smoulders. 🐌

YOU HAVE TO BE MAD TO WORK HERE

GARETH ELLIS on the latest corporate trend: employing court jesters to say the unsayable

Managers are now employing corporate jesters to dispel madness within corporate life. Inspired by the Fool in *King Lear*, their job is to bring wisdom through their comic antics. Now companies have become like medieval courts. Fooling is serious business.

"Fools pinpoint absurdity by acting out the absurd," explains Paul Birch, British Airways' first Corporate Jester. "They act as a mirror in which people see their mistakes without having to admit to them. This enables Fools to challenge accepted wisdom and create new alternatives. As such, they're entrusted with the sensitive task of managing and controlling change."

Whilst not every company has an official jester, Birch believes Fooling has an increasingly important role within the workplace, where folly challenges the predictable Human Question Mark, asking all the questions that no one else will — as well as the really stupid sounding ones.

"The Fool sees things as they really are. The Fool says things as they really are. Fooling is fun," claims David Firth, an innovation consultant, who runs a school for Fools and a Foolish clinic that tours conferences giving Foolish advice — advice that seems ludicrous but actually makes you re-think the situation afresh.

"We do not suffer fools gladly in our organisations — which is one of the reasons we're short on wisdom too," says Firth. "Our Emperors remain naked. Our cultures vibrate with the tension of people thinking, 'They must be able to see what's wrong? Why don't they ask us? Why don't they change? '— but not having the power, the authority or the skills to do anything about it."

Corporate Fools trace their lineage back to the 12th century, where their precursors were granted license to speak out in court. Absurdity freed the Fool from conventional restraints: he could do the undoable and say the unthinkable, exposing genuine absurdity that would otherwise have lain unmentioned. When the Fool became the Queen's pampered lap dog — nothing more than the butt of perennial jokes — then the court was lost. Without its voice of Foolish reason it would slide into decadence.

Paul Birch was appointed by then CEO Sir Colin Marshall to tackle the collective insanity that had seized parts of the World's Favourite Airline. He told Birch to "swan around, stick your nose in and be a pain in the arse — as long as it's all measurable".

Birch despaired of British Airways' culture of autocracy and sycophancy. "The board were like courtiers, jealous of their baronies. They fought out their petty feuds through lackies and brand managers. No one ever admitted they were wrong." As a sane man in an insane world he prescribed

WITH A HEY NONNY NO: DO BIG COMPANIES NEED FOOLS ON THE TEAM?

a hearty dose of creative Folly, hoping to encourage honesty and creativity amidst the corporate bullying.

As a corporate jester Birch held sessions where he turned reality on its head so others might discover understanding. A professional trouble starter, Birch encouraged managers to chase each other with water guns. Or he would create confrontational scenarios that challenged status: participants had to pretend to be giants ("shouting"), witches ("casting spells") or dwarves ("beating people's knees") — and then work within these roles to redesign a new seat allocation system.

Only the truly sane can turn reality on its head. Foolishness requires a sanguine perspective on the role of work and the need to reject the reward and punishment systems that underpin modern corporate life. "Whilst anyone can be a fool," says Birch, "it helps if you've a great future behind you."

Birch held his Foolish post for two years until Bob Ayling became CEO and made him redundant — for "taking the piss". Given British Airways' recent plummet, Birch feels history has shown only one fool remained. ◉

DOTTY COM

Struggling dot com adopts Big Brother eviction system to cut staff levels, reveals MATTHEW DE ABAITUA

CHRIS WATSON

The worldwide phenomenon of Big Brother may be all over now, but its influence lives on in the most unexpected places. Struggling internet company eezygoodies.com has announced that over the next two months, they are adopting the Big Brother eviction system as a way of cutting staffing levels.

The Clerkenwell-based dot com has been losing two million pounds a month since its launch in early 1999. With estimated monthly sales of eight thousand pounds and falling, CEO Mark Westerberg has announced that staff cuts would be necessary if eezygoodies.com was to continue trading. "All of our staff at eezygoodies.com are committed and passionate about their work. Laying them off in the conventional manner would be arbitrary and unfair. So we have decided to give them the opportunity to compete for their jobs."

The store room at eezygoodies.com's fashionable loft space office has been converted into a diary room. Every Friday evening, each member of staff must go in and nominate which fellow worker is to be made redundant. The following Monday the votes are added up, and the unfortunate individual is let go.

Westerberg continues: "As all our staff are freelance, there are no legal problems with the eviction system of redundancy. In fact, I think it is the way forward, as it is a more democratic process than the traditional model of management sitting down and culling the numbers. No-one would vote out a fellow staff member if they liked them, or if they felt their eviction would cause serious disruption to their own work. It's a ruthless system, but it ensures those who are least essential to the on-going success of eezygoodies.com go first."

But doesn't Mark Westerberg himself fear the chop. Surely the boss in this situation is particularly unpopular? "I retain a veto, which means I'm in line to get the grand prize." The grand prize? "Yes, the last person left wins the chance to take all the computer equipment down to Cash Converters when we finally go under. If I win, I was thinking of giving all the money to my mentally retarded cousin. Imagine how many Pingu videos she could buy with £70,000." ✎

PET DEATHS

**They just come apart in your hands.
This issue: poodles, budgies, dogs.**

I'm interested in your pets. I want true stories about how your pets, or the pets of your friends, met their end. Submit all pet death or pet near-death stories to admin@idler.co.uk. I believe that by sharing the tragic deaths of pets we can all come closer to a fuller apprehension of our own terrifying mortality.

MDA

"Evelyn was an obsessive-compulsive cleaner. On her daughter's wedding day, she scrubbed the house thoroughly. While cleaning out the budgerigar's cage, she noticed a beige patch of feathers around its tiny arsehole. Tutting, she dabbed bleach onto her cloth and scrubbed the bird's arse clean. The next day, it was dead."

....

"My brother -in law, Andy, once owned a Staffordshire Bull Terrier called Sinbad. It was a nutter, forever locked out in the yard, gnawing at wood. I saw it fleetingly, once. A fetid dirty white hulk stalking the patio. My sister had to beat it back with a brush. Once she had moved in with Andy, it was clear Sinbad had to go. Its departure was hastened by the time it leapt snarling off

the compost heap and threw itself into Andy's chest. Fortunately, he is a strong man and the dog bounced off and landed in the bin.

When the time came for Sinbad to be put down, Andy came over all sentimental about the dog and instead put it up for adoption. Sinbad was taken from him and he went away on holiday to Greece. A week late, he woke up on a beach in Naxos and realised what a terrible mistake he had

LORNA MILLER

made. He had meant to tell the dog's home to make sure that Sinbad was not adopted by a family, and was kept purely as a guard dog, but it had slipped his mind. For the rest of the holiday, he worried about Sinbad.

"Upon his return home, Andy picked up the free sheet newspaper lying on the doormat. The headline read: 'Police shoot devil dog'. The subline underneath read: 'Family held hostage by new dog for six hours'. And there was a picture of Sinbad."

THE SECRETS OF COMEDY...

AN ENGLISHMAN, A SCOTSMAN, AND AN IRISHMAN — ALL WANKING EACH OTHER OFF.

OH, FUCK OFF MATE, I DON'T HEAR YOU TELLING ANY JOKES.

GWYN

PET NEAR-DEATHS

"A 14 year old poodle called Jet recently went missing in Fareham. Jet's owner searched frantically for her all over the house and adjacent garden, but to no avail. Fortunately, Jet turned up in the toilet. It turns out the poodle had leapt into the bowl only to have the seat close after her. A photograph in the *Daily Star* dramatically re-stages this incident. Surprisingly, they resist the pun on poodle. Yet they had no compunction in recreating what was no doubt a traumatic time in Jet's life just for a half-page story."

....

"My enjoyment of a recent Premiership game was somewhat overshadowed by a distressing phone conversation with my friend Adam. I had tried to rally my male friends into watching the game with me on the big screen at my local pub, but now they were backing out.

"'I can't come, I've got to stay in and look after the kitten,' Adam said, when I phoned him up and asked where the hell he was. I was furious. 'What? You're missing the footie because of a fucking kitten?' 'There is blood in her stool,' he replied. 'Well, stop sticking your finger up its arse, then.' I snapped, briskly curtailing the call. As it turned out, there was absolutely nothing wrong with the kitten." ❧

IT'S A BANAL, BANAL WORLD

We asked our roving reporter to go out there and try and find out what's going on. His results make disturbing reading

CHRIS WATSON

10/ SANDWICH SHOP Sign next to the till. "We are committed to great sandwiches."

9/ REVENUE PROTECTION OFFICERS Tannoy announcement on Silverlink trains. "Please make sure you have a valid ticket for your journey as Silverlink Revenue Protection Officers are now in operation." I imagine the run of meetings at which this change from "ticket inspectors" to "revenue protection officers" was discussed, and wince.

8/ HINCHLEY WOOD PRIMARY SCHOOL FETE "Do come and browse. There is something to suit every age and taste" – sign on Mrs Nielsen's White Elephant Stall, Hinchley Wood Primary School Fete. Is this the blandest exhortation to shop ever?

7/ MICHAEL DICESARE presenting his new range of "haircare products to the stars" on QVC. Rainy Saturday afternoon, wondering "Why do hairdressers always get it so wrong when it comes to their own hair?"

6/ EMAIL NEWSLETTERS Until then, they flick open on the desktop and release a stale burp of prose. This, for example, from the twenieth ignored missive from Lastminute.com in my inbox: *"The combined talents of Ben Elton and Andrew Lloyd Webber make this fantastic new musical a must-see show."*

5/ LAP DANCER Disdainfully parting her labia for four junior members of

Advertising sales team.

4/ WEDNESDAY NIGHT Bottle of Jacob's Creek, me on the sofa, her on the armchair, the two of us staring stoneyfaced at Jack Dee on the Paramount Comedy Channel. "Why do I remember this being funny?" she says.

3/ BREAKFAST TV: Still photograph of Anthea Turner, calling from South Africa. She's furious. Whining on about the press. Cut to Lorraine Kelly on the sofa, nodding sympathetically, though I have a strong feeling that she doesn't believe a word.

2/ BRAND MANAGER PowerPoint open on his PowerBook. Still working on his presentation at midnight.

1/ CLARENCE THE ROAD DEFECT LION Scottish roadside poster campaign, accompanied by a phone number for drivers to call if they spot flaws in the highways. "Hi there. Grrrr. This is Clarence the Road Defect Lion. Grrrr. Please report your road defect after the tone. Grrrr." 🐾

VILLAGE IDIOTS

TIM RICHARDSON discovers Gotham, a medieval village whose inhabitants pretended to be mad to avoid taxes – and got away with it.
Illustration by CHRIS WATSON

Acting mad can get you out of all sorts of scrapes, whether it's multiple homicides or family gatherings. However, it takes good organisation for a whole community to present a picture of craziness to the rest of the world. One such place is Gotham (pronounced Goatham) in Nottinghamshire. In about 1200, during ye olde reign of King John, the story goes, the residents realised the implications of the King's visit to Nottingham. He would pass through the village, thus making it a King's Highway, thus making the villagers liable to new taxes. Since madness was considered contagious, the idea of a whole village of lunatics was perfectly feasible, so the villagers acted like idiots when the King's messengers arrived ahead of the royal party. The ploy worked.

This was just the start. Gotham's national reputation for stupidity grew to such an extent that in 1540 an enterprising publisher put together a chap book of old stories and called it *The Merry Tales of the Mad Men of Gotham*. It was a big hit. Among the crazy antics the Gothamites got up to were trying to hedge a cuckoo in a wood, smashing up a watch they found, thinking it contained spirits, throwing the church bell in the sea to hide it from invaders and marking its position

with a notch on the side of the boat, and allowing cheeses to roll themselves to Nottingham market after one accidentally fell out of a bag.

After its first edition, the book was re-titled *The Merry Tales of the Wise Men of Gotham*, and this has led some to describe the Gothamites as *idiots savant*. But this theory does not hold water. What is *savant* about thinking a load of cheeses can go all the way to market all on their own, and then, get this, going to Nottingham market, finding the cheeses are not there, concluding that they misheard you and went to York market instead, and so going off to York in search of them? The Gothamites are just a bunch of jerks. The title change must be an early example of extreme sarcasm.

Batman's Gotham City is related to the Nottinghamshire Gotham because Washington Irving appropriated the name as a satirical alter ego for the crazy city of New York. It was subsequently picked up by the comic people. How fitting that Batman's big enemy is The Joker.

Other cultures also have villages of fools: Phrysia in Asia Minor, Abde'ra in Thrace, Boeo'tia in Ancient Greece, Sabia in Germany. In Israel, Nazereth was the home of fools, which gave Jesus's nickname, Nazarine, a certain piquancy. 🐌

ADAM AND JOE:
ON THE PSYCHIATRIST'S COUCH

**Exclusive to the Idler, radical filmmaker KEN KORDA
gets a grilling from shrink to the stars, DR HANS VERLAG**

Celebrated psychologist Dr Hans Fischer Verlag is the creator of The Verlag Series: a set of questions designed to strip bare the psyche of his patients. Now for the first time he accepts money to put a selection of questions from the Verlag Series to a celebrity guest. Session One: Ken Korda.

VERLAG: Question one. You are walking in a black void. Suddenly you come across a coffin with a man who looks like you inside it. How do you react?

KEN: I don't like the coffin. I'm afraid of the coffin and I run away from it. I feel worried and depressed, especially as the man inside looks like me. Why, what does it mean?

VERLAG: The coffin represents death . The man who looks like you, is in fact you and your feelings of worry and depression indicate that you are reluctant to die. Running away points to a deeper anxiety relating to dying or being killed. The void just adds to the whole creepiness. Question two. You are standing naked in a white room. A woman enters and begins to undress. She looks like Cat Deely. What do you do?

KEN: Hmmm, that's a tough one. I think I'd watch her undress completely then ask her some questions about working with PJ & Duncan, you know, how much input she has at script stage for *SM:TV*. I'd also

be very interested to know how they go about conceiving a segment like Wonky Donkey. I might also have a wank. Is this one about my Mum?

VERLAG: It is interesting you should say that, but no, it's mainly about how much you are attracted to Cat Deely from *CD:UK*. You'll notice that I said the woman just looks like Cat Deely, I never said it actually was her. The fact that you assumed it was points to deep feelings of desire for Ms Deely. Seeing her going out with Huey from Fun Loving Criminals a while ago must have been very hard for you.

KEN: It was hard because me and Huey are so similar. We both make art about life on the streets and how cool criminals are, but we both know how to love too. If Cat's bodyguard had dragged me away from her a few seconds later she may have chosen differently. We'll never know. I've decided Gail Porter is a far superior proposition to Deely anyway but every time I get close to clinching the deal she shacks up with some other low rent "pop" mediocrity.

VERLAG: Yes. Question three. You are walking down the street when you come across a bag filled with money. Beside the bag is a blind man wearing a sign that says "Integrity". How do you proceed?

KEN: I think I would pick up the bag of money very, very quietly so the blind man couldn't hear me, and then I would tip toe away, then break into a run when I felt confident he hadn't heard. What's the significance of the sign in that one?

VERLAG: This question is about your attitude to wealth and whether you value the acquisition of wealth above your own integrity, hence the sign on the blind man. The fact that you take the bag of money indicates that you care very little for integrity and more for money.

KEN: I suppose that's true. On a more pragmatic level, I don't necessarily think it's right for the blind to have all the money, especially if they spend it all on sticks and dogs and things like that. Obviously people like Stevie Wonder deserve money because they make great music for films like *Woman In Red* with Kelly Le Brock, but that's different because they're famous. The guy in the question was just standing around with a sign on his neck like a stupid bastard. If anything I've taught him a valuable lesson he won't soon forget.

VERLAG: Mr Korda, thank you very much for you candour.

KEN: Yes. ◉

IDLE INVENTIONS 1
By JOHN MOORE

THE REVERSIBLE POLAROID
£39.95 +£5 p&p

This revolutionary device is ingenious yet simple. It gets rid of unwanted party bores forever with one satisfying click. Simply position the subjects in front of the lens as you would a normal composition. Get them to say "cheese" then fire. A perfect polaroidal representation with one crucial difference – it fades away. After thirty seconds the paper is blank. Look around you – they've vanished too. Your party-hatted office colleagues, your dull witted associates; an entire family gathering-gone forever

This fabulous and economical device is so new that it's not even illegal yet. Buy one now while stocks last.

IDLE PLEASURES: DAY VANS

Ged Wells

I recently bought a second-hand US-made 1994 Ford Econoline Day Van for taking my small family on camping trips and days on the beach. We have already motored in luxury through Devon and Cornwall, the South Coast, and all the way up to the highlands of Scotland.

A Day Van can seat seven people in total luxury. It has a TV and video, two stereo systems, automatic transmission, a five litre engine, air-conditioning, cruise control, electric windows, leather seats, wood trim, an on-board vacuum cleaner, mood lighting and lots of plugs and switches and cup-holders and things. The back bench seat folds down into a big double bed. It's mega-smooth and ultra-cool. It has a lot more space than one of those puny people movers. It's like a Lear Jet on wheels.

It may not be the most economical car on the road, but it has increased my driving pleasure – and that of my lucky passengers – immeasurably.

See the magazine Classic American for second-hand examples in the £2-£10,000 region. TH

THE SECRETS OF COMEDY...

MY PARENTS...THEY'VE JUST GOT BACK FROM THE HOLIDAY OF A LIFE TIME... THEY BROUGHT ME BACK THIS LOUSY PHLEGMY FUCKING COUGH... AND THE CUNT ISN'T EVEN MY REAL DAD...

YEAH-WELL, WHERE I COME FROM THAT'S FUNNY, MATE.

GWYN

THE MEDIA™

**The game everyone wants to play.
Devised by MATTHEW DE ABAITUA.
Illustrations by LORNA MILLER**

HOW TO PLAY *THE MEDIA™*

Players 3 – 6
Ages 16 – 65

THE MEDIA™ is the new fun card game for all the family from the *Idler*. The aim of the game is to build a successful career in the metropolitan media, while avoiding career hiccups and backstabbing from fellow players.

To build your career in the media, collect COMMISSION cards. Each commission card represents an appearance in the media. These are laid down in the area in front of the player and totalled at the end of the game. The game ends when either there are no more cards left to draw from the pack, or if one player says "I've had enough of this shit. I'm retiring to the country" and plays a "RETIRING TO THE COUNTRY" card.

HOW TO PLAY

Each player is dealt seven cards. The rest of the pack is in the centre of the table. The person sitting to the right of the dealer starts.

The player draws first from the pack, then discards a card, either by putting the card into play, or by throwing it onto the "Spiked" pile.

Players can trade cards with fellow players at the start of their go. Each card to be traded is placed, face down on the table, and exchanged simultaneously.

Will your mates help you you out, or will they stitch you up? This is the dilemma of THE MEDIA™

GETTING STARTED

Before a player can lay commission cards, they must lay a BEGIN YOUR CAREER card!

When a player lays a BEGIN YOUR CAREER card, they must announce that they are "Off to London". There are numerous BEGIN YOUR CAREER card,. confirming to three types:
> Music Press
> Oxbridge
> Please, Daddy

Players who BEGIN YOUR CAREER with a PLEASE, DADDY card get an extra 20% of the total value of their commissions at the end of the game. If two players have the same college marked on their OXBRIDGE cards, they can form an alliance, adding 10% of the total value of their commissions at the end of the game.

Once you have your BEGIN YOUR CAREER card, you can start laying down commission cards.

COMMISSION CARDS

Lay these down as soon as you can. But watch out, the other players will eye them enviously!

Commission cards include, in descending order of value:

BIG COMMISSIONS

There aren't many of these. Cling on to them for dear life.
> Director of brit-flick £500,000
> Own Terrestial TV Show £250,000
> Editing a Newspaper £200,000
> Face of Ad campaign £150,000
> Book deal £100,000
> Broadsheet column £60,000
> Editing a magazine £40,000
> Voice of Ad Campaign £30,000

SMALL COMMISSIONS

These are many of these cards.

> Own On Digital TV show £1000
> Web site content generator £800
> Broadsheet feature £500
> This Morning guest £400
> Newsnight guest £300
> Kilroy guest £200
> QVC presenter £150
> Second Mugged Old Woman in The Bill £50

BUT BEWARE! It's one thing to get a commission. But holding onto it is another matter. There are special cards in the pack that allow the other players to steal them from you. These are the BACKSTAB cards.

THE BACKSTAB CARDS ARE:

> I'm sleeping with the Editor
   (allows player to take lowest value commission card from rivals)
> I've got a regular supply of good cocaine
   (allows player to take one commission card of their choice from rivals)
> I've got a Tragic Private Life
   (allows player to take commission card of highest value from each rival)

For Example: I'm playing I'VE GOT A TRAGIC PRIVATE LIFE so I'll take Mum's BROADSHEET COLUMN, Dad's KILROY GUEST and little Johnny's BOOK DEAL. After playing a BACKSTAB card, the player takes another go. A Backstab card clears all CAREER HICCUP cards (see below).

"WATCH OUT, YOU'VE GOT A CAREER HICCUP!"

It's not just the BACKSTAB cards that allow you to get ahead of your rivals. There are also a whole range of CAREER HICCUP cards you can lay on your opponents.

Sometimes it's worth slapping one of these babies on your rivals rather than just accumulating commission cards.

THE MEDIA™: "DO IT TO THEM, BEFORE THEY DO IT TO YOU"

When someone plays a CAREER HICCUP card on top of your BUILD YOUR CAREER cards, you can't lay any commission cards. The only way to get rid of a CAREER HICCUP card is to play either a BACKSTAB CARD or one of the many "I APOLOGISE ON MORNING TELEVISION" cards.

CAREER HICCUP CARDS INCLUDE:

> I need it to get out of bed in the morning!
> She's bloody jailbait!
> Dead prostitute in a hotel room.
> Waltzing through customs with a handbag of heroin.
> Kiddie fiddling.

THE CAREER HICCUP CARDS are bad. But they're nothing compared to the "I CAN'T GET ARRESTED IN THIS TOWN" cards. Avoid these like the plague. Use every opportunity to fob them off on your rivals. Playing one of these cards during the game will remove one or more of the player's COMMISSION cards. If the game ends and you still have one of the following cards in your hand, deduct the appropriate amount of points. When a "I CAN'T GET ARRESTED IN THIS TOWN" card is played, each player must pass a card, face down, in a clockwise direction. This is your chance to palm off all those nasty cards onto your rivals.

THE "I CAN'T GET ARRESTED IN THIS TOWN" CARDS

> Stuck in Contract Publishing (put all your commissions and your BUILD YOUR CAREER card onto the "Spiked" deck. You'll have to start all over again). Miss two goes. If it's still in your hand at the end of the game: Minus £500,000
> Nervous Exhaustion (put highest commission card onto the "Spiked" deck,

THE MEDIA™:
THE EXCITING NEW CARD GAME OF
DECEIT AND SELF-PROMOTION FROM THE IDLER

lose a go). Minus £250,000
> They're not returning my calls any more! (put lowest commission card onto the "Spiked" deck, lose a go) Minus £100,000
> Voicemail Hell (lose a go. Minus £50,000)

At the end of the game, add up the value of your commission cards, subtract the values of any "I CAN'T GET ARRESTED IN THIS TOWN" cards and note down each player's points. Also, deduct the value of the highest commission card left in your hand. The first to reach £1 Million pounds is declared the winner. ☞

TRACTOR SALE

Cambridge Circus (just behind the clowns dressing room)
November 5th
many bargains...

Massey Ferguson, John Deer, David Brown, Davy Crockett, Fettle and Wettle, Sprokit and Turk, Dirkitt and Webb, Twin Kam Fottie Fottie Tatie Picking kiss my black ass spudlifter. From the people that bought you tea in the morning with biscuits in brackets optional two stroke stroke two options never never payment plans stroke plan for nothing as you never know what's round the corner.com or visit us at our telephone sales sight and listen to 45 minutes of well educated but bored housewife whittle on about semibidoquial valves and double ended fun sticks and fully formed baby-armed dicksticks.

**Free buttmonkey with every 100th tractor sold
Potatoes everywhere...**

The Idler 5000 Model (never knowingly used)

WARNING

THIS IS AN ADVERT FOR THE SHOREDITCH TWAT

never knowingly understood

available monthly from 333

THE SECRETS OF COMEDY...
TAKE MY MOTHER-IN-LAW.... SHE'S GOT ADULT... ONSET... BLINDNESS.
I'M FUNNIER THAN YOU ARE, MATE.
GWYN

UP THE GARY

By pure chance, GREG ROWLAND has disccovered a set of proofs for the Gary Glitter Annual 1975, complete with revealing marginalia allegedly written by Gary's lawyer. Here we reproduce a selection

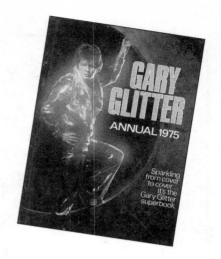

I have deleted some of these

Gary, the pic of 'Jennifer' is perhaps not entirely suitable?

Dear Gary...

Dear Gary,
My friend says you only like girls with red hair (she's got red hair) Please tell me it's not true.

Well she's right, I do like girls with red hair - It's not the colour of hair that counts it's the person underneath it.

Yes, I think we can go with this now

I am pleased to see the boys are now wearing shorts, despite your protestations.

HOW TO SKIN A CAT

**Confessions of a teenage taxidermist. By VICTORIA ISHERWOOD.
Illustration by MARC BAINES**

"**A**re you the girl with the dead cat in the freezer?"

It's a Saturday afternoon, and I'm sitting on the museum steps, reading the lyric sheet of the new Smiths album (the specky kid's version of hanging round the shopping precinct) and I'm getting hassled by a bunch of scallies.

"Well, are you?"

"Yes. And?"

"That's disgustin'"

"Why? Bet you've got dead cow in your freezer. At least I know where my cat's been."

"You're fuckin' weird weirdo." And they knock my hat off, which isn't so bad. In the park, they'd have thrown rocks.

I blamed it on the change of school. When you're a kid growing up in a small village, neighbours come to accept each other's little quirks. It's all part of life's rich tapestry. Then, in those sensitive teenage years comes a new school, new people and questions. So the Geography teacher pauses in her description of the artesian bore, to ask: "Victoria. Have you *really* got a dead cat in the freezer?" Well, yes. "With the food?" Yep, in between the mini-milks and the sun lollies, in a bin bag sealed with novelty gift tape bearing the legend "dead cat enclosed". My explanation, that I loved Gingerbits very much and was going to stuff her, somehow failed to satisfy. My fate was sealed: Merseyside's Boo Radley.

What can I say? It was the Seventies: it was this, or Bunty, and as hobbies go, at least it was cheap, and, hell, was it really any more peculiar than lusting after ponies, or worshipping the God Keegan, or collecting gonks, or any of the other more hygenic obsessions of my supposedly "normal" peers? Children are morbid, nasty little creatures when left to their own devices, and I was fortunate enough to have a mother who believed a child should be free to express itself, and if it chose to express itself by disappearing into dark corners of the garden with a trowel to see how the dead kitty's "getting on", then so be it.

And it wasn't really morbidity, OK, so I'm wearing black, and I do own some Joy Division albums, and, yes, I don't get out much and yes I did spend a year living alone with my mother in a rambling house, stuffing birds, badly, but it wasn't morbidity that drove the obsession. It was curiosity. I mean, I'd love to have spent five years sailing round the coast of Tierra Del Fuego with a mad captain, digging up the bones of extinct animals, coming up with a novel theory of natural selection, and, as an extra added bonus, pissing off an awful lot of Christians. But I was seven years old, and lived in the sort of village John Betjemen wrote doggerel about. Still, I did my best, becoming the kid that people brought wounded animals to, on the dubious grounds that "she wants to be a vet" – not actually a qualification, but there you go. And when, having prolonged their suffering for a day or two, I found them, stiff and stark, I thought, well, why should the fun end there?

The baroque little funerals were just for starters. Where my peers had *Little House on the Prairie* to look forward to, I had the weekly saga of insect folk, played

NOTES FROM THE COUCH

out on Malteser boxes and Peak Freans tins in various parts of the garden. And Roger Corman didn't lie – those little corpses really did turn to green slime, just like M Valdemar. Then, as I got more professional, I began to devise elaborate structures of chicken wire, letting flies in, but keeping foxes out, thus allowing me to observe the more instantly gratifying delights of bodily corruption above ground. Ah! And what delights! Like a gardener watching his prize orchids bloom, I'd visit them morning, noon and night, watering them to keep them moist, and watching the bloating belly, the eggs hatch in deflating eyeballs, arse and mouth, the lips drawing back from pearly little teeth in a Spaghetti Western sneer. Then came "Foom", the chaos stage, when fat little maggots turned the whole thing into an omelette of liquefied flesh and sharp little bones, and, if you looked closely, you could see each individual spine or feather move in tiny gyrations, as the maggots gnawed away at the roots. As work progressed, I'd provide them with a cover – an upturned fruit box – because maggots, like the murder squad, prefer to work in a tent. Then, at the end of the summer, when the ants had picked the little corpses clean, the skulls and bones would join the pet mausoleum on the bedroom bookshelves.

Sundays, I'd go down to the lighthouse, where all the crap from down river and borne in by the incoming tide would collect amongst the pink psychedelic rocks, dead dogs from Widnes and dead sheep from Wales in amongst the usual condoms and jam rags and doll limbs that make up yer Scouse detritus. And I'd have fun, me and my pen knife, dismembering crusty old seagulls, then cycle home, dodging the Big Kids From the Estate, with bags of heads and wings and little

orange feet slung over the handlebars. And so, naturally, when they raided Jeffrey Dahmer's fridge, we got phone calls; "You want to watch her," just because young Jeffrey spent his formative years cycling round his neighbourhood with pockets stuffed with plastic bags, looking for roadkill to take home and hang in trees. Well, you've got to hang them in trees, otherwise the foxes get them.

And not all the neighbours were hostile. OK, so the kids next door rigged up an outdoor karaoke tannoy system to shout "Witch lady hee hee hee…" at me, and dared their mates to run the whole length of our privet hedge. Oh, and they *did* spread the rumour that I'd killed a kid (it was a doll, right? A life-size doll). But some, accepting as a legitimate career move the explanation that I'd switched role models from James Herriot to Quincy MD, would drop round bearing gifts of fresh roadkill, whilst an emigrating taxidermist bequeathed me the entire contents of his freezer: "be careful when you're skinning the weasel's gonads". I was easy to please.

Still, it's a strange thing: if I'd gone out with a shotgun, killing things, everyone would have thought I was normal, But collecting dead stuff? Oh, and I'm a vegetarian, too, something which my fascination with the body and all its works has only reinforced, in a pantheistic, Fotherington-Thomas kind of way: you know – the intricate beauty of fur and feathers, the elegant mechanics of flesh and bone; the sweet mystery of life: I'm buggered if I'm going to destroy all that, just to put it in a bun.

But I'll eat roadkill. Well, why the hell not? I'd skinned a wren. It looked like an action man Xmas Turkey. I cooked it. I ate it. I didn't die. What-the-cat-dragged-in is guilt-free meat, and fun, in a fat–fingered,

Peter-Ustinov-Nero kind of way. Basically, if it's vegetarian or insectivorous, has clear eyes, a clean arse, and isn't bloating or maggoty, it's probably edible: just pick out the sharp bits and cook till you smell it. The irony is that the flatmates who thought this was a disgusting practise were quite happy to eat a pheasant that had died of multiple trauma injuries inflicted by toxic lead shot care of some trigger happy Rollo, then left hanging for a fortnight outside a poulterer's.

Which leaves you with the skin. Back in the Long Hot Summer of '76 my cousin did the Tarzan thing in the paddling pool with my beloved stuffed crocodile. He swelled up like a teabag. Attempting to pacify her screaming brat, mum slit open the belly of the beast and disgorged its sopping sawdust insides. A little bit of childhood died that day, true, but the seeds of a new obsession were sown. A couple of years later, "Brendon Chase" revealed the secrets of the black art, as Mr JD Watkins-Pritchard generously, and with malice aforethought, devotes an entire chapter to skinning a jay. Then what? "Pepper'll cure a skin," he promised, assuming correctly that the Victorian preference, arsenic, was beyond the bounds of the Puffin Club. It didn't. They stank. And then the cat ate them. Oh, but who cares? To be honest, I use "taxidermist" as a flag of convenience; its the whole skinning bit that's the thing I love, not merely the pleasingly Zen process itself, but that whole voyage of discovery thing when you first encounter something's insides: Mouse, truly, I never knew you.

In the end, ambition was my undoing. I got hold of a copy of Metcalf, the Taxidermist's Bible, and it rapidly became clear that professional taxidermic practice was utterly incompatible with a life in bedsit-land: *chez* Metcalf is kitted out with meat hooks and pulleys, fleshing boards and chemical baths, the whole Clive Barker kit. I wasn't even allowed Blu-Tak. And then there's the appendix; "checklist of diseases contagious to man". Hmm. "Bubonic Plague. Anthrax. Brucellosis. Shigellosis. Aspergillosis. Vervet Monkey Disease. Q Fever." (you're making these up), "Psittacosis". (Neighbour had that… Nasty.) "Tuberculosis". No BCG. And coming up the inside, "CJD", which did for a friend's dad. Hmm. OK. So.

Fuck.

So I gave it up, for health reasons. No more afternoons spent up to my wrists in badger, trying to saw its head off with a titchy Swan-Morton scalpel; no more driving back from Llandudno with my Nan complaining all the way home that she can't taste her chips 'cos of the stinking herring gull in the boot ("But mum, it's so rare to find a fresh one"). I've been clean for ten years now. I've still got the habit, but now I buy my stuff pre-stuffed from South Ken auction rooms, and poncey shops in Notting Hill ("Ninety quid for a dingo's head? You can get three whole dingoes for that Up North!") But I'm still the girl with the dead cat in the freezer. Three, to be precise.

SKINNING A CAT

Acquire your cat. Not as easy as it sounds. If you choose to stuff your own cat, your family will make you a pariah. If you stuff someone else's, everyone will make you a pariah. Your best bet is to drive round a bit, and if you pass the same corpse two days running, chances are no-one loves it: remember the Nilsen-Dhalmer principle: no one misses a stray. Even so, it is only fair to knock on the doors of nearby houses, and ask, solemnly,

if they've lost a cat. Do not ring their bell and say "D'you mind if I stuff this?", because you will only get punched. Bear in mind stray cats have feline AIDS or leukaemia, so maybe your best bet would be to go to the RSPCA, 'cos they kill hundreds of healthy animals every day.

1. A word of warning. The residents of a freshly killed and rapidly cooling cat will do a Titanic job, gathering on the highest promontory of their late host on the lookout for a nice warm lifeboat. That's you. (Historical note: It is said that the exodus of lice from the corpse of Saint Thomas à Becket betokened his extreme holiness. It's a line I've tried anyway).

2. Bag it up: accident victims tend to leak.

3. Take it home, and keep it at room temperature until rigor mortis has worn off. Don't leave it anywhere where it might distress or excite your pets, or anyone else for that matter.

4. Table, light, newspaper, scalpel, shears, latex gloves, tissue paper and friend who can be called in to scratch itches, change TV channel, answer front door, etc at inopportune moments. Remember what happened to Thomas Hardy's corpse, and remove pets.

5. Put the animal on its back, and make a centre-parting in the belly-fur, below the rib-cage. If the fur is loose, and slips off, your patient is too far gone: bury it. If not, lightly stroke the scalpel along the parting, gently: you want to slice right through the skin – think Richey Manic's arm – but not burst through the membrane into the guts and the putrefying Kit-e-Kat within. Now peel back the skin from the body, using fingers and a blunt knife to slice through the connective tissue – fingernails are ideal, perfect, honed by two million years of evolution for this very purpose: peeling.

Rabbis still use them – they keep their thumbnail long. And it's strangely satisfying, like picking scabs. Unfortunately, it's also incredibly unhygienic. Pity.

6. Shear the legs off at the hips, mopping up the blood with Kleenex or sawdust, pull the tail out, then peel up to the shoulders, shearing through the joints, and peel the skin back to the ears; like taking off a skinny-rib sweater. When you reach the ears, cut them off at the root. Be careful cutting round the eyelids and the nose, and cut the gums near the teeth. Now you've got to de-flesh the legs and feet, de-flesh the paw pads from the outside, and scrape off all the fat. By now you will understand why Norman Bates stuck to birds.

7. Marinade in a bath of fixative; Metcalf's cocktail is 7 litres water, 700g salt, 700g alum, 110g borax and 10g of carbolic acid. I tried acetone instead. Well, it worked for Mr. Dahlmer.

8. Pare, degrease with petrol, wash, and preserve with borax, or salt and alum, or whatever. I can't vouch for any of these, because by this stage my scabby little mongrel Biff, had run off with the skin.

9. Stuff.

Please note: there is more than one way to skin a cat.

USES FOR A DEAD CAT

1. Annoy angry dogs. Place the cat near them and enjoy the confusion on their little faces.

2. Disconcert elderly relatives. Place the cat near them and enjoy the confusion.

3. Rent it out to Vic and Bob, and watch them destroy it. Some people have no respect for the taxidermist's art.

4. Get pissed off when people use it as the butt of hilarious jokes about "stuffing" and "pussy". ◉

TRAVEL TWISTER

An anonymous Idler reader sent us this ingenious miniature version of the popular game

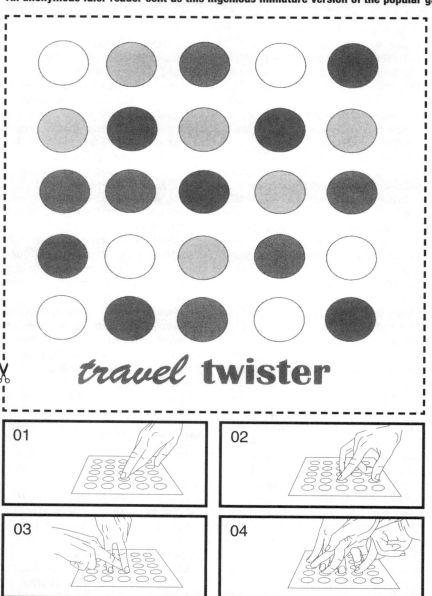

01

02

03

04

DIARY: ARTHUR SMITH

He's got a lovely voice, ARTHUR SMITH. And he knows all there is to know about doing nothing. Illustration by LORNA MILLER

I'm amazed when people want more hours in the day. I think there are far too many already. The most brilliant and exciting moments of a lifetime are just that – moments. If you add them all together, they come to about twenty five minutes. There are 700,805 hours in a person's life. Oh yes, you can do stuff. You can have a job, children, climb Mount Everest, go bungee jumping, but it's all a lie. People who lead busy, interesting lives are in denial. People like myself, who get up in the early afternoon and wrestle boredom to the floor – we're the true heroes. Don't you see? You can't stop time. Have you ever been so bored that you'd rather check into a hotel than change your duvet cover? Have you ever been so bored that you could scream?

10am Wake up. Have piss. Decide not to go swimming. Go back to bed.
11am Wake up. Get dressed. Have piss. Go back to bed.
11.30am Wake up. Get undressed. Go back to bed.
12.41pm Get up. Turn on telly.
8.00pm Turn off telly.
8.02pm Go to pub.
8.04 – 9.27pm Feel fantastic. World is my Oyster. Meet Geoff and his attractive wife Denise. Rejoice in infinite variety of human personality.
9.57pm Geoff is a wanker. Don't know what Denise sees in him. They leave, probably to have sex together.
10.15pm Middle-aged woman on neighbouring table does not wish to go to bed with me.
10.32pm Life has no meaning. Am plunged into black depression. Resolve to go swimming every day, start work on novel and not drink for a fortnight.
10.59pm Order pint, large scotch, and bottle of white wine to take home.
12.27pm Arrive at club in West End. Fail to gain entry. Notice Geoff and Denise inside. Get taxi home.
1.15am Call ex-girlfriend. Put phone down after one ring
1.16am Call ex-girlfriend. Put down phone after two rings.
1.19am Begin work on novel
1.20am Decide to check email.
1.21am Realise I don't own a computer.
1.22am Go to bed.
10am Wake up. Have piss. Decide not to go swimming. Go back to bed. ✆

From Arthur Smith Sings Leonard Cohen

HENRY CYRIL PAGET

The Ffith Marquess of Anglesey converted the family chapel into a theatre and squandered his fortune on fancy jewellery for his band of amateur players. The family tried to erase his memory, but SIMON McAUSLANE has the inside story. Illustration by LORNA MILLER

Henry Cyril Paget, Fifth Marquess of Anglesey, died bankrupt aged just 29 in 1905. His life had been devoted to the unbridled and unashamed squandering of a very large private fortune. Like Des Esseintes, the dissolute, infinitely wealthy antihero of Huysmans' *A Rebours*, Paget spent everything on the creation of his own opulent world, driven by an obsessional pursuit of aesthetic fulfilment. Whereas Des Esseintes became insular and retreated into private darkness, Henry Cyril Paget did quite the opposite — an extremely flamboyant extrovert, his principle interests were dressing up, collecting and wearing very expensive jewellery, dancing and staging lavish theatrical extravaganzas.

The Pagets were a particularly illustrious and respected Victorian dynasty. Henry Cyril's grandfather, Sir Henry William Paget MP had raised a regiment of infantry, served in Flanders and commanded the cavalry with great distinction in Spain. It was at Waterloo, however, that he established the Paget name forever, or, at least until his grandson was to come along some sixty years later. He lost a leg during one of the early assaults, but insisted on carrying on until the battle was won. His extraordinary, stoic bravery earned him unconditional tributory awe from the Establishment, and the affectionate family nickname "One Leg".

Henry Cyril's nickname was 'The Dancing Marquess', and was probably used less than affectionately by the rest of his family. He was born in 1875 and brought up in France, largely in the company of theatrical people. These formative years clearly instilled a deep love of showing off, and, sure enough, his first *fait accompli* upon entering the family seat at Plas Newydd was to convert the centuries old chapel into a theatre. From 1901 onwards, he staged a series of productions whose scale and cost were boundless. Casts of 50 or 60 were clad in luxurious, fantastic costumes and large amounts of jewellery. Paget was especially fond of "Aladdin", and it is believed this light opera was the most performed work by his company. He played the part of Pekoe, and during the interval would perform his celebrated "Butterfly Dance". What this actually consisted of is unclear, although large gossamer-effect wings and huge clusters of colourful jewels, and a great deal of running around with arms flapping can be guessed at. Hence "The Dancing Marquess".

In just four years, Paget blew his entire fortune on luxurious goods, clothes, jewels and the upkeep of very large casts of actors for his productions which would tour in Britain and the Continent. It is not known how much he actually spent, but the jewellery alone for his own Henry V costume cost £40,000, or for over four million pounds by today's values. That was just one costume out of hundreds made for his company over the years.

Sadly, very little information about Henry Cyril Paget exists today. Unlike his forebears and successors, he is not listed in Who Was Who. After his death he was succeeded by his cousin, the Sixth Marquess of Anglesey, whose first priority was to reconvert the chapel and systematically destroy all evidence that Henry Cyril Paget had ever existed. There are no private papers, correspondence, diaries or itineraries left at all. The existence today of cast lists, visitors' books and theatre programmes would be especially invaluable, for it will now never be known who his friends and, of course, large casts of players actually were, who they performed to, and where. It's not inconceivable that Paget was at least known to Oscar Wilde, Saki, Winston Churchill and Edwardian Society. Nonetheless, his outrageous life proved to be literally so, for it was clearly a fit of outrage that his successor unhesitantly condemned him to obscurity and disgrace.

This seems a shame, for Henry Cyril Paget was almost certainly an exuberant, popular and, in his own way, brave man, both ahead of his time and of it too. He died in Monte Carlo — the circumstances are unclear, but it would seem he had

IN JUST FOUR YEARS, PAGET BLEW HIS ENTIRE FORTUNE ON LUXURIOUS GOODS, CLOTHES, JEWELS AND THE UPKEEP OF VERY LARGE CASTS OF ACTORS

completely burnt himself out and spent his huge fortune. The bankruptcy sale of his effects lasted an incredible seventeen days. An obituary in "The Bystander" cruelly compared him to his heroic grandfather and stated: "His example will remain one of the strongest arguments against our hereditary system that the most ardent revolutionary would wish for."

Perhaps one step towards the rehabilitation of Paget would be a less cruel comparison to his heroic grandfather. Both, in their very different ways, displayed an indomitable spirit, originality, and determination and courage which an unkind view could say wavered into the realm of abject stupidity. Both, too, were surely in posession of great charisma and a primal joie de vivre, for how else could they have bonded large groups of people, be they actors or cavalry, and turned them into disciples?

"The Bystander's" obituary did, however, go on to concede that Henry Cyril Paget was much loved by estate workers and locals in Anglesey. The high likelihood of finding stray emeralds and rubies in the locale could have been a factor, of course, but true affection for a riotously amusing eccentric who lived in the most glorious manner of all — that of not caring a damn — seems likely too. ◉

CRAZY TIME

IT WAS A CRAZY TIME-ME AND THE GUYS
HAD PILED INTO A 1963 CADILLAC
SEDAN DE VILLE

THEN WE JUMPED INTO A PONTIAC
1965 CATALINA CONVERTIBLE

THEN ONE OF THE GUYS WAS SICK
OVER THE WHEEL ARCH OF A
1965 LINCOLN CONTINENTAL

THE WISDOM OF WC FIELDS
By Dan Kieran

No *Idler* devoted to the fool would be complete without some reference to WC Fields, the original cranky old man. A bulbous-nosed, self-obsessed, alcoholic who hated pretty much everything except drinking, he was a true eccentric and an unknown quantity in a time of Puritanism in the burgeoning American film industry. He was a breath of fresh air, and a stink bomb at the same time, almost uniquely finding huge success both on the Vaudeville stages of antebellum America and the cinema screens of the early 1900s.

At the time Fields received better reviews than many of his contemporaries, including Chaplin, the Marx Brothers and Buster Keaton but he was to be forever over-shadowed by his arch nemesis, Houdini, whose successes always seemed to out-do his own, and who ultimately stole his place in history as the greatest entertainer of his generation.

A comic genius and juggler extraordinaire, John Cleese heralds him as "the greatest of all comics" and although many of his early films have been lost forever, he did succeed in leaving his own special brand of wisdom. Here are some of the best examples;

FIELDSIAN PHILOSOPHIES

On the whole, I would rather be in Philadelphia *Epitaph*

I was in love with a beautiful blonde once, she drove me to drink. It's the one thing I'm indebted to her for...
From *Never Give a Sucker an Even Break 1941*

Sleep...the most beautiful experience in life — except drink.
My Little Chickadee. 1940

Secretary: "Someday you'll drown in a vat of whiskey."
WC: Drown in a vat of whiskey? Oh death, where is thy sting?
From *Never Give a Sucker an Even Break*

When asked to give money to charity, Fields gave this excuse for refusing:

WC: You see, I am a member of the FEBF
Man: The what?
WC: Fuck everybody but Fields.

On reading the Bible:
I admit I scanned it once, searching for some movie plots [but found] only a pack of wild lies.

I never vote for anyone. I always vote against.

I was married once — in San Francisco. I haven't seen her for many years. The great earthquake and fire in 1906 destroyed the marriage certificate. There's no legal proof. Which proves that earthquakes aren't all bad.

Man (to WC): You're drunk!
WC: Yeah, and you're crazy. And I'll be

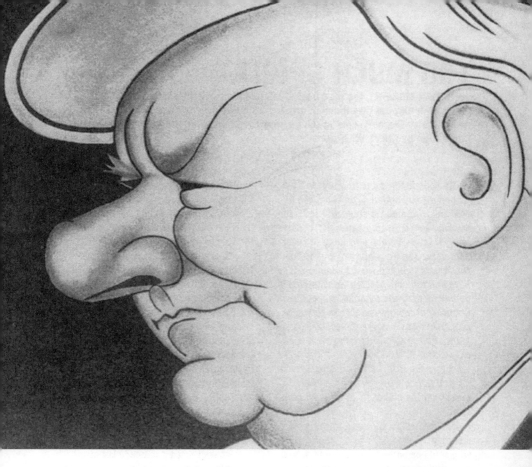

sober tomorrow and you'll be crazy for the rest of your life.
It's a Gift, 1934

If at first you don't succeed, try again. Then quit. There's no use being a damn fool about it.

Man:I have no sympathy for a man who is intoxicated all the time.
WC:A man who's intoxicated all the time doesn't need sympathy.

A plumber's idea of Cleopatra
On *My Little Chickadee* co-star Mae West.

It's a funny old world — a man's lucky if he gets out of it alive. *You're Telling Me.1934*

When asked why he never drank water:
Fish fuck in it.

Invited to play golf by someone he didn't like, Fields responded:
When I want to play with a prick, I'll play with my own.

WC Fields in Four Classic Comedy Shorts including *The Dentist, The Barber Shop, The Fatal Glass of Beer* and *The Golf Specialist* is available on video priced £11.99.

TOO MUCH SPIRIT

JONATHAN MOBERLY, the man behind Ellipsis the publishers and Foundry the Shoreditch bar, got fifty Russian artists and poets over to London. Then his crew went over to Moscow. Lots of things happened, including maggot racing. Illustration by CHRIS WATSON

" *The Foundry is going to Moscow. Dom is coming to London. Dom is a place in Moscow with a bar, a stage and walls for sticking art to. From August 20 to 27 we are giving the Foundry to Dom. In LATE September the Russians are giving Dom to the Foundry. If you want to come sign here and tell us what you want to do. We do have a few quid (thanks to the British Council) but money is tight. So the more people who can pay for themselves, the more of us can get there. Flights are cheap. This is the application form. Make your own job title, make your own dream job and tell us why you are the best person on the planet to do what you want to do.*"

This invitation appeared in the New Foundry a few months ago. Open to anyone who could be bothered to respond with a ballpoint pen, a job title and a fitting job description. Offers to contribute towards the cost of the trip also helped. Every one pound contribution liberated a similar pound from the British Council Paupers Relief Fund. From this mixture of self-assistance and government propaganda largesse, a mobbled troupe of fifty Foundry barflys mounted an all-out anarchic alco-art assault on Russia. Storming Russia's Channel One TV station on our first day in the manner of a Seventies bank raid with plastic guns and clown masks set the tone for a week of chaotic intervention that brought Foundry-inspired noise, geeks, circus and opera to the DOM, out onto the streets of Moscow and into the homes of a

million Russians for primetime breakfast TV. Our final act, as part of a week-long Moscow Trail inspired by the names of British Cold War nuclear warheads, was the sowing of poppy seeds in Red Square (the tolerance of Kremlin Guards was tested prior to this with night fireworks in front of Lenin's tomb). One month earlier thirty five Domovites had descended upon the Foundry with a catalogue of events both outside – naked street performance and burning pavements – and (explosively) inside the Foundry. Greeted by a British cold war air-to-air Firestreak missile the party continued for a week with an infusion of Russian sounds visuals vodka and graffiti. The world's first alcofilm festival was launched and samogon – Russian moonshine – distilled. Rain-soaked dried fish heads lay strewn around the pavements of Shoreditch as the russians departed.Functionally equivalent to the Foundry (which ellipsis runs with Gimpo and Bill Drummond) but in style quite opposite. Where Foundry is more Moscow than Shoreditch, DOM is all New Hoxton white walls and gymnasium floor, so a bar swap seemed necessary to sort out our identity crisis.

THE MAGGOT RACES

Isobel Clouter writes: A last minute decision was made to move the annual Shoreditch maggot races to Moscow in an attempt to escape the heavy handed racketeers of London's East End although the frantic wagering was quick to attract

THE TROUBLE WITH RACING THREE-DAY-OLDS IS THAT AFTER A WEEK THE MAGGOTS START TO PUPATE, WHICH MAKES IT VERY DIFFICULT TO BUILD UP FORM

the attention of the Russian mafioso. The host for the event was The Dom in Moscow.

The shock of the favourite Mr Wiggler's early demise at last nights final stage of the championships came amidst accusations of serious tampering during the event. Aside from the turbulence one man was very happy. Maggot trainer Stephen Haines regarded the event as a success and blamed the crowd's behaviour for the chaotic finish.

"The spectators were getting too excited. They were crowding in and it was getting very difficult to get the maggots in the stalls. Contrary to what people might think maggots are very receptive. They pick up on the feverish atmosphere of the meeting and it disturbs them. I think we lost at least three good racing maggots apart from the ones that Kenny ate!"

Stephen Haines is the owner of the "Larvadrome", the track used in the event. It's a standard 18 inch track, which is the only official track length over which maggots are allowed to race in this country. There are only six lanes.

"The main problem is getting the maggots to race all at once. By the time you've put the sixth one in the stalls the first one has already wriggled out and gone somewhere else. One of the other problems is getting them all to face in the same direction. Some of them would get half way up the track and then turn round and go in the opposite direction."

I asked Gimpo, manager of the winning team, if he had any tips on how to pick a winner.

"We had three breeds - red ones , yellow ones and white ones. If you're looking for a result I'd say that the red ones are the best!"

From a stable of nearly 1,000 maggots building up a close relationship with individuals is rather difficult. This is compounded by the trouble with racing three-day-olds in that after a week they start to pupate which makes it very difficult to build up form. Haines is adamant however that the real enemy of the maggot race is maggot tampering.

"They are on their best form if they haven't eaten for at least eight hours before hand. People often try and sneak in with the odd bit of bacon to excite them before the race. If you give them a hunk of bacon it is more likely that they'll eat and then go to sleep and change their skin and before you know it you've got flies!"

THE ABSINTHE COMPETITION

Last issue we asked you to write, in no more than 300 words, why absinthe should be banned. The standard of the entries was abysmal. No, they were OK. The best one ignored the rules and came in the form of a cartoon, reproduced below. Overall, we detected a lot of anger from you. Are you all right?

The following readers wowed the judges with their persuasive arguments and all will receive a bottle of Hill's Absinth for their pains.

Dan Lewis, Stratford-upon-Avon; Melissa Rossi, US; Sam Redlark, Southend-on-Sea; Antony de Heveningham, by e-mail; Harry Horse, by e-mail; Richard Smith, London; Andrew Osmond, Watford; Max, London; Ben Myers, London; Sean Steele, Wallasey.

We have reprinted an extract from Richard Smith's entry on the right. The appalling pun made us laugh.

And below you'll find the winning cartoon, penned by one Harry Horse. Go to idler.co.uk to see all the winners. Salut!

WHY ABSINTHE SHOULD BE BANNED
By Richard Smith

Consider the following salutary tale reported by Absinthe Abusers Anonymous: Chubby Scott and erstwhile master of the oche, Jocky Wilson, once crashed to a first round defeat at The Crucible after Eric "The Crafty Cockney" Bristow persuaded him to substitute his customary tipple of a pint of vodka for absinthe. Jocky Wilson said, "It tasted like petrol 'n polo mints and it ruined ma game; one or two wee sips and I couldnae hit an elephants arse wi' a banjo, let alone a double-top. Aye, no doubt about it, absinthe makes the dart throw wander."

WHY ABSINTHE SHOULD BE BANNED By Harry Horse

BILL & ZED'S Bad Advice

"WE'VE FUCKED UP OUR LIVES, NOW IT'S YOUR TURN"

Bill is temporarily out of order.

....

Dear Bill and Zed

When I approach women they look at me as if I'm a tumour and always flick me off like some gum from a puma. Can you help me bury it?

Mixmaster Moose
Los Angeles

[Zed] The crux of your dilemma is evident in your very first sentence: "When you approach women." No, no, no, one never approaches a woman, that's tantamount to walking up to some young girl in a nightclub, whipping out your cock and saying "Do you want to suck this, it tastes of shit."

The thing about bitches is that they all need to be the centre of attention and if you're the one guy in the room that isn't paying any attention you can bet your bottom dollar that slagfeatures is going to bend over backwards to get your attention.

The cool, aloof, loner at the bar technique. I've been using that one for years and believe me son, my dick rarely stays dry for long.

Of course I am ridiculously good looking and radiate a potent, sexual charisma that has women orgasming in their knickers

before they even talk to me, that probably has quite a lot to do with my amazing success with women but don't worry, if you're an ugly tosser I'm sure my snaggle toothed, gangly, mong, spazmo friend Bill's advice will be of much more use.

....

Dear Bill and Zed

I have recently noticed that everybody is looking at me. When I turn my back, they point at me and laugh. My friends hold secret meetings to discuss my faults and I don't feel able to take a holiday because I know that if I do all my colleagues will hold a massive party, dance jigs on the furniture and sing jubilant songs about my absence. I can't relax for a second. Please help me.

Jules I, South London.

[Zed] Usually paranoia which has developed to such a degree as yours has a tendency to be based on some element of truth. You are obviously a deeply unpleasant person, Jules, and I would suggest that you do all of us a favour and throw yourself under a tube train immediately.

....

Dear Bill and Zed

The Greek philosopher Heraclitus said that

according to the principle of "rather not" (*ou mallon*), everything is one. I want to apply this principle to my life but am at a loss where to start?
Mark S, Bryanston

[Zed] What the fuck are you talking about you student fucking arsehole?

....

Dear Bill and Zed

I spent three years studying hard for a degree in Classics. Two years later it has still not come in handy. My shoes are becoming increasingly down-at-heel. How can I turn my hard labour to profit?
Over educated under-achiever,
Sam J, Lancaster.

[Zed] Why not get a job at a publishing house editing the work of people who are far more intelligent, witty and better looking than you, that's what people with Classics degrees usually do isn't it? You cunt.

....

Dear Bill and Zed

My best friend has decided to become a stand-up comedian. But neither myself nor my husband have ever found him funny. Recently, we went to see him perform at an open mike slot and, sure enough, he was terrible. Should I take him aside and dissuade him from the foolish dream, or should I wait for him to realise what an idiot he is being?
Sarah B, Winchester.

[Zed] Why don't you mind your own business, you lesbian slag.

....

Dear Bill and Zed

I have started experiencing difficulty sleeping. A combination of tense work pressures and what I can only describe as an unease about losing consciousness means I lie awake every night. Can you recommend some action or cure for my insomnia?
Peter L, Norfolk

[Zed] Rape and murder. It works for me.

IDLE INVENTIONS 2
By JOHN MOORE

THE RUDE PHONE £39.95 +£5 p&p
An intelligent communication device that ensures no call to or from your home lasts for more than your preferred duration. After five minutes of continuous conversation the phone emits an audible yawn. This is followed two minutes later by an irritated tapping sound. Should this fail, the Rude Phone will advance to Deluxe phase. It begins to tut and say "yeah yeah" during every pause. Two minutes later,

it switches to Ultra phase, simulating a cross line, interrupting and issuing threats in exotic accents. The Gold Plus model impersonates the caller's dead relatives and accusing them from beyond the grave of murdering them. If this does not cause the receiver to be slammed down at both ends , the Rude Phone reaches its final Tourette's PhaseTM, repeating the words "Cunt, Cunt, Cunt" ad infinitum.
Comes with a choice of covers.

FOOL CHILDREN

Picture and poem by GED WELLS

Fool children of the revolution.
Safe as trousers, free as absurd,
Close to the hedge, your bets even as odds on,
Minding the gaps, gaps minding own business,
Uncomfort blanket, soggy chewed corners of the world,
Evening standard deliver, highway man is rubbery,
Bandits at six o'clock, privet dancers.
Hovering midges play hard to get,
Blown leaves pretending to be frogs,
Frogs pretending to be insulted,
Let's play a more dangerous game
Push the bound and gagged,
Blank stares this way only, reading signs of life,
Must goes up, what comes down, skate and disturb,
Zoo breaker, crocodile tearing some fresh flesh,
Carefree in community,
Bad tripping, a student loan, lost of noodle,
Acid rain dancing for the dragon face poodle.
Cockney and bull story, plate of meat and two veg,
Insider deal from a dirty raincoat.
Wind stop, kite drop, head pop,
A single mother doubling as brother,
Inbred violence breeding violently,
Creative drunks improvise post-modern urinals,
Pets mean prizes of fecal surprised,
Bandstand with standard band,
Brass polished, something for a weak end.
Grass polished, crown green for a week ending,
Bowling oldies, white and pink as dentures,
Open mouths of empty deckchairs,
Don't walk on the sensitive grass.
Escaped goats look for scape goats modelling pigskin coats,
Litter itching to move on, chewed gum settled.
An army of ants take home the shopping,
A sandwich cheese and pickle, a discarded jogger's nipple,
Leisure terminator, the park keeper,
In the dark park, the grim reaper.

GEO WELLS ©

CONVERSATIONS

LLOYD LOON

PAUL HAMILTON of Bedazzled, the Peter Cook fanzine, shoots the breeze with JOHN LLOYD, comedy producer extraordinaire. The picture on the left is an accurate likeness of Lloyd done by WALERY of Piccadilly Circus

L ike a cherub's piss whistle, the TV CV of writer-producer-director John Lloyd is small but perfectly formed: *Not The Nine O'Clock News, Blackadder, Spitting Image, A Life In Pieces* and, er, that's it. I had interviewed Lloyd before for *Publish and Bedazzled*, the (ahem) "coughicial Peter Cook fagazine", about his collaborations with the magic Wisty 'un, and was impressed by his singular lack of pomposity, his generosity with his thoughts, and his readiness to blow any trumpet other than his own. (It was only with the greatest reluctance that he would admit to being responsible for anything remotely creative or original.) A Decent Cove, I thought; the sort of chap with whom one could have an interesting chat, an even more interesting drink and then go off with to merrily let off stinkbombs at a gala film première or a funeral service.

The past decade has seen John Lloyd curb his workaholic tendencies to concentrate on producing a family instead of more TV series. He has developed a profitable sideline in directing television commercials to subsidise this tide change. In his absence, TV comedy has been descending the long bloody slide to redundancy. Chris Morris and Caroline Aherne notwithstanding, British TV comedy is a bloated, poisoned corpse raddled by instantly forgettable knuckle-dragging pub quizzes and post-modern (whatever that means these days) chat shows, all with the same fat, rich, stupid faces making the same poor stupid witless cheesy carefully-rehearsed ad libs.

I began the interview asking John if he'd been anywhere interesting lately. The answer sounded like the title of a long-lost lump of avant-garbage by rockin' combo The Fall...

LLOYD: David Frost's Summer Garden Party. Wonderful. It's held in this square opposite his house in Chelsea and its quite phenomenal because anyone who has ever been famous in the whole world is there. Frostie, although he's got a bit of a mixed reputation partly through *Private Eye* making mock of him, is a fantastically nice bloke, a very loyal friend, and if you ever get on the list for his garden party you'll never get knocked off it because he won't forget you when he

doesn't need you any more. I mean – God – I don't think I've worked with him in about twelve years, but he still asks me along. There you'll see some of the Royal Family, three or four Prime Ministers, Elton John...

HAMILTON: ...Martin Bormann...

LLOYD: ...Bormann, he was there; looking rather well, I thought. Gandhi was there, looking a picture in his lovely little gold-lined casket. There's Fergie, half the Beatles... This year there must've been over a thousand people there. I had a peculiar conversation with Terry Waite. I don't know him from Adam so I introduced myself – "Hello, Mr Waite, I used to produce *Spitting Image*" – and he went (*bellows*) "Ohhh! That wonderful sketch you did about me and Runcie! It was the funniest thing we'd ever seen." The sketch was tiny Archbishop Runcie in church praying away, and then you'd hear the sound of big Terry clumping up the aisle behind him, carrying two bags of Duty Frees: "I managed to get the gin and the whisky but I couldn't get the 200 Silk Cut." The reason they found it so funny was that Runcie and Waite used to do these mercy missions all around the world and when they came back, Mrs Runcie – Rosalind – would always say, "Did you remember the Silk Cut?" Quite unwittingly and by accident that sort of thing would happen on *Spitting Image*. You'd think up the nuttiest, maddest idea and – blow you down – they would turn out to be true.

HAMILTON: A favourite *Spitting Image* sketch for me was the "20 Drunken Greats" album, and there's Ollie Reed, Dennis Thatcher, and Peter O'Toole or someone in a shopping trolley, all smashed out of their minds yelling tunelessly into the night air.

LLOYD: Ah, that one was a bit after my time.

HAMILTON: These mad, red-eyed drinkers in the streets on Saturday nights always sound to me like they're calling Rodney Bewes.

(*Laughter. Both faux-pissheadedly crooning "Rod-nib-heyewwes."*)

LLOYD: ...but the thing with David is he loves the bizarreness of it. The sheer incongruousness of (*Frosts voice*) "You, Lloyd Honeygan – do you know the Bee Gees?" and there they'll be – Barry, Maurice and whatever the other one's called. One time Frostie got quite sozzled and he introduced me to this bloke. He said (*slurred Frost Voice*) "And errrm... Do you know – John! Lloyd! Comedy! Genius! – do you know errr... King?!" I looked at this bloke and it was King Constantine. Frostie couldn't remember the fucking guy's name! All he knew was that he was a king. (*Laughter.*) I guarantee you that, at David's parties, if you don't recognise them, they are fantastically powerful.

HAMILTON: You're not dissimilar from them – and you have one-up on the likes of Rowan Atkinson and Hugh Laurie – in that you're rich but not famous. You're not going to get people in the street coming up to you and saying "I have a cunning plan'" or "Tally-ho! With a bing and a bong and a buzz buzz buzz!"

LLOYD: And Cleese getting "Oi! Monty, show us your funny walk!" all day long. A lot of those guys find it dreadfully painful. After the first six months – when it's wonderful, apparently – they go off the idea pretty quickly. Except Angus Deayton, who loves it. He's got a great life and he's very cheerful.

I badly wanted to be famous in my twenties. I liked the idea of being a David Frost-type frontman for a show. In about '87 I did some presenting and found being looked at very disturbing. You go to the pub and someone goes, "Oh! How are you" ... "I've never met you before." ... "Well, where have I seen you before?" It's strange, a bit like if a pretty girl's in the street and everyone's looking her up and down, you know? Peculiar. It didn't suit me, the idea of being famous. Didn't like it.

HAMILTON: I've done loads of research on you so what's all this guff about you being brought up by a malteser?

LLOYD: I lived in *Malta* when I was small – nothing to do with packets of Maltesers. My Dad was in the Navy and we were stationed there when I was eight and nine. I didn't really go to school till I was nine and a half because we were always going round the world.

HAMILTON: Did you have an idealisation of England in your mind as a boy whilst you were overseas? Was there a "home" in your head?

LLOYD: Hmm, not really. I was born in Dover which is a pretty grey town at the best of times. I just remember 1950s England as being amazingly grey. Grey towns. If you went to lunch with your parents – we lived in Norwood for a while – and you'd go to some caff with pretensions to grandeur with their lace tablecloths. The mushy food. People nowadays would not accept the food that the average English person shoved down then. Lunch was mince. Perhaps some cabbage to go with it. There were no hamburgers then. If you wanted a pizza you'd have to go to Italy. I'd never heard of pizza until I was twentysomething.

We always used to go on holiday to Ireland – a country I've always liked a lot, wonderful people. But again, we always stayed in this place called The Hotel in Duncannon, Wexford. They'd have a tennis court but there'd be holes in the concrete, holes in the netting. And the food! They always gave us milk that smelled like it was three months old, and you could bounce the fried eggs off the floor. The cream was off because then only Americans had fridges. And then you'd get chucked in the sea by your Dad and you'd come out *blue*, it was so freezing.

It's amazing how colourful life is for kids now, the variety of possibilities that weren't open to me as a kid. My hobby in Malta was collecting lollysticks off the streets. Me and my two friends would go round and pick up suck-lollysticks out of the gutters and drains and see how many we could get.

HAMILTON: Were they the ones that had jokes on?

LLOYD: Yeah, some were but most of them were just sticks. The idea that anyone would allow a child to do that today – '"Get that out of your mouth! Go and wash your hands!" But then it didn't seem to matter very much that we'd been stricken with impetigo. Such a simple thing but I remember those times as incredibly happy, albeit with a diseased face caused by sucking sticks that have been up goats' arses.

(*Laughter*)

I did a Goldfish commercial with Billy Connolly and there was a young actor in that, and he said before the age of five the children's only present for Christmas and birthdays was a tin can sellotaped up with a stone inside it – and they had a whale of a time rattling these things.

We moved house recently and being, you know, a modern indulgent middle-class parent my children have got *stuff* – you know, a computer, software, electronic toys – but I tell you, for the first three months we were in this new house all they wanted to play with was the boxes the stuff came in. They made a huge den out of the removers' boxes and had an absolutely brilliant time. And so did I.

Materialism – though I'm not disapproving in a spiritual or ethical way – is counterproductive; it doesn't actually make people any happier. It's a very temporary thing. The things that really make people happy are *immaterial* – like friendship and love. Sex, I suppose, is sort of material.

HAMILTON: This is strange, you saying this when you're basically earning a crust making little films telling us to buy things that won't make us happy.

LLOYD: It's completely, utterly amoral and without justification apart from the fact that I've put in my time as a public servant on very small wages for very long hours, and this is a way for me to see my children which is more important to me than certainly any sort of career I might have had. And it's important to them.

HAMILTON: How much do you get for directing an advert – 89 million quid, isn't it?

LLOYD: 89 million pounds exactly, and all I can eat. So many things in this world are the wrong way up, it's mad. You have these runners on films who are paid nothing – £30 a week or something. You know, they don't have any shoes yet they're expected to get to work under their own steam, whereas the director is paid a fortune, is whisked to work in a limo, gets pocket money and free meals, but the people who desperately need free meals have to pay for their own lunch. It's not fair, is it?

HAMILTON: It's criminal, isn't it?

LLOYD: (*Peter Cook Cockney voice*) "Criminal, yess..." And this is the way of the world: the more worthless your profession – PR people, advertising and marketing people, bankers, for God's sake! – the more you're paid. It's an inverse law of worth. It's rotten to the core, really. And I know it sounds awful and pretentious but, you know, advertising's going to happen anyway, so if I can get in there and at least make it as honest as I can and also to add value – make them funny, entertaining and not ruin your day. 'Cos for most people advertising is entertainment; they like them, the funny ones particularly. It is selfish, ultimately. I suppose I should be working in a relief camp or making important documentaries about the meaning of life but just in the last few years I've been too busy having a family and thinking.

HAMILTON: Paul Morley said something similar recently. He's written a book with the brilliant title of *Nothing* – so if your asked what are you reading? You can say "*Nothing* by Paul Morley". He said that for about fifteen years all he cared about was Pop music, the cultural zeitgeist, style, all that stuff, but now he says that what is more fascinating and important is the family.

LLOYD: I must say, my children have taught me all the worthwhile things that I've learned. Everything that's of

MATERIALISM DOESN'T ACTUALLY MAKE PEOPLE ANY HAPPIER. THE THINGS THAT REALLY MAKE PEOPLE HAPPY ARE IMMATERIAL — LIKE FRIENDSHIP AND LOVE

value ultimately I've learned by watching them, being told things by them, learning how to behave towards children – or trying to. It's a fantastical, mystical, amazingly rewarding experience. And if you behave well, kindly, patiently, intelligently unpatronisingly towards your children they give you so much back; they give you forty times more than you give them in terms of attention, of love.

HAMILTON: How old are your children?

LLOYD: Nine, seven and four.

HAMILTON: Ah! They haven't yet reached that horrid age where if you mention a poem they go, "Poetry's sad. Get a life."

LLOYD: I read that every day you spend with your children before they're three and you're completely there for them and not thinking (*impatient voice*) "Yes, alright, I'll do Lego with you but only 20 minutes because I want to read the paper", then that time and commitment repays itself in adolescence. People will have shit relationships with their adolescent children because they had shit relationships with them before. Parents are all screwed up, angry, tired and selfish and so we'll shout to the children, "shut up, go away, do it yourself" and getting obsessed about "Tidy your room and do your homework". Who likes to do homework? I never did.

Nobody has any working philosophy for life. It obsesses me, this. If your lawnmower doesn't work you either take it to someone who can fix it, you fix it yourself or buy a new one. The same with an aeroplane. You wouldn't get in an aeroplane that only had one wing. But when it comes to human nature, people just accept their faults: "Well, I fucked up my marriage, I can't talk to my kids, my Dad hates me. But I am the way that I am. I'm greedy, selfish, fearful, lazy, spiteful – and you can't change human nature." Why don't they decide, "Well, what's wrong here? That road rage stuff I do every single fucking morning just makes me feel unhappy and tense," – why don't they get rid of it?

With marriage, after the honeymoon period, everyone starts yakking on about how they've married a lunatic, a slattern, a drunk or whatever, and they just moan on and on and making excuses for themselves. They're always looking outwards and see how wrong everything else is, but if they fix themselves first, the problems start to go away.

I can't control the world. I tried for years and years as a satirical television producer to better the world. I just made it worse, actually.

HAMILTON: D'you think?

LLOYD: I think *Spitting Image* kept Mrs Thatcher in power for years longer than she would naturally have been. We offered her a safety valve. At the time we did the show she was widely

hated. We used to get hundreds of letters every week which could roughly be divided into two piles. There were the "You cunts! You Bastards! You should all be shot!" category, and there were the others that said, "I was going to kill myself last week because I've been unemployed for four years, my wife's left me and I'm such a useless person, but I thought I'd just watch *Spitting Image* before I go, and I had such a good laugh about Thatcher being beaten over the head with a truncheon that I thought I'd give it another week." So the response went from completely prejudiced, ludicrous rantings to heart-warming letters from people who felt disenfranchised and used those Sunday nights to get the bile out of their systems.

HAMILTON: So *Spitting Image* acted as a kind of anaesthetic, numbing people from going out and rioting?

LLOYD: Yeah, we thought we'd be making Thatcher squirm and bring down the Government but really we made it better for them. Although we had writers from every political colour, from extreme right-wing to Communist, it generally panned out as a left of centre show, but we did Neil Kinnock a great disservice, I think. We'd just have him going "Lovely voters, lovely lesbos, lovely, lovely lesbos" in a pub and – because the Opposition never do anything anyway – we made him and the Labour Party look totally ineffective, thus making Thatcher look more powerful. I was on *Breakfast with Frost* not long ago and Portillo was there and he said, "This Blair government need a damn good kicking. You should bring back *Spitting Image*." That's the certain way to keep Blair in power for another ten years.

HAMILTON: We're back to David Frost again. Is it true he has a little curly tail?

LLOYD: No!

HAMILTON: Tail or not, why is it, with all his dosh, David Frost propels himself out of bed at the dawning of every Sunday morning to present a show that no one watches?

LLOYD: Everybody's money is relative. People get used to any amount of money. Someone wins ten million on the lottery and it's gone in three years. I've been rich and I've been poor and like they say, "Money doesn't make you happy but at least you can be miserable in comfort." I was talking to Griff [Rhys Jones] the other day, and he's just sold his share of Talkback productions and made himself £23 million or something, but that won't change him a bit. He'll have a week of going "*YES!!!*" but it won't make him get on better with his life or stop the worry. Those that don't have it want it desperately – even if it's 10p off a tin of beans – and those that do have it will always want more. I don't know anyone whose happy with the amount of money they've got.

As for David Frost getting up at 3am and all that – well, he's a broadcaster down to his toenails and he loves his job. I don't think at his time of life he's going to give it all up and take up quantum physics or abseiling. I often wonder about movie stars like Tom Cruise who must be worth, I dunno, hundreds of millions of dollars. All these stars own a handful of islands and stuff. Probably half their films are absolutely awful and very hard work, so why do they go on doing it? Because it defines their life. A movie star perpetually worries about "I'm

only Number Three on the chart and last year I was Number One!"

HAMILTON: There's no point in climbing a ladder if you're not going to be happy on it.

LLOYD: And what about all those on the bottom rungs? *You've* got this Peter Cook thing in your life which is a wonderful obsession but what have most other people got to spend their time on? Pub, a football team, read a couple of crappy thrillers. The human mind is extraordinary and capable of so much and it's not being used. I don't mean that disparagingly because at the top there are people doing crap movies, crap TV, running crap governments, who have never really thought to any great degree about the meaning of anything very much. People are just going along a tramline, doing things by rote, like their fathers did or how the newspapers tell them. It's rather depressing really.

The principle difference between us and children, apart from height –

HAMILTON: And mountains of pubic hair, garages of the stuff…

LLOYD: …and *that*, of course, is that adults are in possession of more information. They're not more intelligent – they're less open minded than children – and about 98% of that information is wrong, in my view.

HAMILTON: A bit like the scene in *Monty Python's The Meaning of Life* where all these bigwigs are having a boardroom meeting and number seven on the agenda is the meaning of life. One exec's findings are, "One – people aren't wearing enough hats. Two – the meaning of life cannot be found because humans are too easily distracted by trivia." Another bigwig asks, "What's that about hats again?"

IF THIS WERE THE 18TH CENTURY PEOPLE WOULD BE INTERESTED IN THESE THINGS. THERE'D BE AN ALCHEMIST'S LAIR UPSTAIRS, A GIANT TELESCOPE ON THE ROOF, WE'D BE IN A SALON DISCUSSING LITERATURE AND PLAYING THE SPINNET

LLOYD: There was quite a famous journalist who wrote for the *Daily Telegraph* and was noted for his waspish, sharp and nasty views and writings. Can't remember his name. Anyway, he got a fatal disease – I think it was cancer – and he wrote a full page article, an incredibly moving piece saying that now he was facing death he was changing his outlook on everything. As John Diamond says about his cancer, he has been more happy since he knew he was going to die at any moment than he has ever been. Jonathan Swift said, "May you live every day of your life," and that's important. Anyway, this article about what he thought the meaning of life was inspired more letters to the *Telegraph* than any other subject and a few days later a double page was given over to readers' responses. Amongst these insightful, truthful and touching stories was a letter from one guy who wrote that he too had looked for the meaning of life. He had studied religions, science, philosophy, name it, and his conclusion about life was the one question – "Why?" and only one answer: "To love."

I was really broken up by that. The sense of hopelessness and despair when a crisis comes – like when your parents get sick or a friend dies and you go to the funeral and think, "What the fuck was that all about?", and suddenly the panic, the dread of the Universe and the meaninglessness of it floods in on you – it's too late, then! I've spent years sitting down, before the big crisis happens, trying while the sun's still shining to find something to cling onto for when the rain starts falling. The money I make from advertising I spend on books and any free time I have I spend reading them. And if there's any time after that I try applying what I've read to real life.

Philosophy means "the love of wisdom" and why aren't people interested in that? Mention it to people and they say, "Oh, Philosophy's boring."
HAMILTON: The image of Philosophy is white-bearded pooftahs roaming around in togas. Philosophy, along with Sociology, is being cut from school curriculums.
LLOYD: That's so mindless. That bloke who's the Chief Inspector of Schools, I read about his ideal for education: "Lots of lovely dates learnt by rote; times tables; spelling – very important to be able to spell; long division." You know, utterly vacuous. What education should be about is endless curiosity about the nature of the world. I'd make Philosophy and Human Behaviour a compulsory subject. I wouldn't bother to teach History; I think it's pointless. History is just the record of human crime. It's battles and murders and pogroms, but there's a secret history and that's the record of human goodness. The little acts of kindness aren't recorded anywhere. Little deeds of altruism: The lady in the baker's shop who runs after you saying, "Here, you left a fiver on the

counter." That sort of thing is never recorded, but that's what actually keeps the world going.

HAMILTON: Do you think there's been a slow concrete wave of cynicism that's engulfed us, smothered us?

LLOYD: Yeah. If this were the 18th century people would be interested in these things. There'd be an alchemist's lair upstairs, a giant telescope on the roof, we'd be in a salon discussing literature and playing the spinnet. But now, you know, you go in to any newsagents and there's naked birds on every single magazine from Wildfowling Weekly to Yachts Today. There's a fucking naked bird on every cover as if the only thing anyone ever wanted to do was shag. What's up with people, what's up with the world, that they haven't got another idea?

HAMILTON: Bob Dylan, in 1985, said we're living in the age of masturbation. Do you see the situation getting only worse?

LLOYD: Cycles are part of how the world operates and we're going through a very materialistic and meaningless bit of history at the moment. But I think it'll turn around. We are up against the buffers, materially speaking. Like, when you've just got your record collection it's made redundant by CDs so you buy the records again in that format. And then they unveil the MiniDisc.

HAMILTON: And DVDs are here now to replace your videos.

LLOYD: Absolutely, and it's our fault. We get the culture we deserve. But here I am, banging on about how crap the culture is; I should be out there, making good programmes, making an effort. Yes, Lloyd, that's the answer: Get off your fat arse and stop making

money doing cheese commercials. And I'm definitely going to do that. This year.

HAMILTON: What are you doing?

LLOYD: I'm going to start a company that'll make radio and TV programmes.

HAMILTON: Plus there's a film with Rowan Atkinson that you're going to direct.

LLOYD: Well, I don't know if that's going to happen now. We've spent four months trying to rewrite a not-very-good, overcomplicated script and I think Rowan's gone a bit cold-feety about it. It's a spy movie based on the Barclaycard telly ads we made, and though I don't want to be a movie director I *do* like the idea of making a good movie. It's difficult to do a great movie because you have to have a great script, there's no two ways about it. Hitchcock's three secrets to great movie making were a script, a script and a script. In that order. You have a crap script, you get a crap movie. The problem with the movie business is this thinking that "We'll start with a crap script; don't worry, we'll fix it as we go along," which they never do.

HAMILTON: *Casino Royale* was the classic example of that attitude.

LLOYD: Was it?

HAMILTON: Yeah. Charlie Feldman produced *What's New, Pussycat* from a Woody Allen screenplay, but as filming progressed Peter Sellers and Peter O'Toole said, "Oh this script's useless. We'll improvise some funny stuff and make it good." And Allen had no clout, this being his first film. The film was a box office hit and Feldman, believing lightning can strike twice, went totally bananas. "I'll get the hottest directors doing scenes by the best writers, get the top stars, loadsa sexy chicks, make it freewheelin' and groovy. It's godda be a smash!" Of course, when *Casino Royale* was put together it was a totally incoherent mess, with all these embarrassed-looking stars walking about, wandering what the fuck's going on. It's money madness.

LLOYD: What moguls don't know is how much people don't like modern movies. The crew I work with in America – normal working-class New Yorkers – they *hate* the movies, they think they're rubbish, by and large. This never shows up in the figures. *MI:2* in its opening weekend took 31 million dollars or something preposterous, so the Big Boys think everything's fine. I said to my producer on this film, "I don't want to do a film like *MI:2* because it hasn't got an idea." He replied, "So what? Millions of people went to see it so why do we need an idea?" I hate films like that. I hate it when I've spent an evening watching a load of crap and a few explosions, and when you go to the pub to talk about it you can't think of what to say. I don't want to impose another one of *those* on the world. I remember my Dad taking me to see *Lawrence of Arabia* when I was about ten. Unforgettable. I love that film. *The Magnificent Seven, The Godfather*. It's my pleasure and my duty, I suppose, to entertain people. That's why I do it; I love it.

HAMILTON: Apart from the Coen brothers I don't think there's anyone making intelligent mainstream films. It's just soulless, aggressive, big bangs, big tits, cheap laughs, no brains nonsense.

LLOYD: Yes, it's just appealing to immediate, visceral sensationalism.

The Navajo have a proverb: "Everything easy is evil, everything difficult is good" and that's a pretty good rule of thumb. If something's a cinch, then it probably isn't worth doing; you're just wasting your life. Things are constructed to be difficult for some reason, be it a painting, a movie or building a wall – it's tough work, an effort, but the reward is immense. I don't want to sound like an old buffer, but people don't want to put the work in. They don't want to study for seven years to do something really fucking well, whatever it is. They want it all *now*: "Where's my Porsche?"

HAMILTON: Like instant talent: "I've just bought a guitar. Sign me!"

LLOYD: I started in broadcasting in radio. Five years in radio. I was happy there, felt privileged to be there. Nowadays people are in radio for a *year* and they want to get straight in to the telly and then making their first film. We're getting films made by 24, 26 year olds who don't have anything to say. I'm not saying they shouldn't be allowed to do movies but they haven't had much of a life and their work reflects that. It's all gangsters and shagging.

HAMILTON: Shallow, like Pitt the Younger's ghastly teenage poem in *Blackadder*. "*Why do girls hate me?*"

LLOYD: Yes. I'm fascinated by the process of creativity. Cézanne painted Mont Sainte-Victoire something like 2,000 times from every conceivable angle – "What is it? What is it about this mountain?" – and he went on and on doing the same thing, trying to find the secret of whatever he was looking for.

HAMILTON: Talking about creativity, I'd

like to know about the *Meaning of Liff*, the book by you and Douglas Adams. It's an extremely funny and original work using the simple idea of ascribing definitions to strange but actual place names.

LLOYD: All great ideas are simple, and that applies to the laws of physics as much as great jokes. If you've made up a really good joke you automatically think, "I must have heard it before, it's so perfect", but you haven't. Well, you *might* have, but not usually. E=MC² – that's how the Universe runs and it's only four letters, for God's sake. Incredibly simple, yet very hard to achieve that kind of simplicity.

The Meaning of Liff came out when Douglas Adams and I had booked a holiday on the basis of the *Hitch-Hiker's Guide To The Galaxy* book we were going to write jointly in Corfu. Then Douglas sacked me – the bastard! – but, as I was poor and I'd already spent all the money, I went anyway and whilst Douglas was sitting in the villa typing and looking out of the window being a novelist, I was in the taverna getting drunk. When he got fed up of being a novelist, which would be after ten minutes, he would come down and join me and get drunk as well. We used to play word games, one being a game his English master taught him. During a free period or at the end of term he would ask the class "What's a York? or a Richmond?" We loved this game and by the end of the holiday I'd written a load of them down. At that time I was doing *Not The Nine O'Clock News* and we did these spin-off big fat calendars with two jokes a day that used to eat up material like nobody's business. I reached a point where we were out of material

and I thought, "Oh, let's use those definitions." The Chairman of Faber called me up: "Those dictionary definitions are the best thing in it. You should do a book of them." Writing *Meaning Of Liff* with Douglas was the nicest job I ever had because Douglas by then was seriously well off, had houses all over the world, and he was all "Johnny, I'm afraid I can't reach you. Unless of course you come to Malibu. I'm staying at Donna Summer's beach house for the summer." We wrote the first one in Malibu and the second volume at Palm Beach near Sydney on another book-tour-cum-holiday of Douglas'.

Those *Liff* definitions… You'd be staring at these town names and trying to think of things there are no words for and you'd be stuck for a week when suddenly you'd get ten in a row.

HAMILTON: Do you remember what a burbage is?

LLOYD: No. Go on.

HAMILTON: "The sound made by an elevator full of people all trying to breathe through their noses." (*Laughter*)

LLOYD: The wonderful thing about writing that book was I'd say, "Hey, Douglas, you know that thing in the lavatory when such-and-such happens?" and he'd be "*No*! That's *never* happened to me." The best are the height-of-embarassment ones that touch a nerve, when the reader thinks 'I've done that, I didn't think anyone else knew I did that".

HAMILTON: How did you write it? Did you rip a map of Britain in half and delegate, like; "I'll do Lancashire, you do Dorset"?

LLOYD: No. Douglas is a very old friend of mine but he *is* the laziest person. So I would buy a gazetteer and pick out the interesting names. Like, Mapledurham has got to mean something. I'd put these names on a series of cards and provide him with, say, fifty to work on – you know, definitions of Berriwillock or Moffat. Then I'd collect the cards and do a draft, then we'd do a re-draft. Jon Canter, who has a particularly bitter Jewish sense of humor, supplied a couple of excellent ones like Lemvig – "someone who can be relied upon to be doing worse than you". (*Laughter. Hamilton hands Lloyd a copy of Liff to leaf through. He reads* :) "Kowloon – one who goes to an Indian restaurant and orders an omlette." (*More giggling.*)

HAMILTON: I'm afraid that's me. I'm also a Nybster – the type who uses the lift to go up one floor.

LLOYD: Of all the things I've ever done, I think I'm most proud of this book.

HAMILTON: Have you any Grand Doomed Projects?

LLOYD: Doomed? Yeah. Only I do so little that what I choose to do – I'm very stubborn – are things I totally believe in. So if I do a crap first series, which is often the case, I don't give in, I just go on past the point where most sane people would say, "Oh, this is *never* gonna work, this is *awful!*" However, I did do a show called *Stephenson's Rocket* which is said to be the worst half-hour of television ever made.

HAMILTON: Who was in that?

LLOYD: Pamela Stephenson, when she was famous, after *Not the Nine O'Clock News.* She got pally with David Mallet, a pop video director who did Kenny Everett's shows, and Mallet was *the* sexiest director around. I got big-headed, thought I was a genius because I'd got a BAFTA award. We

all thought we were geniuses and, of course, the show was absolutely awful.

HAMILTON: Was it just one show?

LLOYD: Yeah, a pilot. David was used to pop video budgets and spent the entire budget on the opening number of the show and we ran out of money. A terrible mess but for one good, salvageable moment: It was a mock ad for the Super Absorbo Tampon, where we saw Pamela dreamily taking the Tampons out of her dressing table and going outside in a white swimsuit – because with Super Absorbo you could do whatever you wanted – and dived into a swimming pool whereupon there's this *SSHHHLURRRP!!* And there she was, like a beached sardine, at the bottom of an empty pool.

If that show taught me anything it is A Star Can't Save Anything At All. I've since been suspicious of star-based projects; I'd much rather work with people I've never heard of that I like.

HAMILTON: What you were saying about carrying on with an idea... I recall the first series of *The Black Adder* being, um, well...

LLOYD: ...a shambles. Total shambles. That came up after the last series of *Not the Nine O'Clock News.* I worked far too hard on that show; I felt about 80 years old. Richard Curtis and Rowan came up with this show, the original title was King Edmund And His Three Friends – a rather weedy thing. They did a pilot with John Howard Davies producing and I didn't think it was very interesting, really. It wasn't *about* anything, it was set in a mythic period of history. I didn't want to do it but I succumbed to their kindly blandishments. They wanted castles, horses, huge-scale sets. The sets were so big we couldn't fit into the studio a bleacher for an audience. The series consequently had no audience, which meant the cast had no focus. Rowan is used to performing to an audience; that's what edits his performance and makes it real…

Someone told me there's only seven magic tricks in the world but there's loads of variants, and I think that applies to jokes too.

HAMILTON: Yes, I had heard about there being only seven jokes and I've tried to list them. I came up with Slapstick, Exploitation, Class Consciousness (which may be an offshoot of Exploitation, come to think of it), Concealment, Crime, Dramatic Irony and Misunderstanding (be it with language, customs, foreigners).

LLOYD: Yes, and Surprise should be in there. But you can simplify it further. The Greeks believed everything came down to Sameness and Difference, and that's the essence of the Universe. I think they're probably right. One joke is when you think something is definitely the same and it turns out to be different. A pun is very good at Sameness and Difference. A pun is like a Stargate; it's a wormhole that connects two entirely different universes instantly. John Cleese is very anti-puns but he's not right. A good pun is mind-expanding and can suddenly take you to different pictorial worlds. But if you know what the Seven Jokes are, it wouldn't help you one bit to write a funny line.

HAMILTON: How do *you* write comedy? Do you have to be totally relaxed, phone off the hook, peace and quiet? Or do you work best under pressure in an office full of noise? You told me that when you wrote with Peter Cook, Peter worked in a "drinking-too-

> **THE GREAT SKILL IN GOING TO WORK IS GETTING RID OF YOUR PERSONALITY AND ALLOWING THE THING TO OPERATE FOR YOU. YOU SEE THAT IN MUSIC: YOU DON'T THINK, YOU JUST DO THE WORK. MOZART SAID HE COULDN'T WORK UNLESS HE WAS TOTALLY RELAXED**

muchy" kind of way.

LLOYD: Yeah, Peter couldn't really write sober. I mean, not totally sober, He'd try for an hour and then he'd have to have a vodka and tonic or something.

The great skill in going to work is principally getting rid of your personality and allowing the thing to operate for you. You see that in music: You let go, you don't think, you just do the work. Mozart said he couldn't work unless he was totally relaxed. He would say, "I never composed anything; I was just listening to God." And certainly with Cooky, he just *let go*. He was speaking far too quickly for any of his comedy to be consciously thought through. But I'm not a Peter Cook. *Blackadder* was a group effort, a well-knitted team of people who really believe in what they're doing. And *luck*, too. Like the last scene in the final series. There's the sense that you've touched something that isn't usually touched. A kind of epiphany, I suppose, where you realise you've put your finger through that invisible membrane into a reality of something. It's extraordinary and to this day I feel a fantastic privilege that I was *allowed*, as it were, in the room where something as wonderful as that happened. ☻

FEATURES

WHY I LOVE TOMMY COOPER

**The legendary comedian was a true artist, says DAMIEN HIRST.
Illustration by JOE HARRISON**

When I was a student the artist Bruce McLean told me that the surest way to success was "the double 'O' syndrome". I didn't follow, so he explained it to me. "Jeff Koons, Larry Poons, Willem de Kooning, Tommy Cooper. Get a double 'O' in your surname and success is assured, Brooce Mcloon, Doomioon Hoost." Yeah maybe, I thought, but more importantly, what is a comedian doing in a list of important Twentieth Century artists? So I bought a fez and the rest is history.

I once tried to explain Tommy Cooper to an American artist. It's totally fucking impossible: "... and he's walking about on stage going 'oooo sore, ooo arghsore, so sore ow' clutching his side. The audience has been laughing since he walked on stage. You see, he's so funny he only has to walk on stage and people fall about" – blank American face – "and then he pulls a saw out from inside his jacket and the audience go hysterical" – blanker puzzled American face – "you see, sore-saw, get it? Oh and he wears a fez" – totally puzzled – "you'd love him, you've just got to see him." It's the same if you try and explain Vic and Bob to Americans. They are only just getting Monty Python. But why is Tommy Cooper so funny? You either love or hate him. Most people love him. My Mum can't stand him "because he's so stupid," but she likes some of the jokes in this article. She proofread it for me. My Dad took her to see him twice, because he thought he was great.

Where did the fez come from? One evening he forgot the pith helmet that he needed whilst performing. So he took a fez from the head of the waiter who was walking past the stage at the time and this got him so much of a laugh that it stayed. If you look into Tommy's career the answer to most of the ponderables is simple, like where the fez came from. He simply had the ability to fill a space with laughter by emanating humour. In his life, as in his art, on stage and off. At a Royal Variety performance he asked the Queen "Do you like football?" "Not really," she replied. "Can I have your World Cup tickets then?"

He walked on stage one evening and said, "it's lovely to be here." He paused and moved a few feet across the stage and said, "It's lovely here as well". You had to be there!

Eric Sykes, a fellow comedian, swears that Tommy turned up late to meet him in a busy pub wearing a bowler hat and pyjamas, saying, "Sorry I'm late, I couldn't get up."

He is also known to have handed a particularly friendly taxi driver something saying, "Have a drink on me." It turned out to be a tea bag.

Q. What's the secret to good timing, er, good comedy, I mean?

A. Timing

Tommy Cooper had great timing. He only had to stand on a stage and people laughed. There is speculation that this must have made him feel awfully lonely at times but who really wants to know? "There's only one trick that Tommy does successfully," claimed his wife. "And that's making a drink disappear."

Van Gogh and Francis Bacon both painted several self-portraits titled "The Artist On His Way To Work" playing with the idea of identity. I mean, if you're an artist then you're an artist at home and you're an artist at work. So what the hell are you supposed to be when you're on your way to work? Tommy Cooper stood up to accept a "Thirty Years Working in Comedy" award and the whole audience put on fezes. He pulled a fisherman's cap from his pocket and donned it, to laughter from the audience.

There's an infinite number of ways to get to the same point and unlike most stand-ups, Cooper didn't think that he was inventing the future. He believed he was discovering it, and this allowed the audience to discover it with him. Whether that audience was a small pub, a packed theatre or a taxi driver, there's a feeling of an incredibly generous man. He's a stand-up, a magician whose tricks go wrong, which makes him funny, and he's a performer who tells bad jokes and bungles magic tricks with impeccable timing. There's a generosity in creating something magical without pulling the wool over anyone's eyes that is normally

"THERE'S ONLY ONE TRICK THAT TOMMY DOES SUCCESSFULLY," CLAIMED HIS WIFE. "AND THAT'S MAKING A DRINK DISAPPEAR"

associated with art. Maybe that's why it's difficult to explain Tommy Cooper to someone who's never seen him.

Cooper in no way had a one-gag repertoire. The wealth and breadth of his material was enormous, how much of it came naturally and how much of it he laboured over I've got no idea. I guess a bit of both, it doesn't really matter. Here's one of my favourite sketches that occurred shortly after he got into television (the transition from theatre to TV came easily):

So he's walking down the street dressed as a painter and decorator, wearing a bowler hat and carrying a tin of paint in one hand. He walks up to one house and knocks on the door.

A sombrely suited man answers the door.

"Is Fred in?" asks Tommy

"Oh" says the man. "Fred passed away peacefully in his sleep last night. We're just having the wake now."

"Oh," says Tommy. "He didn't mention a tin of paint did he?"

Stand-up, entertainer, funny man, comedian, magician, performer, artist, whatever you want to call him, he was magic.

I slept like a log last night, I woke up in the fireplace.

I was cleaning out the attic with the wife the other day. Filthy, dirty and covered in cobwebs but she's good with the kids.

So I went to the dentist the other day. He said, "say aaah". I said, "why?" He said, "because my dog's died".

So I got home and the phone was ringing. I picked it up and said, "who's speaking?" and a voice said, "you are!"

And then there's the story of when Tommy Cooper gave someone some money buy a round in a bar. They bought the round and left the change on the bar. Cooper was visibly disturbed when asked why he was fretting about the change. He said "It's not the principle, it's the money."

Bruce Nauman made a neon wall sculpture that has writing going into the centre of a spiral that reads "the true artist helps the world by revealing mystic truths". Think what you like. I personally, at the moment, am far too worried about my own work to worry about anyone else's – I think I'm flogging a dead horse... just like that...not like that, like that!

Francis Bacon, the artist, when asked what he wanted to happen to his body after he died, replied: "Just stuff me in a dustbin sack and throw me in the gutter." Tommy Cooper died on stage of a heart attack amidst peals of hysterical laughter.

On the 15th April 1984, Tommy Cooper collapsed during a live television broadcast at her Majesty's Theatre. The people in the audience were still laughing as Tommy, lying on the stage, had the curtain brought down on him. The show's host, one of Tommy's great friends, Jimmy Tarbuck, recalled the moment. "As usual, he was supposed to make a mess of the last trick. He was wearing a long black coat from which he was supposed to start bringing out large objects. Then a ladder would come through his legs followed by a milk churn and a long pole. When Tommy fell backwards I thought he'd put another gag in. I thought he was going to do some levitation from under his cloak. We all expected him to get up and we waited for the roar of laughter. It was terrible when he didn't."

Tommy Cooper died ten minutes later on the way to hospital... just like that! ☉

I PERSONALLY, AT THE MOMENT, AM FAR TOO WORRIED ABOUT MY OWN WORK TO WORRY ABOUT ANYONE ELSE'S – I THINK I'M FLOGGING A DEAD HORSE... JUST LIKE THAT

ASK A SILLY QUESTION

It's time for the media to embrace naivety, argues BRIAN DEAN

BRIAN DEAN

A few years ago there was a minor public outcry when the BBC admitted to spending millions on the evening news opening graphics. These ten second bursts of visual expensiveness were apparently intended to convey a sense of importance, authority and restrained urgency, so the viewers at home would sit up and pay attention.

Judging from this ultra-high spending, TV bosses are anxious to have their news programmes taken seriously. This has led to a presentation of the news which, in its fanfare and gloss, is similar to professionally staged business seminars and political conferences. Unlike those events, however, TV news isn't meant to be about persuading, hypnotising or dazzling an audience – so why spend millions on its presentation?

Well, for one thing it costs money to create a convincing illusion. The news presents one of the most impressive magic tricks since the Emperor's New Clothes. The illusion is of a serious, businesslike, adult world – economics, politics, stock market indexes and inflation rates – full of "experts" and presided over by "The Authorities". Naturally we feel powerless as individuals to influence this world since it can be accessed only on TV. The slick presentation of the illusion – immaculate suits, gleaming studios, intimidating presenters and those costly visuals – has the effect of reducing most (relatively shabby) viewers to a state of infantile awe and low self-esteem.

This news world is built on conventional wisdom, "adult" assumptions which can't be questioned, because to do so would be an admission of childlike innocence. Pundits obviously like to be seen as authoritative, so they tend to fall back on safe assumptions rather than explore unknown areas and risk looking naive.

Unfortunately, it's precisely this lack of naivety which leads to the stagnation of media debate. These childlike qualities are valuable – they have the potential to embarrass the "experts" and expose the banality behind the adult gloss. For example, a child might ask: "why is Daddy always so tired and sad when he comes home from work?" No economics pundit has ever provided a satisfactory answer to that question.

Taking such "childish" questions as an inspiring starting point, I've compiled my own list of "naïve" questions and "foolish" answers which I'd like to see featured on a serious news or current affairs show:

NAIVE QUESTION: Is school education a good thing?
FOOLISH ANSWER: Yes. It's producing exactly what society needs: economically frightened clones ready to slot straight into low-paid menial jobs.

NAIVE QUESTION: Do we have to be tough on crime?
FOOLISH ANSWER: Without crime there'd be no need for police, lawyers, courts or prisons. That would mean mass unemployment and the end of society as we know it. The "tough on crime" policy is okay as long as it doesn't reduce crime.

NAIVE QUESTION: Does advertising make any sense?
FOOLISH ANSWER: The huge number of car commercials on TV makes no sense at all. How can the UK market for new cars be big enough to justify that amount of advertising? It's not as if everyone can afford a new car – most people have trouble paying their electricity bills. The saturation advertising for Amoy noodles is similarly puzzling.

NAIVE QUESTION: Is the "free market" a good thing?
FOOLISH ANSWER: Many people claim the existing system is not a "free market" but "Monopoly Capitalism" based on protection rackets (eg land ownership) and usury (eg banking). This apparently goes back to the Bronze Age, when spear-wielding thugs extracted rent from peaceful settlements. These thugs were the first land "owners" (and the first land "lords", barons and kings). The people they exploited and turned into slaves were the true wealth creators – they grew the food, raised the livestock, made the tools and built the dwellings.

NAIVE QUESTION: Why do adherents of the "free market" support the BBC?
FOOLISH ANSWER: The market can be trusted to provide our water, food, transport, electricity, gas, communications and refuse disposal, but it can't be trusted to provide our television programmes. We need the BBC for that.

NAIVE QUESTION: Why does the BBC compete for viewers?
FOOLISH ANSWER: It seems that the BBC is pretending to be part of the competitive market, possibly to disguise the fact that, with its public hand-out funding, it is essentially the country's largest welfare recipient.

NAIVE QUESTION: The BBC allegedly employs 2000 journalists. What do they all do?
FOOLISH ANSWER: That will probably remain a mystery.

NAIVE QUESTION: Is crime the biggest concern people have?
FOOLISH ANSWER: Statistically, people are more concerned about their dentist appointments than about crime.

NAIVE QUESTION: If TV reflects real-life concerns, why do crime shows outnumber dentistry shows by a

thousand to one?
FOOLISH ANSWER: Exactly! And why do TV shows never feature landlords or bankers?

NAIVE QUESTION: Nobody seems to care when neighbours' burglar alarms go off. Would it help to restore our sense of civic duty if the alarms had a louder, more piercing sound?
FOOLISH ANSWER: Research indicates there would be an increase in violent incidents due to noise-related stress.

NAIVE QUESTION: Is food safe?
FOOLISH ANSWER: If manufacturers can't prevent traces of nuts getting into food, then what other contaminants can get in? To restore public faith in the honesty of the food producers, warning labels should be extended to say: "may contain traces of nuts, rat faeces, rat urine, rat parts, dead insects, live insects, human effluvia, human skin, human hair, toenails, fingernails and assorted dormant and active bacteria of known and unknown origin."

NAIVE QUESTION: Should we teach children to be competitive (putting self first), or to be considerate (putting others first)?
FOOLISH ANSWER: Both. Then we should teach them the importance of behavioral consistency.

NAIVE QUESTION: Are money makers the real heroes of society?
FOOLISH ANSWER: Making money shouldn't be confused with creating wealth. Real wealth is what supports

IT SEEMS THAT THE BBC IS PRETENDING TO BE PART OF THE COMPETITIVE MARKET, POSSIBLY TO DISGUISE THE FACT THAT, WITH ITS PUBLIC HAND-OUT FUNDING, IT IS ESSENTIALLY THE COUNTRY'S LARGEST WELFARE RECIPIENT

and enhances human life, whereas money is just numbers in a database. Many wealth creators (inventors, artists, mothers, etc) are penniless, and many money makers are useless bloodsuckers.

NAIVE QUESTION: Are banks friendly, like in the adverts?
FOOLISH ANSWER: Banks make large profits from "unauthorised overdraft" charges. Credit card companies make large profits from "late payment" fees. But they tell us not to go overdrawn or pay late. So they're fucking with our heads while they rob us blind. But otherwise they're friendly.

NAIVE QUESTION: Is it really cheating if athletes use performance-enhancing substances?
FOOLISH ANSWER: Only if the substances are ingested. It's not considered cheating to enhance performance with anything worn or surgically implanted (muscle grafts, organ transplants, bionic limbs, etc).

NAIVE QUESTION: Why have breakfast cereals adopted sensible names (eg Sustain, Perfect Balance, Just Right and Advantage)?
FOOLISH ANSWER: Because marketing consultants determined that 51% of cereal consumers have anal fixations about diet, health and fitness. Watch out for forthcoming name changes: Bran Flakes to Nice'n'Regular and Frosties to Blood-Glucose Boost.

NAIVE QUESTION: Why are there so many beggars in a booming economy like Britain?
FOOLISH ANSWER: It pays more, and humiliates less, than work in telesales.

NAIVE QUESTION: Is there anything bad about full employment?
FOOLISH ANSWER: Not if you're happy to condemn half the population to minimum-wage slavery, flushing creative potential down the economic toilet, so a politician can tell the country how prudent he is. Or to quote Henry Hazlitt: "Hitler provided full employment. Prisons and chain gangs have full employment. Coercion can always provide full employment."

NAIVE QUESTION: How much does it cost to create a job?
FOOLISH ANSWER: The New Deal cost over £5bn, and has created 50,000 jobs which otherwise wouldn't exist. That means each job created cost the taxpayer £100,000.

NAIVE QUESTION: If labour-saving technology is getting better and cheaper, why are corporate employees working longer hours?
FOOLISH ANSWER: Because they're slaves.

NAIVE QUESTION: Is it true that hard work never hurt anybody?
FOOLISH ANSWER: According to a government report (Mental Health & Stress in the Workplace), working over 48 hours per week doubles the risk of coronary heart disease.

NAIVE QUESTION: Why do successful business people want less regulation and smaller government?
FOOLISH ANSWER: Ironically, big business depends on a complex legal framework and a powerful state apparatus (to enforce the laws under which businesses and lawyers prosper). Business people don't really want less regulation and smaller government – they just want less state interference in their own activities. They're quite happy to see everybody else (particularly the less well off) be regulated and controlled. Many business people love the US system, where the government is powerful enough to fill the prisons with millions of relatively harmless people who are then available to corporations as cheap, captive labour.

NAIVE QUESTION: Is unemployment high or low at the moment?
FOOLISH ANSWER: When governments talk about their performance in managing the economy, unemployment is low. But when they talk of "cracking down on dependency culture" or "getting tough on the workshy", unemployment is "high".

NAIVE QUESTION: ... spending so high?
FOOLISH ANSWER: The welfare budget is £99bn. half of that goes on pension amount spent on pensions is increasing because the population is getting older. Only £5bn is spent annually on unemployment benefits. The amount spent on unemployment decreased by £1bn over the last year. As a cost comparison, bear in mind that a new British-US fighter plane has a development price-tag of £250bn.

NAIVE QUESTION: Why should people get pensions?
FOOLISH ANSWER: The cost of state pensions is huge, yet there is widespread poverty amongst old people. Many elderly people are able-bodied, so let's put them to work. There's no excuse for laziness and dependence – if they can use a phone or walk a dog, they can take jobs in telesales or supermarket trolley shepherding.

NAIVE QUESTION: Who really wants strong leaders?
FOOLISH ANSWER: Only sexually repressed people want strong leaders (according to psychologists). ◑

Brian Dean is editor of anxietyculture.com webzine

THE HISTORY OF FOLLY

**Is foolishness next to godliness?
NICHOLAS LEZARD examines the
evidence**

*A*fter *our heads ache with thinking, it is
fair to play the fool.* – Hazlitt,
"Merry England". What was the
last foolish thing you did?

There is a good chance you've done
something foolish today. We may do stupid
things in the heat of the moment, but we
also do them perfectly readily at room
temperature. You could have lit a cigarette;
opened the fridge and then forgotten what
you were looking in it for; had sex ("the
foolishest act a wise man ever commits",
according to Thomas Browne), anything.
But most of the time the most typically
foolish act anyone does in the course of the
day is get out of bed; and that is very
foolish indeed.

IN EVERY AGE THAT HAS EVER EXISTED IT HASN'T BEEN HARD TO FIND EXAMPLES OF IDIOCY; AND AT OUR MOMENTS OF GREATEST FOLLY, WE IMAGINE THAT WE STAND ALONE, AN ISLAND OF GOOD SENSE IN A SEA OF DAFTNESS

We like the idea of being wise; failing that, we like to think of ourselves as capable of wisdom; and, failing that, we keep our mouths shut. Better to have others think of you as a fool than to open your mouth and have them confirm it. In every age that has ever existed it hasn't been hard to find examples of idiocy; and at our moments of greatest folly, we imagine that each of us stands alone, a forlorn island of good sense marooned in a vast sea of daftness. "I'm surrounded by IDIOTS" sounds like a plausible personal motto but, if adopted by everyone, it means that we are constantly being considered an idiot by someone, somewhere.

Our mythology is steeped in stories of folly, whether in the Judaeo-Christian tradition of eating a fruit we had been expressly told not to (which was only eaten with the specific intention of making us wise, of knowing good from evil; fat lot of good *that* did us); or in the ancient Akkadian legend of Adapa, who was offered a meal by Anu, the god of heaven. This is an interesting version of what happens when mortals are offered divine grub, and certainly offers a revealing gloss – for our Bible stories are often twisted hand-me-downs from Sumerian sources –

on the story of Genesis' forbidden fruit. Adapa, who cursed the West wind for overturning his boat, had been called to account by Anu; Ea, the Promethean demiurge, had told Adapa not to eat anything offered by Anu, because it was the fruit of death. Adapa said thanks, but no thanks, to Anu; who then laughed, as what he had offered Adapa was actually the fruit of eternal life. We could be immortal now, but for Adapa's hesitancy; but as to whether it was Ea or Anu who was making a fool of humanity we won't ever know, as the seal on which the legend is written breaks off at that point. The point of God's laughter at us.

Sahu, the word for laughter used in the legend, specifically refers to mocking laughter, the laughter at others' misfortunes; and that's what fools are for: to fuck up, so we can laugh at them. Until we fuck up too. And we do. Socrates called himself the most foolish man on earth; Goethe's Faust was the most learned man on the planet, but he at least has insight into his own condition:

Da steh ich nun, ich armer Tor!
Und bin so klug als wie zuvor;
[There he stands, the poor fool
No cleverer than he was before]

Faust fucks up royally; but Goethe is always tender towards him, and it becomes clear from this very first speech that Faust is a stand-in for us. But if Socrates and Faust can bemoan themselves as fools, what hope is there for the rest of us?

None. Even knowing what is wrong with you will not save you. The fool, as the Bible reminds us, persists in his folly. The Bible abounds in warnings about folly; its greatest reproaches, and those of its explicators, are directed towards atheism, and may be seen as practically synonymous with it: the fool hath said in his heart, There is no God. It is the most common insult, the default setting, for the human condition. This represents a problem for those who see humanity – and themselves in particular – as the pinnacle of divine achievement; or, if you prefer, of billions of years of adaptive evolution. To think we have the nerve to understand the mind of God, to decode the arcane language of macrocosm and microcosm, when we can't even walk down the street without stepping in a turd or poking someone's eye out with an umbrella or getting drunk or committing adultery; or, as I am sorry to admit I have done, *more than once*, driving half the length of the M1 without having left the oil filler cap on the roof of the car?

There is a book of the Bible called *Wisdom*, which is short for "The Wisdom of Solomon". It is a particularly ballsaching book of the Bible, theologically meretricious and strikingly insulting, and as such considered fit only for Catholics to read. (Curious Protestants may find it published, individually, in the Canongate pocket edition, with a miserably pious introduction by the God-bothering novelist Piers Paul Read.) Its second book begins with a speech by an imaginary, or rhetorical, fool: the atheist who says "come on therefore, let us enjoy the good things that are present: and lets us speedily use the creatures like as in youth. Let us fill ourselves with costly wine and ointments: and let no flower of the spring pass us by. Let us crown ourselves with rosebuds, before they be withered. Let none of us go without his part of our voluptuousness: let us leave tokens of our joyfulness in every place: for this is our portion, and our lot is this."

Nothing wrong with that, you may think, so the author – and I hardly think it could be Solomon, who knew how to have a good time, although he might have written it with a ferocious, guilty hangover – somewhat distorts the picture by adding that these hedonists are little more than Anthony Burgess's Droogs a long time *avant la lettre*: "Let us oppress the poor righteous man, let us not spare the widow, nor reverence the ancient gray hairs of the aged. Let our strength be the law of justice: for that which is feeble is found to be nothing worth." The link is proclaimed between hedonism, atheism, and the complete breakdown of moral law; and, the title of the book being *Wisdom*, everything it condemns is folly. It is a handbook of intolerant thinking. But things are more complicated than that, as its rejection by the Church of England implicitly acknowledges.

Evidence of human folly, as I said, is stretched out in front of you under the covers when you open your eyes in the morning. (At least one of my children, and a surprising number of those of my friends, were conceived – how shall I put this? – stupidly. I hasten to add that I love them all to pieces.) There are two reasonable approaches to this. One is to try and become wise and minimize your opportunities for making mischief of your very existence; the other is to try and find some way you can turn the wretched spectacle of yourself to some advantage.

One technique is to imagine that, stupid as you may be, you are at least not as stupid as an animal; but often humans are turned into animals by their stupidity. The most potent parental rebuke that can be delivered without profanity in American English is the word "jackass", symbol of the stubbornness which works against its own best interests; the pedigree goes back, probably, to the first time someone saw a donkey and compared it to a horse. Another symbol of stupidity was the pig, this time carrying suggestions of gluttony[1]. The symbolism of each is ancient, and persists. Lucius Apuleius was turned into a donkey when what he really wanted was to be turned into an owl, despite owls being considered birds of ill-omen in second-century Thessaly, a region that had witches the way New York restaurants have cockroaches.

And then I put off all my garments, and greedily thrust my hand into the box, and took out a good deale of oyntment and rubbed my selfe withall[2].

After that I had well rubbed every part and member of my body, I hovered with myne armes, and moved my selfe, looking still when I should bee changed into a Bird as Pamphiles was, and behold neither feathers nor appearance of feathers did burgen out, but verily my haire did turne in ruggednesse, and my tender skin waxed tough and hard, my fingers and toes losing the number of five, changed into hoofes, and out of myne arse grew a great taile, now my face became monstrous, my nosthrils wide, my lips hanging downe, and myne eares rugged with haire: neither could I see any comfort of my transformation, for my members encreased likewise, and so without all helpe (viewing every part of my poore body) I perceived that I was no bird, but a plaine Asse.

We do not soar: we are donkeys, is the lesson from that text. It's worth thinking of Folly's opposite in representational art: the owl, Wisdom, *sapienta*, symbol of Minerva, bird of ill-omen in so many cultures; but not in Gnostic iconography. Buy an airline ticket to Madrid. Go to the Prado and find Hieronymous Bosch's *The Garden of Earthly Delights*, more properly known as *The Millennium.* Take a ruler and pencil and draw two lines which intersect in the exact dead centre of the left-hand panel, which represents the Fountain of Life in the Garden of Eden. You will notice an owl, peeping out

---

1. The problem with the pig, as moralists saw, was not so much that it performed wicked acts, but that it [I] wallowed; and it is the [I] wallowing in one's pleasures that turns them both into sin, and fun, at the same time.
2. Andrew Rudgely, in his [italics] Encyclopedia of Psychoactive Substances, and elsewhere, suggests that legends of witches flying on broomsticks can be explained by the fact that a paste composed of henbane, belladonna and mandrake, or wolfsbane, aconite and others grouped under the term Saturnian herbs ("offensive to the understanding", Pliny called them), too dangerous to be swallowed, can be more safely absorbed by being rubbed on to the skin; and more effectively absorbed by being rubbed onto a mucous membrane. The most sensitive, not to mention exciting, method of doing this would be to introduce it "per vaginum" or "per anum", using,say, the end of a broomstick; the sensation most commonly experienced under the influence of the "psychotropic" ointment is that of flying.

of a little hole in the fountain of life
itself. The hole reminds you of an
eyeball's pupil, does it not? This
charming vignette of symbolic
shorthand represents the wisdom
that, in a perfect state, makes sense of
the world for us. The world revolves
around that little eye-piece, as the
world revolves around each of us;
but the interior of the orb is black
and fathomless; except for this
symbol of thought. Now find, if you
can, reproductions of two more of
Hieronymous Bosch's paintings
(easy-peasy on the Internet): *The Ship
of Fools*, and *The Haywain*. You will
notice owls in them, too. In *The Ship*,
an owl sits in the tree or maypole
which is the ship's mast; it looks
down philosophically, ambiguously,
like a cat. In another of Bosch's
paintings, *The Prodigal Son*, it ruffles
its feathers angrily, or perhaps in
consternation, from the Tree of Life
at the antics of the debauched young
man. But in *The Haywain* – which
depicts the casual sin, stupidity and
greed which will send us all to the
hell of the right-hand panel – the owl
makes the only fitting and
unmistakably eloquent expression of
its disgust and repudiation of the
world that it can: a blobby pendulum
of shit dangles from a thread
suspended from its arse. It cannot
even be bothered to shit on anyone;
it just shits.

But it is the position of the owl in
The Ship of Fools that concerns us.
Some anonymous, probably
unsymbolic cretin, Everydolt, is
trying to climb up the mast – another
Tree of Life in Bosch's work – and
either feed it something that looks
like a kipper; or perhaps he is trying

to scare it away. But the owl just sits there. Is it there just to bide its time, or to act as an example? Six centuries on, and the iconography is debatable. But two things, at least, are clear: the owl isn't moving, and it certainly isn't shitting. (If it is – and, now I come to think of it, its expression is very like a cat doing a Richard the Third in the bushes – it's doing its business discreetly, in the foliage.) There would appear to be a connection – not an intimate one, but a connection nonetheless – between Folly and Wisdom.

Let us consider some dates. In 1494, Sebastian Brant, and two or more wood-engravers, produce one of the most successful of all early Renaissance books: *Das Narrenschiff*, or the *Ship of Fools*. Somewhere between 1490 and 1500, Bosch completes his own *Narrenschiff*. And in 1509, suffering from an unspecified kidney ailment, or maybe just a bad cold, Erasmus of Rotterdam, staying at his friend Thomas More's gaff and waiting for his books to arrive, writes the *Encomium Moriae*[3], or *The Praise of Folly*, in a week. Given the standards of communication (quality, not speed) in those days, these three works can almost be said to have appeared contemporaneously. Certainly, Erasmus knew of Brant, and called him "incomparable"; this may have been diplomacy. Brant's *Narrenschiff* consists of 111 chapters in rhyming couplets, averaging I would say about 100 lines each, maybe fewer, in which a wide range of vices

[3]. The title is a benignly mischievous pun on More's name.

and customs are held up for abuse. The first one, which tickles all scholars, rails against idiots with big libraries: "Of splendid books I own no end,/But few that I can comprehend." (Usually one couplet suffices to bring out the flavour of the entire chapter.) The woodcut accompanying this shows a fool looking through exactly the same kind of goggly proto-spectacles that Sean Connery uses in *The Name of the Rose*. More or less everything else is pretty straightforwardly bad: Greed, Causing Discord, stupid fashions, bad manners... read it today and you will learn that people have been complaining that the world has been going to pot for at least five hundred years. No-one respects their parents any more, people wear the most idiotic clothes, no-one fears God, people work on the Sabbath or other Holy Days, no-one even considers adultery a sin any more... at times you might feel that you're reading a contemporary conservative bemoaning the awful state into which we have fallen. Each woodcut depicts one or more of the characters of the following verses dressed in the standard fools' headgear, the cap and bells of the jester (the female characters are not thus adorned; whether or not it is because they are already foolish it is hard to say). These characters, we are told, are universal, and although lip-service is paid to the idea that you and I could be included in this parade of folly, it is more to be understood that what we have is a freak show of heedlessness and stupidity, leading us to the fires of hell. The idea is given stronger visual force at the same time, and a few days' journey to the north, in the paintings of Hieronymous Bosch, with the depiction of hell in the right-hand panels of *The Haywain* and *The Millennium*: the emblem of the bagpipes was symbolic of the empty rhetoric, the senseless wheezing in and out of air that is all that fools can produce. Bagpipes appear in both the verse and images of *Das Narrenschiff* and in the huge, squatting monster of Bosch's hell: in the latter, the bagpipes not only appear on the monster's head, but on a flag stuck into his rump. Those who find the instrument a somewhat tiresome symbol of Scottish national pride, or simply a ghastly racket, may take some kind of evil satisfaction in this.

Brant's treatment of folly is one-dimensional, a conflation, unwitting or not, of the separate yet related branches of folly: stultitia, or stupidity, is dressed in the cap-and-bells of *dementia*, or insanity. The two could once be easily confused: if stupidity was a punishable sin, or at least an avoidable trait that, if indulged, could lead one to eternal punishment (and one would only have to be stupid, and not necessarily evil) to so risk one's immortal soul would be nothing less than insane.

It took a genius like Erasmus to notice that folly is the soft target in the war against ignorance, and when a philosopher or moralist rails against it you should treat the device with as much respect as you would a machine politician who rails against anarchy or disobedience. Erasmus up-ended the conventional wisdom by writing a book praising folly, and indeed it is narrated by her. Folly is female, as I suppose she would have had to have been at the time, but this is not a sexist decision on his part. Erasmus's Folly is given the mythological parentage of drunkenness and ignorance, placing her as a near cousin of Comus, the god of revelry; she, too, knows how to have a good time. And it is thanks to her that we do, too. The very word "fun" comes from the old sense of the word "fond", meaning foolish, and indeed the first meaning of "fun" was a trick, a joke at someone else's expense. This twist survives in the American usage, "I was only funning around", usually delivered after some humiliating practical joke.

We begin Erasmus's book by taking it for a satire, that inverted vision that allows us to see the world in a new light, where what was previously shaded is made clear; it ends as rather more than a satire, and states that true Christian wisdom is impossible without folly. This is radical, and went very much against the dour Old Testament view of religious feeling that had dominated the church for over a thousand years; but it is sanctioned, if you know where to look, in the New; you had to become as a child, to liberate yourself from the trappings of reason, before you could begin to glimpse the divine. For, after all, how could a rational mind grasp what was beyond its powers to imagine? Transcendent ecstasy was very much then what it became in raves across the world a decade or more ago. Every once in a while, as Seal put it, you have to go a little crazy.

That Folly became a champion in this way fitted very well with the already ancient Feast of Fools, a carnival which had survived in various forms for, it is safe to speculate, longer than verbally recorded human history. From a circular letter of the Paris School of Theology in 1444: The Feast of Fools was necessary "so that foolishness, which is our second nature and seems to be inherent in man might freely spend itself at least once a year. Wine barrels burst if from time to time we do not open them and let in some air. All of us men are barrels poorly put together, which would burst from the wine of wisdom, if this wine remains in a state of constant fermentation of piousness and fear of God. We must give it air in order not to let it spoil. This is why we permit folly on certain days so that we may later return with greater zeal to the service of God." The first proper dramatic play after the misery of the Dark Ages, Adam de la Halle's *Le Jeu de la Feuillée*, orig. *Jeus de le feullie* (13th century) was not only the originator, or at least first preserved instance, of the Rabelaisian idiom, but a praise of Folly itself. From the introduction by Richard Axton and John Stevens (Blackwell, 1971): "The *fuellie* is traditionally seen as a *feuillée* or canopy of green leaves, such as was constructed over the shrine of Notre Dame exhibited in one of two public squares in Arras in summer, between Pentecost and the Assumption. The alternative explanation is that *feullie* means *folie*. The square in which the Confrerie held their summer festival on Assumption Eve was known in Arras as *la place de la folie* ["mad square"], the place of executions and public exhibition of sacred relics. Either interpretation enriches one's appreciation of the milieu in which the play was produced; both may have been apt for the pun-loving Arrageois." And indeed Folly, like a pun, is seeing things as they are not; it is a holiday from reality.

Man is not as rational an animal as he would like to be; and folly is the proof of it. A world without it is unimaginable and unsustainable; communism, in its high bureaucratic phase, officially conceived of society as subject to almost mathematical rules, and the contradictions inherent in that proposition led to its collapse. Irreproachably lofty and beautiful the idea of total equality may be, something in us prevents it from working.

The conundrum at the heart of rationality – that the more you know, the more you know how little you know – finds its counterpart in the Christian tradition of the Holy Fool. Some may think of Christianity's useful idiots, e.g. most clerics in the C of E, or Parsifal, whose virtue is impregnable precisely because of his near-cretinism, but the archetype is St Symeon, who after 29 years in the desert doing little else apart from praying, having the odd vision and being pious, turns up in the city of Emesa with a dead dog tied to his belt, shitting in the street, acting like a cunt but somehow managing to be an inspiration for potential converts. That he may not even have existed, and may indeed be a satirical version of the Cynics ("dogs" in Greek, hard-core moralists who deliberately outraged convention; their founder, Diogenes, would toss himself off in public and then say if only hunger could be satisfied by rubbing one's belly) is something the scholars are still tussling over to this day. It is problematic for Christians, too. As I have implied, the entire recruitment policy of our national church consists of giving a certain kind of idiot something useful to do, but there is a clear line between being a twit and an outright embarrassment. (On which note, I recall that the pious John Tavener has composed a series of motets on the subject of Holy Folly, with lyrics by the Greek Orthodox Mother Thekla; having been reported (*Private Eye*, 20/10/00) as saying "it's a mark of what society has come to that you can't have a joke with a black man and call him a nig-nog any more", one could say that as far as being a fool goes, he not only talks the talk, he walks the walk. One would have preferred, however, the dead dog.)

But in these pages, we have to salute folly, even if it goes against the grain of the Enlightenment, whose boots we are still not yet fit to lick. The very name of this publication is an affront to the industrious ant, who scorns the grasshopper for having fucked about all summer. But you can't have fun without folly; and you can't begin to be wise without having fun. Being a fool at least means you are more likely to be doing it at your expense rather than someone else's. So let us all tie a dead dog to our belts and shit in the streets. In the global village, we are all world-class idiots. But I would suggest you leave the bagpipes at home. There are limits. ◉

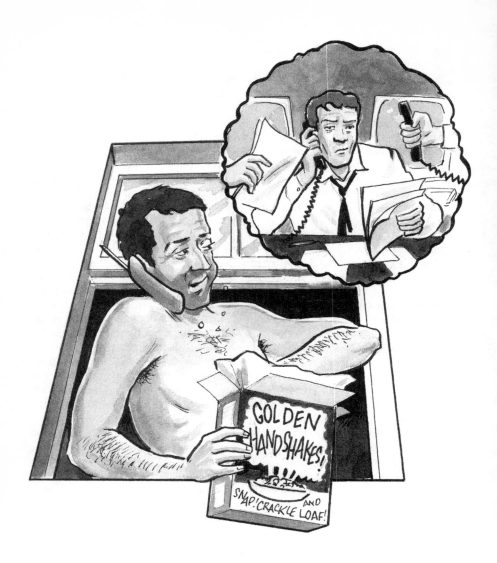

LAID OFF, LAID BACK

Longtime contributor TIM RICHARDSON enjoys a rare period of enforced idleness. Illustration by JOE HARRISON

Like most contributors to the *Idler* – in both its 18th and 20th Century incarnations – I am a competitive, busy, career-minded arse for whom the concept of Idleness is a kind of ironic, subversive conceit. Idleness in this sense has little to do with laziness, merely a kind of leisureliness of mind which one hopes might produce unusual and diverting opinions. However, now as in the 18th Century, most people contributing to the *Idler* are media hacks of one sort or another, unable to spend weeks meditating on the subject of their essay. Precious though it is, the *Idler* commission is subject to all the usual deadline frenzy, and it is a challenge for writers to find the headspace to generate ideas from idleness.

Until now. Due to the sudden and irritating closure, by jealous executives, of the magazine I edited, I find myself unemployed and, due to a contractural vagary, obliged NOT to work for a period. This has meant that after ten years of office life, I have been suddenly catapulted into a world of slow decision-making, an interest in the weather and the option of spending the whole day nude.

I am now in the third month of this strange netherworld existence. A chunk of me had been lopped off: I had no e-mail and most of my contacts only knew my office telephone number, a number I had had for ten years. Suddenly, from a world where people wanted to speak to me every day, I had the option of speaking to no one.

In fact, I did speak to people. I rang people at their workplaces to explain (at length) what had happened and how I was not at fault. I had the strange sensation, after fifteen minutes or so, that they were trying to get me off the phone. They were interested and sympathetic, but they were busy. They had other fish to fry. When I put the phone down I experienced another strange sensation. I had no fish to fry. In fact I could have made shrimp ceviche and personally overseen the whole marinading process.

When the phone rings at home nowadays, I pick it up. Not because I need, want or am allowed to work, but because it does not seem like a chore. Like everyone else, when I was working, I answered the phone or responded to voicemails scores of times every day. When I came home from the office I enjoyed a freedom from the tyranny of the phone and screened compulsively. Now I am once again enjoying the sensation of answering the phone first time. I have even experimented briefly with the old-school way of saying hello followed by a quick recitation of the phone number. All right!

In the first days of unemployment I didn't need to wear clothes for breakfast and its environs. What was the point? The novelty soon palled. I have discovered that my natural body clock demands I sleep or nap for a short period between 3.30 and 4.30. Why not? Churchill had a nap every afternoon, even at the height of the Battle of Britain. Conversely, my interest in lunch has waned. When I worked, I found it painful that few compadres liked to lunch properly, preferring some kind of

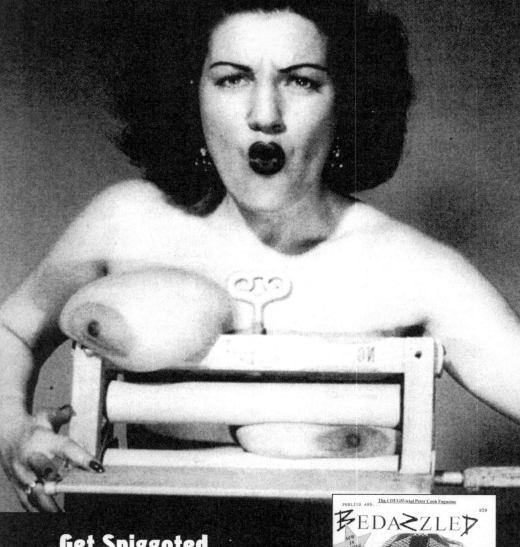

Get Spiggoted

The Peter Cook Appreciation Scoiety has been up and meandering for almost exactly 94 years, celebrating the non-stop dancing, the heroic smoking, the beer and loafing, and – lest we forget – the comic twinklies of Sting Thundercock, inventor of the horizontal bubble.

For a whole new lease of death, send £8 (to us, preferably) for a year's worth of our quarterly fagazine, Publish and Bedazzled, plus one (count it!) ghastly badge.

"It's like a breath of hot air"

PETER COOK APPRECIATION SOCIETY

15 Temple Dwellings
Temple Street
London
E2 6QG

The COUGH-icial Peter Cook Fagazine

PUBLISH AND... #20

BEDAZZLED

NOW IN BORING COLOUR!

GIRTHDAY EDITION

HOUND OF THE BASKERVILLES: The Mutt's Nuts Or Finest Dog Dressage?

MOCK AGAINST THATCHER: That 'Saturday Live' Show in Full!

disgusting sandwich or wrap to expensive restaurant food. Now, I don't mind a modest cold platter, with no alcohol. I think it's because I used to see lunch as a kind of reward or compensation for hired work: the consolation of gluttony.

It now seems to take a long time to get things done. In an office one performs many small tasks every day, arranging things, sorting things out, finding things out. You can do at least 30 such things a day in an office environment. At home, things are much harder to do. I can do up to three things a day, and quite often none at all. I am not lazy, though. I just feel disenfranchised from the world of getting things done. The other day I managed to chase up an insurance payment for some ironic ornaments and Elvis videos I had left in the car and which had been stolen. I got the cheque yesterday, which proves that I can still do things.

I have also achieved familiarity with shopkeepers, the particular makeup of the weekday population and a variety of radio stations. I have gone shopping without extreme pressure of time, and the weekend has crept up without me noticing, sensations I have not had since I was a student. I am aware of the local post-box times, get nervous in restaurants and now take a keen interest in weather developments. I have not drifted into drugs or prostitution, thank goodness! I saw a show the other night that said anyone could make 150 bucks on the street. The risks must be high, though.

I was suprised to find that daytime television was just a fleeting interest. My unemployment coincided – holy mother of God! – with a complete revamp of BBC1 afternoon programmes, and in those early days I hunkered down to watch them with a kind of patronising smirk. So this is daytime TV? Wow, and I'm not even ill... Initially I was upset by *The Weakest Link*, the new quiz show hosted by Anne Robinson, in which contestants eliminate each other and are then encouraged to be rude about one another. The show generates an unpleasant frisson. Only now do I realise that experiencing a frisson of any kind is a bonus for a proportion of the daytime audience.

Well, I must be getting on. I am conducting an experiment with the bank. I know banks close early, but can't remember when. I am leaving the house with my baby son (who has made these months so much better than working) at slightly different times in order to find out when it closes. I have these cheques to pay in. The past few days the bank has been closed at just before 5 and just after 4.30. I reckon it closes at 4.30. Today I will find out whether that is true. ◉

YOU SILLY SAUSAGE

The foolish acts of a foolish man by BEN MOOR

By the way, let me start by saying this isn't one of those confessional things where a writer boasts about all the crazy things they've done and tries to get the reader to be all impressed. I don't want your admiration, I don't think I deserve it and I honestly have nowhere to put it if you gave it to me anyway (I can hardly move in here for admiration).

No, what this is, is a bit of me thinking about what makes someone a temporary fool and how, while this is often a bad thing, it puts a lot of normalcy into perspective.

Good word, normalcy. It was made up by Warren Harding, a president of the US sometime in the last century. Everyone knew it wasn't a real word, but he was the president and nobody was going to say anything. Who were the real fools there, huh? If you don't know the answer to that, maybe you are a fool. In which case, this whole article isn't going to mean much to you. I should skim on if I were you, find something else to read. There is plenty. Just so you know, the fools were the other people. Not Warren Harding. He was plain straight-down-the-line stupid. The fool is the person that can see sense but just goes ahead and ignores it.

Here are some examples when I have been such a fool.

ACT OF FOLLY 1: AGREEING TO DRINK A PINT OF MINDFUCK. *

Reason For It

This was the evening of the Christmas dinner at my college. I was 21. I was drunk. I had had a lot of food and drink already that evening and believed that just a little more drink would make me happier; seeing as how that previous drink had got me this happy. Mindfuck was a cocktail made by putting in a double shot of every spirit by passing a pint glass along a row of bar optics and then filling the glass up with orange juice. It would have given Oliver Reed (GRHS) pause.

Effect

After maybe ten seconds inside my body, this aptly named drink returned to the outside world whence it came. I puked all over myself and the person sitting next to me. It was all in front of over two hundred people, who, up to that point, had quite respected me. I instantly lost their respect, lost my self-respect and lost the trust of the person next to me. She now moves away whenever she sees me. I gained a reputation as a fool.

Lesson Learned

That when you are already drunk, drinking more is largely wrong. The fact is though, that I have rarely taken this lesson to heart. When I have drunk enough, I still often drink more. I remain, sadly, a fool.

ACT OF FOLLY 2: TELLING MY (THEN) GIRLFRIEND THAT I HAD ONCE FANCIED HER COUSIN.

Reason For It

Basically, I did it because I felt guilty about having once fancied her cousin.

Effect

My girlfriend said she was unhappy that I had once fancied her cousin, but after I assured her that I no longer fancied her cousin and in fact fancied her, she became less unhappy and we shared many fabulous times. Secretly though, I think she continued to suspect that I still fancied her cousin.

Lesson Learned

I have never since told a girl I have been going out with that I have ever fancied her cousin.

ACT OF FOLLY 3: RUNNING NAKED THROUGH THE STREETS OF CROYDE IN CORNWALL ONE NEW YEAR'S NIGHT IN THE EARLY NINETIES. 1992, MAYBE.*

Reason For It

I was drunk and I wanted to emulate my hero Ken Campbell who, in his excellent show "Memoirs of a Furtive Nudist" spoke movingly of the time he took all his clothes off for a midnight streak through Croyde. Having found myself in the same town I let myself go, quite literally, and streaked.

Effect

Some scratches, wet feet, the pity of my friends. I saw a policeman and some other people celebrating the New Year, which, as I say was probably 1992, but it might have been 1993. I avoided them however and returned to the cottage my friends and I had rented, later to return to the beach and sing to the stars of my achievement. The song should reach them sometime after Easter in the year 3862.

Lesson Learned

Streaking is fun. I did it on the spur of the moment and don't really regret it. It's on this list as it was a foolish thing to do, but foolish can be fun. In this case, a whole streak of fun.

ACT OF FOLLY 4: GOING TO BRITISH COLUMBIA TO TRY AND FIND THE TOWN OF JACKSON BAY.

Reason For it

Ken Campbell clearly inspires a great deal of foolishness. I had heard him talk about Geographical Acupuncture at the ICA (in summary, between these brackets, you are the needle, the world is the body, find the place you have to be) and when I got home I found the town of Jackson Bay circled in an old atlas. I must have circled it for some reason years previously, but couldn't remember why, so I decided to make my way there and see if that was the place I had to be.

STREAKING IS FUN. I DID IT ON THE SPUR OF THE MOMENT AND DON'T REALLY REGRET IT. IT'S ON THIS LIST AS IT WAS A FOOLISH THING TO DO, BUT FOOLISH CAN BE FUN. IN THIS CASE, A WHOLE STREAK OF FUN

Effect

I got to Vancouver and found no mention of the town on any map of the Province. I did my best to get to where it should really have been, but it would have involved a bus that ran only once a week and hiring boats and really I would rather have gone to Seattle where there were cool bands and interesting examples of Space Age architecture.

Lesson Learned

That setting yourself a mission, finding it is just a little bit too hard to achieve and therefore not completing it, isn't failure. It just means that the mission was foolhardy to begin with.

ACT OF FOLLY 5: WALKING HOME AFTER A FANCY DRESS PARTY TO WHICH I HAD COME DRESSED AS A TERRORIST. I WAS STOPPED BY THE POLICE WHO ASKED TO SEE MY GUN TO MAKE SURE IT WAS, AS I CLAIMED, PLASTIC AND I WAS NOT, AS I ALSO CLAIMED, IN ANY WAY ABOUT TO BLOW ANYTHING UP OR SHOOT ANYTHING.*

Reason For It

I didn't have a lift home from the party so decided to walk the eight miles from Canterbury to Whitstable. It was winter, I was cold, so I put on my balaclava and combat jacket and slung my toy gun over my shoulder. I was, incidentally, drunk.

Effect

The police made me feel stupid, which, along with enforcing the law, is their main function in society.

Lesson Learned

That it doesn't matter how big a fool you think you are, the police will always make you feel a bigger one. Also: always get a lift if you can, as everywhere's further than you think.

✱ At this point it is worth pointing out that three of the five acts of folly above have been asterisked. This asterisk serves the following purpose: it represents moments when alcohol has influenced my behaviour to such an extent that foolishness, if not inevitable, is at least more likely. This isn't an excuse. It's just a fact and one which I hardly need defend.

Now a lot of people like this effect alcohol has on them, and I guess I have to count myself as one of them. It's why alcohol remains the world's number one recreational drug of choice. Inhibitions? "I free you of them," says booze. Consequences? "Ignore them," it says. Social conventions? "So what," it slurs, "run naked through coastal towns if you like, what does it matter?"

Childhood is like drunkenness in this way. Speaking for myself now, when I was young I was just learning about consequences, bits of behaviour I now find foolish as a sober adult were socially convinced out of me by teachers and parents through negative reinforcement.

Saying what I actually thought about people, believing I could eat or drink anything, wearing what I wanted, or indeed nothing at all; things that I now understand are not the done thing, were things I did all the time back then. Grown-ups may have found them funny, but I was punished for them and learnt that society doesn't really accept such activity.

Hence the popularity of *Kids Say the Funniest Things* where people who just happen to be young are held up as entertaining idiots for their uninhibited opinions and confused logic. You might just as well have a show called "Drunks Make the Funniest Fools" as all that show is doing is liberating its audience from how we expect non-foolish adults to speak and act.

The important thing about being a fool is that you ignore consequences. Or you acknowledge them but just wish they'd go away. Those friends of President Harding that let him invent the word normalcy didn't care what would happen once it got out. Now lexicographers and sub-editors twinge whenever it comes up.

But what if there really were no consequences? What if what you did now didn't have any impact on the future?

I think the church vs. orgy question arises here: The world is about to end – what do you do? Do you go and pray in a church in the belief that when this world ends you will still see the consequences of your actions or do you join the nearest orgy and hope that there will be no consequences? This isn't just a

DO YOU GO AND PRAY IN A CHURCH IN THE BELIEF THAT WHEN THIS WORLD ENDS YOU WILL STILL SEE THE CONSEQUENCES OF YOUR ACTIONS OR DO YOU JOIN THE NEAREST ORGY AND HOPE THAT THERE WILL BE NO CONSEQUENCES?

religious question, it's about how you perceive your capacity for pleasure. The fool assumes that pleasure is infinite and should never be avoided; the non-fool wonders about the cost of glee somewhere down the road.

Now I know a bit about the end of the world, as, in my foolishness, I have collected movies and programmes to do with it.

For example, I love the first hour of *The Stand* and *Survivors* from the Seventies which concentrated on bad diseases. I like a couple of nuclear war ones, but I currently adore doom-from-space scenarios. For example, there was that episode of *Sliders* and recently there were the movies *Deep Impact, Armageddon* and *Last Night*. Of these, *Deep Impact* always struck me as the one movie that explored this best.

Last Night had David Cronenberg going around telling people they'd still be getting gas until the last moment which would end the world in a very Canadian manner. *Armageddon* made, um, Armageddon, look like a Coca Cola commercial (although any movie that include Steve Buscemi delivering the line "Embrace the horror" does have at least one good point). And the *Sliders* episode (though heavily featuring orgies and churches) was resolved by the Professor inventing nuclear weapons to save the planet. Hmmm.

Deep Impact suggests that if you know there's an asteroid on its way to kill us all – an Extinction Level Event, indeed – what you shouldn't do is head towards the big cave

where the American government is saving its boffins and lottery winners, but go and cuddle your Dad on a beach. Survival be damned. Tea Leoni's character (who had a place in the cave all sewn up) expresses herself in a supreme act of foolishness; when faced with the infinite she ignores sense and does whatever the heck she likes. And she's not even drunk.

But, Extinction Level Event folly aside, the other thing is that even normal foolish acts have benefits. It's only by doing them that we realise what potential morons we all are and how deeply unsatisfying an existence moronity generally is. It's good to remind ourselves regularly that below our civilised surface, there is an idiot just waiting to get out and spoil everything. How evolution must have cheered when it started to select for sensible. And how near we totter to the edge of barmy. I have just listed five of mine. I'm sure you could do the same. So be on your guard for nonsense. Arm yourselves against insanity. And while you're doing that, have a drink and ask yourself, "What's the worse that could happen if I just..."

This piece was going to consist of just five things, but after thinking about it and getting a few beers in I decided to do one more foolish thing and put on my video of *Deep Impact* (1997 Dir: Mimi Leder).

ACT OF FOLLY 6: WATCHING *DEEP IMPACT* AGAIN.

Reason For It

To see how people behave without consequences. I remembered the scene on the beach right except for the inexplicable foreignness of Tea Leoni's father, but a lot of the other characters cried and/or killed themselves when faced with the end.

Effect

I wasted a couple of hours that I could more valuably have spent playing Vib Ribbon on the Playstation.

Lesson Learned

That meteors are bad and it doesn't matter if loads of people die so long as they die fairly spectacularly. In the last scene, Morgan Freeman, playing President Plot Exposition, speaks to a big crowd. A tidal wave has just destroyed a model of New York and killed millions, but he pledges a return to normalcy. Lots of fools cheer. ◉

Ben Moor has just been playing a fool in the West End production of A Busy Day. *He is currently working on a play called* Three Wishes.

IT'S GOOD TO REMIND OURSELVES REGULARLY THAT BELOW OUR CIVILISED SURFACE, THERE IS AN IDIOT JUST WAITING TO GET OUT AND SPOIL EVERYTHING

FUNNY BUSINESS

BABS BABYLON recalls a disappointingly unfunny encounter with the world of New York comedy in the Eighties. Pictures from Dr Katz, courtesy of Paramount Comedy Channel

July 17, 1985 was a typical mid-summer Thursday for New Yorkers, another sidewalk sauna of stinking subway steam, rotting trash smells and waddling tour groups clogging up transportation arteries. But it was a special day for me in sweltering Manhattan, where the air was so thick it felt like Vaseline and my makeup was sliding off and forming plastic globules on the sidewalk.

That particular day, I was convinced, was going to be the funniest of my entire existence: I was

going to a taping of *Late Night With David Letterman.* Even better: I would be sitting backstage, no doubt partaking in the hilarious scene on the other side of the TV screen.

This was a very big deal. Despite obvious dental flaws, David Letterman at that time was as close as you could get to a saint, a national hero, the King of America. He was transforming the culture, making the US far more amusing than it had been the year before and enticing the natives to finally learn how to use VCRs. That summer, the beginning of his reign, Letterman had graced the cover of *Rolling Stone* and was changing the face of everyday chit chat. Mornings began with a smile and a conversational "Hey did you catch Dave last night? That guy!"

Dave yelled at strangers from his eighth floor window: "I'm not wearing any pants!" and tried to screw up other talk shows; he sent inept correspondents around the world and used monkeys strapped with "Monkeycams" as the cameraman; he had machines that shot golf balls and guests that cursed, stripped and got married as a result of a well-placed Letterman call. He made fun of his own network. And his wicked wit proved that Americans can be as ruthlessly funny as Brits, on occasion.

Letterman was also ushering in a comedy renaissance: *Late Night* was *the* showcase – standups from Jay Leno to Richard Lewis, Roseanne Barr to Ellen Degeneres were showered with instant fame – and comedy clubs were blossoming like dandelions in every town with a population over three.

I was then a lightly seasoned comedy critic for a news weekly in Portland, Oregon. With six months of comedy shows under my belt, I should have seen what would lie ahead that particular Thursday. I knew enough comedians to notice they tended to fall into three categories: neurotically needy and/or amazingly annoying and/or terminally miserable and tense.

The animated show *Dr Katz* sheds light on merrymakers' bizarre off-stage behaviour with comedians taking to the psychiatrist's couch – the difference being that the show is hilarious, and the off-stage standup often isn't. Not that he doesn't try.

Profession punsters can be pathetic, like puppies seeking attention: you deeply wound them if you don't laugh at their little jokes, which gurgle out nonstop. Friends, relatives, strangers? Simply guinea pigs for their test balloons – and sources of material, which comedians guiltlessly steal. They always despise their parents – or so says Letterman's ex, Merrill Markoe; many seem to loathe themselves. The same emotional material that might drive a sane man to suicide can drive the fool to the mike. For whatever reason, comedians are often twisted, and I'm not the only one who thinks so.

In an article skewering Mike Myers in the October 2000 issue of *Vanity Fair*, an industry insider gives their take: "Comedians are not people. They look like people, but... They're angry... really, really difficult... [sometimes] maniacal and out of control and full of rage." Humour-robots who can't stop blurting out jokes on stage, they're often a huge headache once they step off.

Take the beloved and talented Lily Tomlin who, I'm chagrined to report, was alarmingly paranoid when she showed up in Portland to test-run *The Search For Intelligent Life In The Universe*. Though the local media had formed a drooling cheering squad, the comedienne – after reading a

foot-kissing, positively slobbering review in the local daily – cancelled all interviews and threatened to sue: Lily thought the reporter had taped the show. I'd been sitting behind said reporter who'd simply taken notes with a voracity that would make a top executive secretary wince.

Carol Leifer, later head writer of *Seinfeld*, was remarkably boring, saying little of interest save that she was the offspring of a psychiatrist and a psychologist; Richard Lewis, to judge by the one time I met him, could have used Leifer's parents since he seemed to be mid-anxiety attack. Roseanne Barr and Rosie O'Donnell have reputations for being less than a laughfest on the set; Jay Leno was so crazed about taking over Johnny Carson's desk that he once hid in a closet to spy on his former best friend David Letterman, also up for the job. A night out with comedians is a nightmare full of faked laughs and competitive one-upmanship, and let's not get into how many comedy writers have nervous breakdowns searching for jokes.

Granted, not all comics are egocentric, paranoid and grating. Paula Poundstone, the former Boston bus girl who, when mad at customers, would "touch their eggs", is wonderfully engaging, even though we were kicked out of a shopping mall for disrupting a fashion show. Seinfeld seemed likable and level-headed, Bobcat Goldwaite is sweet and silly; Dana Carvey and A. Whitney Brown can crash my dinner parties whenever they desire.

But of all the comedians making the rounds, there was one I positively adored, though he was the oddest of the bunch: Emo Philips. With bowl cut 'do, slinky body that wheezed like a vertical accordion, and his habit of fiddling around with a trombone that he never assembled, wide-eyed Emo was an original – he stood out in a field filled with clones telling the same slick, memorised jokes in the same slick, memorised style.

From his simple jokes – "I found my girlfriend in bed with another man. I was crushed. I said 'Get off me you two!'" – to his longwinded stories that jabbed at religious righteousness, Emo was brilliant.

I spent a day with him in Portland, during which our conversation frequently drifted back to his preformulated jokes, which he tossed out like nervous tics. No matter: between his unusualness and "possible alien" looks, the article I wrote about Emo was easy to sell to *Spin* magazine.

Emo, who'd never snagged national press before – he'd soon have a mountain – was touched. So he invited me to be his guest at *Late Night*. He'd been asked to reappear – under the condition that he omit the joke about his new romantic attraction – a real beauty, whom Emo described as lovely from the tip of her nose to "the tag on her toe..." Necrophilia gags apparently weren't playing so big at NBC. The last time Emo had tried them he sent the Censors beeping.

So I flew from the West coast to the East, not knowing that what would follow would be a tragi-comedy of errors, in which Letterman would fall from his pedestal and I would prove myself an utter fool.

It started when the airline lost my luggage – forcing me to do a hurried shopping spree for an outfit. When I turned up at Emo's agent's office,

A NIGHT OUT WITH COMEDIANS IS A NIGHTMARE, FULL OF FAKED LAUGHS AND ONE-UPMANSHIP. AND LET'S NOT GET INTO HOW MANY COMEDY WRITERS HAVE NERVOUS BREAKDOWNS SEARCHING FOR JOKES

bags in hand, the agent informed me first I couldn't go to the show, then that I couldn't sit backstage at Late Night, which Emo had promised.

This prompted a hissy fit – I'd flown five hours to sit in the Green Room, not the studio audience; finally the agent relented. But I was relegated to the role of albatross around neck. The agent – short, squat, pudgy-lipped - whom I shall call Dick since that's what he was acting like – began a long-winded lecture. "Whatever you do, don't talk to Emo!" he warned. "He won't have time for you! And he gets all wound up before shows! Don't talk to him!"

"Don't talk to Emo!" he said as we pushed through the revolving doors into the gaily muralled entryway of NBC. Dick chanted the warning in the elevator up to Studio 8A and chanted it more as we stood waiting in the fluorescently-lit corridor which was so corporately characterless it could have been IBM.

It was immediately clear: something was wrong, something more than Dick's blathering. This was *Late Night* – the funniest show in the universe. People were supposed to be laughing, skipping down the hallways, slapping each other on the back, saying "Hey didja hear the one about..."

They weren't doing that though. No one was chortling, giggling, skipping or jigging. There wasn't a hint of a smile on the faces that briskly marched down the corridor. Everyone looked cranky and tense. The place felt as festive as a morgue, as merry as a war room after an announcement of war.

My back went rigid. I felt like an idiot carrying shopping bags. Dick wasn't helping any either with his constant lecturing, now shouted from across the hall, since he clearly didn't want to be seen standing beside me.

He opened his mouth to bark his agentorial command once again, just as the door to the Censor's room flew open. Out bounded Emo in trademark baggy plaid pants and tight shirt that showed off his skinny, caved-in chest.

"Babs!" he said, ignoring his agent. "How are you?"

I looked up to see Dick positioning himself behind the comedian, making frantic "Time Out" signs. He wasn't joking.

"Happy to be in New York?" Emo asked, as Dick continued his cheers for silence campaign, mouthing "Don't talk! Don't talk!"

"Excited to be at NBC?" Emo asked. Dick was making furious zipping motions across his mouth.

"Why aren't you talking?" asked Emo. I should have pointed to Dick doing his imitation of an idiot, but I shrugged. "Well," Emo said warily, "see you after the show." Emo hadn't seemed uptight initially, but my Dick-imposed silence seemed to unnerve him.

Dick immediately zipped over to hiss in my ear. He was cut short mid-hiss, when a page herded us into a corner, not far from the studio doors. "Thank God," I thought. "Dave's finally here. The Prince of Lightness and Levity – who shows the funny side of everyday life – will know just what to say to sweeten this sour, oppressive mood." I half expected him to cart-wheel down the hall.

One look at Letterman's expression as it came into non-cartwheeling view disavowed me of that notion. "Surly," is a term that comes to mind. So is "really grumpy and generally mean and sorta scary."

As he strode by haughtily, whipping on a blue tie, Dave didn't smile or wave or tell a hilarious joke. Instead he glared at the assembled crowd, disdain evident, as though he was looking at jackasses lined up to be branded. He might as well have spat at us – his foolish fans.

I was shocked. But just as he was turning the corner, Dave did a double take. A smile suddenly overtook his face. He turned and walked back to the crowd, a flash of familiarity in his eyes.

Dave walked right up to me.

"Well hello!" he said. "How are you doing?"

I've been told I'm a dead-ringer for a hotshot Manhattan agent; apparently Dave thought I was her. I wondered if I should play along with my mistaken identity. Instead I said, "Um Dave, you don't know me."

The light flickered out of his eyes, his smiled reassembled into a frown, and he stomped off, more furious than ever.

"Well ya didn't tell me ya knew Dave," Dick said, pushing to get close and taking me by the arm. "He looked so happy to see you! What did he say?"

No time to answer: a page then escorted us into the Green Room.

THIS WAS "LATE NIGHT" – THE FUNNIEST SHOW IN THE UNIVERSE. PEOPLE WERE SUPPOSED TO BE LAUGHING, SKIPPING DOWN THE HALLWAYS, SLAPPING EACH OTHER ON THE BACK, SAYING "HEY DIDJA HEAR THE ONE ABOUT..."

It was upon entering the closet-sized "green room" – which was blue and gray – that I lost the ability to speak. "Hi there," said Larry "Bud" Melman, the diminuitive, bespectacled "character" of many a Letterman sketch. "Hi there," Larry "Bud" repeated, handing me an invitation to his birthday party. "Hi there," Larry "Bud" said to everyone who entered the tiny room, most of whom ignored him and his invitations.

The room, after all, was filled with terribly important people: agents and managers and NBC employees, all of whom seemed professionally nervous. On the couch across from the one where I sat, some sort of inventor was huddled, clutching his invention in a briefcase, and biting his nails. At least fifteen people squeezed into the tiny room, everyone sniffing at each other like "Who are you?"

The band broke into the theme song. We gazed at the monitor hanging in the corner, and I slouched into the blue couch to ensure I didn't block the midget's Melman's view.

The opening monologue was an unmemorable blur: joke after joke nosedived. When they cut to commercials, Letterman was looking quite annoyed at his desk.

When the taping continued, he couldn't fool me with his fakey smile as he narrated a skit starring Larry "Bud" as a farmer. Utterly humourless. "Bad start," someone moaned, while someone else whispered that Dave was in "a mood" because at the last minute baseball great Mickey Mantle had cancelled.

Letterman looked livid during the commercial break. But his enthusiasm seemed sincere when he introduced his guest: Connie Chung, a fetching reporter for an NBC news show.

It was all my fault what happened next. My fault – and Dick's – that he hadn't offered to let me keep my many shopping bags at his office. Because what I hadn't gathered until that moment was that the Green Room – essentially a holding tank – also served as runway to the stage. And my shopping bags were piled up right in the middle of said runway.

When Connie Chung, late for her cue, came barrelling through, her foot caught on the handle of my shopping bag. A horrible slow-motion moment ensued during which she was one second aloft – and the next nearly doing as bad as a nosedive as one of Dave's opening jokes. Right before gravity claimed her, the stage manager Biff caught her and she ran onto the stage.

The collective gasp in the Green Room was not unlike the belch of a rumbling volcano. "Whose bags are those?" demanded a navy blue suit

who was Connie's manager. Dick resumed his hostile, "she's-not-with-me" posture.

"Whosever they are, I'll move them right here," I would have said had I been able to talk. Instead I scooped them up – a clear admission of guilt.

I took deep interest in the TV monitor, upon which Connie was talking about spinning sperm. Then she went on to demonstrate her "Stupid Human Trick": breaking walnuts with her bare hand. Drum roll please. Connie closed the nut in her tiny fist and squeezed. Nothing. She squeezed. Nothing. She squeezed again. Nothing. The walnut might as well have been the Rock of Gibraltar for the effect she was having on it.

"It's because she was tripped on her way to the stage!" declared the manager, and all eyes turned to me. I slunk further into the couch, and Letterman cut to a commercial.

Happily, in the next segment Connie actually cracked her stupid nut. Unhappily, everyone kept sending death stares my way, and I would have crept out, except right then the door shut, and Dave strode through the hallway – merrily chatting with most of the people who'd been in the hallway crowd that he'd glared at not long before. Bullhorn in hand, he strode to the window – and solicited a hilarious black woman from eight floors below to be his guest. "Can I bring my boyfriend?" she asked. "No!" Letterman bellowed back. She brought him anyway – and they threatened to show up Dave with their one-liners. Letterman was again looking annoyed when they cut to a commercial.

The final act was Emo, who ran through the Green Room without incident. Once on stage, he donned his bashful, bugged-eyed, "what planet am I on" act. His first two jokes were stunning. But around the third, he stumbled, and forgot his line.

"I told you not to talk to him," Dick hissed at me. "It's all your fault!" By the time Emo sat down with Dave, the talk show host was fuming, and they quickly ran the credits.

The show was over. Emo ran by, nervously asking, "How was I?" and Letterman was stalking down the hallway looking like he was going to punch something, and I was happy my face wasn't within reach.

I stood there stunned, watching the parade of people leaving, none of them laughing. What I'd imagined would be the funniest day in my life turned out to a top contender for the most horrid.

I don't think Emo was on the show again; if he was, he didn't invite me. Connie Chung, on her next appearance, made a special request: not to enter through the Green Room. And I, clearly not heeding the clues, briefly became a freelance comedy writer, emerging from the experience deciding that ballgame to be more screwy than the evening backstage at *Late Night* ever portended.

Years later, I met Letterman's ex-girlfriend Merrill Markoe, quite the witster and comedy writer herself. "Dave and I could have been the King and Queen of Manhattan," she lamented of their life in the late Eighties. "But he never wanted to go out. He just wanted to stay at home and mope about that night's show."

I sensed a fabulous future friendship brewing, until I said something mildly kind about my parents – and Merrill's anti-parental quirk was struck. I received a loud lecture, during which I recalled that while funny people are great, professional jokemakers are often too much.

The point is this: levity, that ability to find lightness in darkness and turn ennui on its ear, is truly a virtue, a necessary lubricant in keeping the wheels of life turning. But in the same way that a witticism gets ruined when encapsulated in a joke, a funny person is so often doomed once they brand themselves a "comedian" and seek out the din of laughing approval. Alas, purveyors of wit aren't heroes or demi-gods; they're simply mortals, often more wretched than the rest of us fools. ◉

EMPEROR NORTON

In 1859, retired businessman Joshua Norton declared himself Emperor of the United States. JON FORTGANG describes the surprisingly successful life of an arch self-delusionist.
Illustration by HANNAH DYSON

There's something fascinating about human beings in the grip of fierce delusion. Unshakeable conviction, no matter how absurd, generates a thick stew of responses. Partly it's envy at another's careless disregard for the rest of the world. Partly it's contempt for a personality in retreat from reality. And partly it's a quiet but persistent fear that maybe, somehow, they're actually right.

Joshua Norton, first Emperor of the United States and Protector of Mexico, could reasonably claim to have elicited all these responses, and plenty of others besides. He reigned from a fifty-cent-a-night hotel room in San Francisco from 1859 until his death on a street corner in January 1880. During the course of his life he managed to lose more money than most Americans had ever seen. Dressed in a flamboyantly chaotic uniform of army surplus and feathers he wandered the streets of San Francisco, his life entirely subsidised by his adoring subjects, dispensing decrees and ennoblements as the fancy took him.

Born in London to Jewish parents on St Valentines Day 1819, Norton was taken the following year to live in South Africa. Little is known of his childhood but during his twenties he exhibited a serious head for business and, via a succession of cunning food and property deals around the Cape of Good Hope, notched up a significant fortune. In 1849, at thirty years old, and for no very obvious reason, he washed up in San Francisco with $40,000. Catering to the needs of miners and gold prospectors he increased his worth to a cool quarter of a million and by 1852 was among the richest men in America.

But in conventional terms, Norton's luck was about to run out. In the early 1850s, famine in China caused the price of rice in America to increase to nine times its usual worth. Advised to expect a consignment from Peru, Norton staked all his wealth on a single delivery, buying up the lot in the hope of establishing a sort of rice monopoly. The Peruvian ship duly sailed into San Francisco, followed by another, and another, and then another. The city gorged itself on a variety of rice-based dishes, but for Norton it was a disaster. Despite owning two thousand pounds of the stuff, his fortune was irretrievably spent. He called in some favours and struggled on for a while but in 1856 was declared bankrupt. And then Joshua Norton disappeared.

A businessman all his life, it's impossible to guess how Norton spent his time in the wilderness, where he went or what sort of epiphany he experienced. Friends were worried, but with no clue as to his whereabouts there was little they could do. Dead, they might have muttered; curled up with a bottle in Sacramento, or shouting at his shadow in the Nevada dessert. Business was all Norton knew. He was good at it and it had served him well. But clearly the blow dislodged – or re-installed – something deep within him: a series of communications with friends

throughout 1857 indicated that Norton was very much alive, and felt strangely invigorated. He had in fact been reborn as Norton I, Emperor of California.

Strictly speaking, however, California – merely a state – wasn't in a position to recognise Norton's new found eminence, and on 17 September 1859 he delivered the following decree to the San Francisco Evening Bulletin:

"I, Joshua A. Norton, declare and proclaim myself Emperor of the US and in virtue of the authority thereby in me vested do hereby order and direct the representatives of the different states of the Union to assemble in Musical Hall of this city… then and there to make such alteration in the existing laws of the Union as may ameliorate the evils under which the country is labouring."

This announcement, drily notes Catherine Caufield in her book *The Emperor of the United States and Other Magnificent British Eccentrics*, was printed "without comment". If that's the case it was to be the last of Norton's uncommented upon announcements. How indulgent or liberal were the citizens of the city that would a century later spawn The Grateful Dead, Jefferson Airplane and Beat Mecca – The City Lights Bookstore, publishers of Ginsberg's *Howl* – is unrecorded. But Norton's bizarre pronouncement was received calmly and without hysteria. Possibly the people of a confused city, in a confused country, at a confusing time, were relieved to discover who was actually in charge.

And yet, despite the strangeness

surrounding his disappearance and subsequent return, Norton appeared to be deadly serious in his worship of the absurd. Coinciding with his proclamation of sovereignty was the Union's descent into civil war. By 1861 South Carolina, Mississippi, Florida, Alabama, Georgia, Louisiana and Texas had all seceded from the Union. Over the next four years America would suffer 600,000 fatalities. Norton's pragmatic solution in July that year was to declare the Union invalid. Then there'd be no one to fight either for or against. He imposed a sentence "not more than ten, nor less than five years" for anyone ignoring his proclamation. As it happened history overtook him but already his legend was firmly in place. In 1861 a new play opened in San Francisco: *Emperor For A Day*, based on the strange and increasingly eccentric life of Joshua Norton.

EMPEROR NORTON'S VISION WAS FOR A SORT OF NON-HIERARCHICAL, CULTURED LANGUOR: LIFE LIVED IN THE ETERNAL WARMTH OF A SUNNY SUNDAY AFTERNOON

Being Emperor of the United States is, one might imagine, a fairly demanding job, but Norton adopted an admirably hands-off approach. Most days were spent wandering the streets of San Francisco with his dogs Bummer and Lazarus. If the day carried a particularly heavy agenda, he travelled by bike. His vision was for a sort of non-hierarchical, cultured languor: life lived in the eternal warmth of a sunny Sunday afternoon. If someone looked like they needed ennobling – because they'd served him a particularly fine coffee, or told him a good story, or just looked a bit down – Norton declared them King or Queen for a day, the phrase, if not recognition of the rank, passing into everyday use. Most days he ate for free in San Francisco's best restaurants and rewarded his favourites with a plaque declaring "By appointment to his Emperor, Joshua Norton I". The Emperor's new clothes were provided by the city's Board of Supervisors, for which kind act they were ennobled until the end of time. Contemporary pictures show a chubby, cherubic Che-like figure leaning on a stick, heavily bearded and a little dazed, gazing stoically into the middle distance.

Before ascendancy Norton's life had been dedicated to making money, and the impulse never left him. He did however adopt a more literal approach to economics, designing and printing up his own fifty-cent notes. Astonishingly, these bills, marked "The Imperial Government of Norton I" were almost universally accepted, not just by shops and bars, but also by banks. When, in 1867, a police officer new to San Francisco arrested Norton for insanity, there was massive public condemnation. The Chief of Police issued an apology, and his men were told to salute The Emperor whenever they came across him.

Norton was also an enthusiastic supporter of the arts. Three seats were permanently reserved for himself, Lazarus and Bummer in the Metropolitan Theatre, where in 1873 a second biographical play opened: *The Gold Demon.* At around the same time Norton founded the Modern Airies Orchestra. Always forward thinking, only the newest and most novel instruments were allowed in the pit: the saxophone, the bailerphone, the frightening sounding omniphone. Concerts were legendarily dreadful, time having been spent on developing and building the instruments, rather than actually figuring out how to play them. Biographers describe a sort of open-mike policy. Members of the audience could get up and have a go, this perhaps being the only way of preventing them from simply getting up and going. When, incidentally, Bummer died, Mark Twain penned the great dog's eulogy. He also based the character of The King in *Huckleberry Finn* on Norton.

There was a serious side to the Emperor as well. Thinking globally but acting locally. In 1869 he issued a decree ordering that money be sent from the people of San Francisco to early airship designer Frederick Marriott. Tax was to be levied at whatever rate the people of San Francisco felt was reasonable, and in 1872 he began to consider the construction of a suspension bridge joining San Francisco with Oakland. These decrees were accompanied by a further decree declaring that ignorance of his previous decrees be punishable by arrest.

On January 8 1880, on his way to a lecture at The Academy of Natural Sciences, Emperor Norton fell over and died. Two days later he was buried at the Masonic Cemetery in San Francisco. His imaginary majesty, noted the *San Francisco Chronicle*, "is dead and turned to clay," which doesn't sound so bad. He had about five dollars on him.

Thirty thousand people turned up and mourned and partied and mourned.

It's impossible now to gauge how seriously his edicts were delivered, just as it's impossible to know whether Joshua Norton really believed he was Emperor of the United States. Maybe he was, as Robert Louis Stevenson said, just a "harmless madman". But his announcements were remarkably effective at focussing public opinion. In his life he exhibited a sort of will to lunacy, but one of the reasons for his continued status as an underground legend is that almost everything he said made perfectly good sense. He might have been a character in a fairy tale where strange, good men are rewarded with strange, good lives.

At the height of Haight Ashbury the hippies again took up Norton as a mascot, and his story is told in, among many odd places, issue 31 of the *Sandman*. But much of the responsibility for the continuation of his legend lies with chaotic US Cabalists Discordia. A sprawling, surreal "disorganisation" with its own strange taxonomy of the absurd, they officially recognise Norton as a Second Class Saint. (He's in fine company alongside St Edward the Spectacularly Bad, fleetingly known on earth as Ed Wood, and also St. Jarvis Cocker.) "Emperor Norton," Discordians advise with satisfying simplicity, "live like him." ☯

BEFORE ASCENDANCY NORTON'S LIFE HAD BEEN DEDICATED TO MAKING MONEY, AND THE IMPULSE NEVER LEFT HIM. HE DID, HOWEVER, ADOPT A MORE LITERAL APPROACH TO ECONOMICS, DESIGNING AND PRINTING UP HIS OWN FIFTY-CENT NOTES

MY STUPID LIFE

Confessions of utter idiocy, including a doomed scheme to use bubble-wrap as a sleeping bag, by GREG ROWLAND
Illustrations by MARC BAINES

You have to be slightly clever to realise just how stupid you really are. Absolute ignorance is truly a blissful state. Just look at any six-month old baby that you might find to hand. The ignorant little baby has no knowledge of plate tectonics, John Leslie, Wittgenstein, Brian Clough, Ryvita snack recipes or the latest goings on with Anthea Turner. Yet the little baby, floating through an unexplainable ocean of colour and sense, is as happy as Larrys Grayson, Hagman and Flynt combined.

It's possible to continue this ignorance as you progress through your adult life. You may by now be aware of Anthea Turner, but lack the necessary intellectual vigour to form any critical judgements about her – or indeed about a media world that saturates us with the sub-atomic details of the rich and boring. If you have retained this innocence, as you wander the aisles of Tesco's, bathed in the warm light of consumer benediction, picking up a jar of Dolmio and delighting in your Dolce Vita sophistication, then I congratulate you. You're stupid and you've made it stick. You are verily one lucky bleeder.

However, poke your head above the parapets of idiocy and you are lost. You now begin to see just how stupid you really are. You begin to see the piercing light of true intelligence somewhere just beyond the horizon. Just like Prestatyn, you're sure it exists but you don't know how to get there. But as soon as you get the faintest glimmer, a vision of Noam Chomsky in your Coco Pops perhaps, you are destined to drown in a sea of your self-made stupidity.

Many of us therefore live stupid lives, half-knowing that there is something clever out there and are just self-aware enough to know that we have as much chance of finding it as witnessing a sweaty scene of double anal-penetration on an old episode of *The Liver Birds*.

Foremost in the lives of the stupid comes ambition, that murky harlot who teases us with the promise of "personal fulfilment". But the concepts of "personal" and "fulfilment" are bulging non-sequitors, boils on the butt that, if not lanced under proper medical supervision, threaten to fill your pants with puss. Put two non-sequitors together and you get something else entirely. But I'm not sure what that something is. You'd have to ask someone clever.

Fulfilment, as Mistah Buddha said, is impossible in the material world. We compound this problem mistaking fulfilment for desire. From the looks of things, Buddha owed much to the Mr Kipling school of fulfilment. His chubby smile is, in my experience, only achievable after eating an entire box of French Fancies (without the strawberry ones).

So, desire is like an episode of Casualty. (Here is where I begin to differ from the teachings of Buddha.) It goes on and on forever, when you really should be doing something else on a Saturday night, and you feel consequently worthless in its torrid pursuit. And there is no reward or fulfilment at the end, just the promise of another week of someone screaming with a broken pelvis. Neither desire nor ambition can ever be satisfied. Ambition is just the social, externalised form of desire – the "look at me, aren't I great?" part

of the desire mechanism.

Think of those much greater than you and I, my brethren. Think of he who is Bruce Forsyth, king of prime-time game shows for thirty years yet desperate to be accepted in the big site of all our imaginary desires, the United States. Think of how pitifully he chummed up to Sammy Davis Jr and wanted to join the Rat Pack some twenty years after the said rats had packed it in. Or think about Bill Clinton, who had become as powerful as any man could ever become, but still had unfulfilled ambitions in the area of squirting spunk over intern's dresses. Or dear Larry Olivier, whose unfulfilled ambition to play centre-forward for Wolverhampton Wanderers haunted him to his grave.

Bruce, Bill and Larry were all great men. How much do we pale in their shadows? Yet you and I nurse ambitions whose unlikely resolution would just lead us onto yet more and more ambition. Most of us will be disappointed at the first hurdle as the pursuit of drear ambition knocks us flat on the arse.

The alternative to the active pursuit of ambition is equally stupid. It's about being totally passive, a passivity borne of an arrogance that you're too good to pursue anything; an arrogance itself borne out of the insecurity that if you do try anything you will be found out as a talentless git and are no more special than the everyday folk whom you secretly despise. You can sit and wait for your boat to come in – or in my case a flotilla of ceremonial ancient Egyptian barges from the Cheops Dynasty that alight at Blackfriars Bridge.

Few of us have any potential to fulfil, but we are too stupid to realise it. So, if you're like me, you will embrace your lack of potential and celebrate the fact that you can open a packet of crisps without spilling the entire contents over the carpet (one or two examples of "droppage", as the post-structuralists call it, are permissible – you don't want to beat yourself up over a few crumbs of Quavers do you?)

I am now so stupid that I can't think of anything to say to anyone. Woman delights not me, nor man either. And I'm not too crazy about those starfish.

These starfish just lollygag around the ocean floor, smug in their pentagonal contours, waiting for a big break that they think the world owes them. Well I've got news for you starfishies – no-one's interested! Least of all the seahorse, who has a nice steady gig modelling for plastic sand moulds sold in webbed net packs along with small rakes, buckets and sieves at most seaside holiday shops.

The arrogance of the seahorse, an aquatic creature that bases its whole identity on a much larger land-based quadruped that can run fast and go "neigh" never ceases to astound me.

So, most of my life is spent blinking in dumb wonder at the tawdry exhibitions of existence that pockmark the universe. I just can't take it all in. I'm like one of those obscure Massai tribesman who had never

I AM NOW SO STUPID THAT I CAN'T THINK OF ANYTHING TO SAY TO ANYONE. WOMAN DELIGHTS NOT ME, NOR MAN EITHER. AND I'M NOT TOO CRAZY ABOUT THOSE STARFISH

seen a TV before and is suddenly exposed to *Wheel of Fortune* and is unlikely to be propitious in his choice of vowels for "Famous Event" — (Answer: The Post-Modern Apocalypse.)

Blinded by the dim gaslight of a thousand paltry pinpricks of dreariness I find myself surveying My Stupid Life and can find only one answer. The answer is "Yes". Let me share with you some of my most stupid moments.

My Stupid Life begins each day when I wake up and drag myself into the bathroom. Barely able to focus I catch sight of myself in the mirror and am greeted by a soft-focus visage of glowing skin, sparkling eyes and a wistful pre-Raphaelite look of uncommon beauty. This is what I call the Early Morning Honeymoon of the Face. By the time I have finished scrubbing my teeth my vision has returned to its twenty-twenty precision. The gauze effect – used by such effect on Captain Kirk's female conquests in *Star Trek* – has now vanished. I am greeted by the spectre of what I really am: a bleary, blotchy bad blokey face. A face that was drawn and then discarded by a Sixties Underground Comix artist's crappy assistant. Here begins the first disappointment of another day in my stupid life.

I will do many stupid things on any given day in my stupid life. Just yesterday I experimented with cookery. I took a slice of Walls Vienetta and put it in the microwave. This was an astounding success, producing a small portion of a delicious choco-cream syrup drink. Truly, the Vienetta is a milkshake in suspended animation. Flushed with success I decided to strive onwards for other re-formats of my favourite delicacies. This is one of the things that characterises the stupid life. You try something once and it works so you try more stupid variants of the same idea that are doomed to failure. I took three fun-size Milky Ways (though what's fun about having less Milky Way than a normal-sized one is one of those post-modern contricks that slices up my feeble mind like Parma Ham at a smelly Deli) and placed them in a bowl and put them in a microwave on full power for two minutes. Dreams of culinary grandeur can dissolve in such a short time. Within two minutes my hopes of a regular cookery column in *The Observer* faded to a small sludge of caramelised goo that stuck so heartily to the bowl that I couldn't scrape it off and so I consequently had to throw the bowl away. I got told off about this.

But it doesn't stop at microwaves – I am very stupid in the way that I assume technology can solve all problems. This I blame on *Star Trek*. I have spent untold monies on high tech equipment that I feel will turn me into a combination of Orson Welles, Picasso and John Lennon. Needless to say, these dreams too are crushed. The best case scenario is for you not to be able to work the stuff at all. It's far more depressing to find that you can make the equipment work but have less creative inspiration than a hermit crab after a particularly boring day spent inside his shell.

However, this love and trust in technology extends beyond the hi-tech. I was once on tour with my band in Paris. This being a low-budget affair we were staying on the floor of a spacious friend's house. Everyone else had bought sleeping bags to fend off the November nip. But I thought I would be clever. Rather than lug about a big sleeping bag, surely bubble-wrap would provide a more effective blanket against the cold? I discovered that there were a few flaws with this thesis. Bubble-wrap is not warm. The bubbles retain no heat whatsoever. It tears very easily so that you awake with a few sad tatters around your feet. Worst of all, and this is hardly a revelation, bubble-wrap pops. So every time I moved I not only woke up myself but the whole room. I have since eliminated bubble-wrap from the list of sleeping bag substitutes and am now toying with the idea of clingfilm.

But, just as Falstaff was the cause of wit in others, I can cause others to act stupid by my mere presence. It was not long ago when I was stopped by the police in the early hours of the evening and accused of deliberately walking too slowly. Duly chided, I was instructed to walk "more purposefully" if I insisted on walking the streets at 8.30pm. In an unrelated incident, a wig was thrown at me once, which managed to knock me to the floor. It was just a wig, but it's symbolic intent was much more portentous.

My teenage years were also shot through with arrant stupidity. From trying to coax roaming cows out of a tent in Wales by singing the greatest hits of Jimi Hendrix to being overly nice to girls, my foolhardiness was unremitting. Why did no-one ever tell me that being nice to girls was the worst thing you could do if you wanted a snog? On visiting one such girl, I once tired to dodge the fare on the train with a discarded travel card. The inspector asked me if I was over 65. I had stupidly taken an old person's travel card. To experience sarcasm at the hands of the most stupid band of men ever to walk the earth – the British Transport Police – was chastening indeed.

I also envy the dreams of others. My unconscious provides fantasies so bland that they would make vindaloo taste like cottage cheese. A typical dream of mine will involve walking in to a shop – it might be an Argos, it might be a Boots – and asking for a particular item like a plug board or some plasters. After waiting around for a while the assistant will return and say that there are none left, at which point I also realise that I've misplaced the keys to the house. Other people, as they tirelessly inform me, have interesting dreams full of sexual adventure, high surrealism, serendipity and chocolate-covered football pitches. My stupid life, unfortunately, extends far into my unconscious.

My unconscious thinks it rules. Hence I will obey its every whim when gambling. My unconscious tells me that it can see into the future and predict the outcome of sporting events. No matter how many times it is proved wrong, the id still gets one over on the ego and informs it that it will be different this time and that Wimbledon will beat Manchester United 4-0. It is indeed a stupid person who believes that his stupid brain can influence events that happen in the real world — particularly when you can't even influence yourself.

If, like me, you're really stupid, you will see the world through metaphors derived solely from dumb TV shows of the Sixties and Seventies. Because, you see, life is like *Runaround* – the ITV kids game show hosted by a pre-Eastenders Mike Read. After the loveable cockney cunt asked a question, the hordes of kids would have to "runaround" three sections of the game-board. Two would be right and one would be wrong, and you got a yellow ball if you stood in the right area. Much jostling would ensue as the kids chose safety in numbers, assuming that the more people who stood in an area the better the chance of them collectively having the right answer. And normally this worked. But there was always one kid who would dart between the three sections, following and then abandoning the flow, making complex but futile judgements about his probability of success as the blinding lights flashed and the sirens hooted. At the moment of revelation, this one kid would invariably be occupying a section all on his own.

As the answer was revealed he would desperately try to jump next door but would soon be spotted by the cybernetically enhanced eyes of Mr Read. Mike Read would whisk you away with a clip on the ear (this was 1975) and declare to the laughing masses "What a wally!"

Some of us have been standing in that wrong segment for most of our adult lives, sometimes trying to jump into adjacent squares but then changing our minds and sticking to our so-called principles. While all the time a voice of gruff fatherly authority shouts beerily down our lugholes with a Readian equal emphasis on each syllable — "What A Wa Lee!" You could try and jump next door with all the other kids, but if you're stupid like me you'll stay in your lonely segment, hoping that, despite the overwhelming evidence, you've made the right decision. You just had to be different, didn't you? Welcome home my friends, to the tale that never ends — welcome to My Stupid Life. ◉

STORIES

ON THE PISS IN ADDIS

Our friend GAVIN HILLS died in 1997. Penguin have just brought out Bliss To Be Alive, his collected journalism. Here we print his account of a hellish trip to Ethiopia with Zed Nelson. Illustration by MARCUS OAKLEY

The quest was simple. Alas, confusion reigned. I went looking for the Ark of the Covenant and got a golden fleecing. They say pot causes memory loss, but I'm not convinced. My recollections of Ethiopia are vivid and disturbing. The taste remains. Piss washes around my mouth, swilling the shit caught in my teeth.

Just before landing in Addis I'd flicked through the Air Ethiopia in-flight magazine. I chanced upon an article entitled "Ethiopia – seasons all year and sunshine aplenty!" Between the exhilarating passages on the delights of tourist Ethiopia, I chanced upon an amazing sentence: "In the city of Axum lies the famous church of St Mary of Zion, home of the Ark of the Covenant." Hosanna in the highest!

Theologians, scholars and historians have spent centuries in search of this mythical container of the tablets of Moses. They had scoured biblical landscapes and spent lifetimes analysing ageing scripts. I had found the answer in business class of an Air Ethiopia jet, just opposite an advert for Paco Rabanne. Eat shit, Indiana.

I saw fit to make the Ark my quest. Well, I saw fit for about six hours. Then unfit for a couple of days. A combination of dysentery, lethargy and insanity saw to that. My original plan (go to Axum, find church, grab Ark, leg it) was fundamentally flawed: I didn't have enough money for the bus to Axum. I would have had. I am a man of means who can often afford to travel by bus. Why, on some occasions, I even travel by train. No, I was the victim of crime. An innocent abroad. A victim of Solomon's golden fleece.

Addis is a magical city tingling with a warm uncertainty. Apart from a brief fracas with Mussolini, Ethiopia is the only African country never to have been colonised. It understands culture in a European sense. Its ancient orthodox churches mix with a toy-town architecture of Fifties kitsch buildings. The surrealism of Blackpool combined with the heritage of York. And, despite a socialist revolution and subsequent revisionist coup, one man still lives large in Addis. The four-foot-eight-inch frame of Haile Salassie towers over the city. In sculptures, shops and song: Jah lives!

Hotel Ethiopia reeked of underachievement. The decaying grunge of the past it never had was self-evident. My room gave me wonderful views of an Army depot. As dusk fell, vultures and eagles caught the air currents and circled around at window height. I called upon the room of my photographer friend Zik and we decided to venture into town.

On leaving the hotel two things became clear. Firstly, it was very dark. Secondly, we did not know where we were going. Most capitals give way to the aimless wandering of the tourist. Unfortunately, Addis had few tourists and plenty of hawkers, blaggards and conmen. The aimless wanderer must appear to be neither wandering nor aimless. As we strode purposely to nowhere-in-particular, we were soon rumbled. Three guys resembling the Marx Brothers tailed us and soon were keen on conversation. "Hello, my name is Solomon," said Groucho. We grunted replies. Just enough to say we're not interested.

Like insurance salesman who've just found Jehovah, they started a gat-gun spiel. Where where we from? What were our names? What were we doing? What was our job? Did we like it here? Where were we going? What music did we like? Were we married? Where were we going? Did we have sisters? What religion were we? WHERE WERE WE GOING?

"Er, for coffee?" said Zik, with all the command and elegance of a tortured hamster. But where were we going for coffee? Before we knew it, we'd been herded into a restaurant. Our large ears and swinging tails had been obvious. We thought we'd been marching purposefully – unfortunately, it was the swagger of two fat donkeys.

The restaurant was basic. So basic, in fact, that it obviously doubled as someone's living room. After insisting on just a coffee, we buckled under pressure to try the local wine. I could have done with a drink, especially as it seemed to provide a temporary relief for my dysentery. A bottle of off-yellow liquid was placed on the table. This was "honey" wine, a traditional Ethiopian beverage. After much research and deliberation, I have arrived at an unfortunate conclusion. I now believe I spent that evening ploughing through five bottles of what was probably a mixture of orange squash and urine. Apparently this con is quite common in these parts. Further folly occurred after the second bottle. I said I was hungry and ordered the shit.

We dined on traditional Ethiopian fare. A large, circular tray was covered in chapati-style bread. Upon this had been placed some of the finest turds from a selection of the country's indigenous species. While we dined Solomon (Groucho) told us his life story. He was an ex-soldier. He had been trained in Leningrad. He knew David Dimbleby. Like most of his countrymen, he thought Rastafarians were very strange indeed. Once, fighting in Eritrea, his unit was overrun and he and his comrades had to walk for fourteen days through rebel territory without food and water. He'd survived by slashing the throats of cattle and drinking their blood. This, I thought, was a positively mouth-watering prospect compared to the example of the country's cuisine I had been presented with.

As the evening rolled by, the highly spiced crap slipped down, washed by steaming golden nectar.

THE RESTAURANT WAS BASIC. SO BASIC, IN FACT, THAT IT OBVIOUSLY DOUBLED AS SOMEONE'S LIVING ROOM. AFTER INSISTING ON JUST A COFFEE, WE BUCKLED UNDER PRESSURE TO TRY THE LOCAL WINE

'One of the strongest voices of his generation ... His work explained what it meant to be young in the nineties'
Sheryl Garratt

'He was an inspiration and ... a true journalist'
James Brown

A donation from the proceeds of Bliss to be Alive will be made to Amnesty International

OUT NOW IN PAPERBACK
Available at all good bookshops

Soon it was time for coffee. Nescafé was not on the menu. We endured the "traditional coffee ceremony", an hour of suspect shenanigans performed by an attractive local maiden. Some vaguely erotic motions resulted in coffee beans being roasted on a fire of suffocating incense. The only rest from this tedium was the offer of some grass.

They have no Rizla in Addis, and make do by emptying cigarettes and sucking up pure grass into the remnants of the flaccid tube. Apparently this was the stuff the monks grew. Fair play to the monks. I soon realised why they'd based a whole religion around it. One spliff, and things went very uncertain. This was the most powerful substance ever to enter my innocent lungs. Within about two minutes, Zik was doing the coffee dance, then convulsing into uncontrolled hysterics. The crackle of popping brain cells could be heard for miles around. The world was not as it should be and we were both beginning to struggle for our sanity. It was clearly time for the bill.

I was just compos enough to work out we were being shafted. A hundred dollars to feast on urine and shit seemed a tad too much. It had been a fisting worthy of James Herriot. Delirium reigned, but how we roared. Every time we tried to get shirty and complain, fits of laughter would cascade from our pathetic mouths.

I WAS JUST COMPOS ENOUGH TO WORK OUT WE WERE BEING SHAFTED. A HUNDRED DOLLARS TO FEAST ON URINE AND SHIT SEEMED A TAD TOO MUCH

Solomon told us it was time for bed. We followed him, knowing this was the route to certain death. Dogs howled in the darkness. Vultures flapped above. Down back passages we stumbled. Our journey terminating where it began, Hotel Ethiopia. A donkey sanctuary for lightweight Jah warriors such as I.

Two days later, I returned home, without the ark. ☞

MAY ALL WHO APPROACH THE KINGDOM OF GOD ENTER

A tale of God and Mammon by BIDISHA
Illustrations by VINCE RAY

The break-up, like the guy, was short and nasty. When people asked about him, I just shrugged and said "Dick by name, dick by nature. Maximum baldness, minimum compassion." That was my line, the official quote. When they pressed for further details I got exasperated: "What d'you want me to tell you? He sweated on me. He didn't use toothpaste when he brushed his teeth." There was something else, too: he watched porno films with all the action pixelated out. There the celluloid couple would be, moaning and groaning, but anything below the navel was a grid of coloured squares. Finally I figured it out: it was the pixels that got him off.

I only discovered Dick had snuffed it when his brother Roy phoned to invite me to the funeral. Roy was a thin manky-looking thing who spoke very slowly. Hair-wise, he had the opposite problem to his (late) brother: his body was covered in matte deep-shag curls. "If ever I need my floors sanding I'll call you over for a game of Twister." I believe those were the very first words I said to Roy.

The dead-Dick conversation didn't exactly demonstrate the peaks of etiquette and empathy to which I sometimes ascended. The phone rang: "Yes?" That was how I always answered. It frightened off the telecoms cold-callers and any psycho exes who'd gotten special dispensation from their respective community day-care centres. "Leila, this is Roy. I've got some news and I don't know how to say it, I wanted to wait until we had it all in hand. Right, OK, I'll just tell you. The thing is, you know Dick went skiing this Easter. Well..."

I interrupted him: "The cable-car snapped and he plummeted to his death. He slalomed off the edge of a black slope and plummeted to his death. He was taking in the view from the roofside cocktail bar at his chalet, a big gust of wind came along and he plummeted to his death."

There was a long, shocked silence. Finally, in a choked voice, Roy said, "No. On the way home the plane crashed. He'd been meaning to drive through Europe and take the Eurostar but he changed his mind at the last minute. First class. It was meant to be a birthday present to himself." He drew another deep breath: "It was on the news."

I never watched the news. As soon as you got a handle on the "atrocities" of one country a thousand other "terrible tragedies" occurred in an entirely different area of the globe. Current affairs weren't my bag. The world was too big, and my attention span was too small.

I took down the address of the boneyard and hung up. I didn't care about Dick. With pulse, without pulse, no diff. He was a jerk, now he was a dead jerk. I met him at a party and fucked him for three months, so what? There wasn't any connection going on there. But his brother and his mother liked me. I was dealing them both the young-girl-voodoo routine. You gave them a close look at your peachy skin and your shiny hair and they fell in love with your innocence. You brought into their lives that aching nostalgia for liberty and zest. They should have seen through me from the start. Liberty

and zest? Life was just failure and pain. Why was nobody reading my screenplays? You worked, you showed your work to someone, they slapped you in the face. When they weren't slapping you in the face, they were stabbing you in the back.

Dick had been loaded. When I got to the funeral there were fat bouquets everywhere, giving off a smell so dense and bland it seemed synthetic. There was a mini-marquee around the grave, like those vinyl builders' tents you see by the motorway. It was striped blue and white. We had to squeeze in there and teeter at the edge. Next to the grave was a fancy, gleaming, engraved coffin. It seemed much bigger than they do on telly. But no amount of dough could hide the truth – Dick was not a man who had enjoyed the pleasures of human contact and friendship. There was his mother, Roy, me, and maybe four people who worked for the undertaker's firm. Roy took up his place next to me. I turned to him: "I do a good impression of being gainfully employed, don't I?" I wore a smart black suit and white shirt that I'd bought at Oxfam. Roy gave me a vaguely disapproving look and turned back to the oblong gap in the ground. Suddenly a thought occurred to me and I dug him in the ribs: "There's nothing in the box, is there? It's empty." He nodded sadly. Nothing in the box. They'd spent thousands of pounds on an empty box. I was attending a fake funeral. We were directing our grief at a half-ton of beautifully varnished wood. This wasn't a burial, it was a carpentry exhibition.

When the vicar-type finished,

everyone filed out and stood in the graveyard smoking cigarettes. I wanted to split. People were standing mournfully by kiddies' graves and murmuring about the brevity of life while they ground their fag-butts on the headstones. I went up to Dick's mother. Her eyes were perfectly mascara'd. She looked upon her kids as something she'd bought on impulse and couldn't return. I could get that. Most of the time I felt like my life was something assigned to me by mistake – the King's Cross bedsit, the greasy mattress, the geriatric Amstrad. I was twenty-five. Time was passing fast. "Hello," I said to Dick's ma, who inclined her head graciously, "Sorry about Dick."

Ma gave a big, strange smile. "Oh, he had no soul," she told me. "Even when he was little. I always said so." She reached out and took my wrist: "Never have children. You have children and the next thing you know, thirty years have passed."

I turned away and let myself into the church. It was a new building, and it looked like a council house, all neat yellow bricks with a snazzy red accent on the window-frames. It still had that new carpet smell. The original church had been burnt to the ground by schoolkids two years ago. I was pretty impressed by that. All it took to obliterate the House of God was a truant and a box of Swan Vestas. Before I had time to collect myself, a soft-looking lady bustled up to me: "Are you here for the History of Multi-Ethnic Faith class? Because, you see, it's been postponed. I've got a new timetable for you." I gaped at her while she gave me a big smile. Only God could make you smile like

I WALKED RIGHT UP TO THE ALTAR AND FACED THE REST OF THE ROOM. "YES, MY PEOPLE," I BELLOWED IN A TEXAN ACCENT, "I AM THE VOICE OF THE LORD, AND THE LORD SPEAKS THROUGH ME"

that. I'd seen it on doorsteppers and tube-train nuts a thousand times. She thrust a piece of paper into my hands then ambled past me and through the door, beaming beatifically all the while.

I crumpled the paper up and threw it into the corner. Empty pews stretched ahead. The altar and pulpit looked like self-assembly jobs, bedecked with jumble-sale gewgaws. On the red noticeboard were leaflets advertising a singalong with a "renowned Christian Rock Band" that Sunday.

I walked right up to the altar and faced the rest of the room. "Yes, my people," I bellowed in a Texan accent, "I am the voice of the Lord, and the Lord speaks through me." If screenwriting didn't work out, I could always make it as a televangelist. Me, I could testify. I heard a sniff and froze. There was someone sitting in the second pew. At first I thought it was a lady-vicar in dark robes, but what vicar would have a pentangle tattooed on the side of their neck? The girl looked up and her face was wet. She had brown hair, expensively cut. The outfit was designer, too. It had an upper-tax-bracket sheen.

"I think you may have come to the wrong place," I said, indicating the tattoo. I knew she'd been crying but I didn't know what to do about it. My spontaneous-sympathy quotient was low. But she laughed gamely, wiped her hand across her face and said, "I was a pretty dedicated Goth for about two months when I was thirteen." She had an interesting look. I went and sat facing the same way she was: towards a crucifix upon which a Tom of Finland Jesus (with his six-pack,

taut pecs and sinewy quads) writhed in agony. I nodded at the scene a few times and finally said "So what's with him?"

The girl smiled: "It's funny, isn't it?" But she didn't say anything else. Then I looked at her again and realised why her beauty had been bothering me: she was famous, a famous writer. A bolt went through me, and that bolt was jealousy. I knew her face from magazines and I knew her voice from the radio. I had a sudden fantasy of taking her hostage and demanding some kind of international multimedia break as ransom.

I picked up a hymn book that was lying on my pew and leafed through it. The anodyne verses took me straight back to the thousands of school assemblies I'd winced through as the junior choir squeaked *All Things Bright and Beautiful.* I waved the book at her: "This is so lame." She took it from me and ran her fingertips over the cover. I thought, *manicure.* Then she shrugged: "They're not *that* lame, I don't think." I knew what was going to happen – I was going to be dealt the full-on born-again confessional. Finding God meant losing your dignity; you freed your spirit and it loosened your tongue too. Here it came: "Sometimes I try and follow certain rules that you could say were Christian. Like learning to be humble, even when people are shitting on you for no reason. And getting away from the idea that you deserve success or recognition. Or that pain is a learning curve where you eventually get some kind of payback. That's a good way to live, isn't it? It can be very liberating, because everything we do is about getting a reward, a treat for hard work. But maybe there's no karma. There's no destiny. You do not always get repaid for your hard work." She looked hard at the altar: "You have to make yourself into nothing."

"Doesn't seem to have worked for you," I remarked. Even as those words came out of my mouth I felt a little bit bad. It's not like I had the secret meaning of life in my pocket either. But the girl gave a wry grin: "Material things are pretty nice, that's the trouble. If you like to flash your cash, which I do." She sighed and stood up abruptly. There was an impressive Rolex on her wrist. It didn't just look like a watch, it looked like solid, pure, moulded gold. It looked like money. She began walking quickly back to the door. "Hey, what's your name?" I shouted to her. I had to check. She turned and frowned, then said "Marcia. Marcia White." She said her name one more time and then hurried on and went out.

I went home and lay on my grimy sheets turning what she'd said over in my mind. Marcia White was under my skin. I could understand if she was upset. I often cried, at least once or twice a day, in fact whenever I saw the postman bypassing my door on his rounds. But the other things Marcia White had said were burning in my ears. I thought about living a simple life where I made words chime next to other words and never worried about the price tag they could carry. It must be bliss to be without that insatiable feeling of

I HADN'T BEEN OUT IN WEEKS AND THE OPEN AIR SUDDENLY MADE ME FEEL NUMB AND INVISIBLE. CARS AND PEOPLE WERE SWERVING TOO CLOSE TO ME. THE KING'S CROSS NOISE I'D ALWAYS LOVED WAS SCRAPING IN MY EARS

ambition always biting away inside you. I tried to imagine a person who had left the selfish material world so far behind that acclaim meant nothing and you didn't walk around all the time thinking life owed you something, because you knew you were nothing – a worm, a dog. *There's no karma, there's no destiny.* All the parties and the bitchery reduced to unnecessary noise. The ego a small dot.

One night after this I went for a run at nine-thirty and bumped into Roy outside a Hoxton bar. He worked in the City and was ashamed of it. As soon as his day was over he scurried out of the vertiginous all-glass office ripping his silk tie off with one hand and undoing his cufflinks with the other. He stashed his briefcase in his Merc and changed into a cool-dude shirt behind its blacked out windows. Then he hit Shoreditch. The time I saw him, he was out on the terrace of the bar. I didn't want to interrupt my run. I was in the blissful blank-mind zone, my strides eating up the pavement as I went. But there was Roy, his arms and neck furry. He was the type of person who had a five o'clock shadow by midday. Roy was having fun playing the grief-decimated brother. His eyes were troubled, his voice sombre, his brow racked with new lines. You could see he thought how interesting it made him. In a year's time he'd be using the Dick story to pull typing-pool newcomers during the company's annual do.

With Roy was a plain bland Anglo Saxon-type. I could see from his tie-pin alone that he was a bored rich boy looking for a project. When you've got so many diamonds that you have to start buying random naff things to put them on – tie-pins, document clips, fountain pen barrels, key rings – you know you're earning too much. Sure enough, said Roy, his friend Louis here had recently given up City life in order to start up the entertainments empire he'd always dreamed of. He had the penthouse apartment, the car, the cottage in the South of France. He'd now live the life of a bohemian, an artist. "I've always really loved anything creative," he said, "Art, films, ads. Anything visual. Now I can be part of that world."

"You're welcome to it," I said.

"Oh come on," he demurred, "it must be great. Working your own hours, actually *creating* something."

"Yeah," I replied, "I'm working on something really big at the moment. It involves making bathroom-fungus from water and dirt. I'm getting pretty good at it too." The upshot of the evening was that Louis wanted to see a sample script for the production company he "ran". As I sprinted off again at midnight I was excited. As soon as I was out of sight of Roy and Louis I let out a jubilant yell and actually punched the air.

The next morning I got up early and dragged a few boxes of my writing out from the bottom of the wardrobe and under the bed. Six boxes in total, containing every rewrite of every rewrite I'd ever done. The scripts were all about cop-killers and cyborgs and gangsters. All my paranoiac fantasies were set down there. I was good on fights and car chases. I could get the pace. But essentially it was schlock. In the afternoon I sat down with my hands poised suggestively over the keyboard. I watched people walking past outside. I made coffee. For two weeks I repeated this routine. I just couldn't get over how bad a writer I was. It was like standing next to an impressively tall and wide building: you could only marvel at its magnitude. Artistic frustration brought me out in an anxiety rash that covered my palms and throat. Eventually the itching got so bad that I had to see the doctor, who told me I'd become allergic to dust. I cleaned my room and the kitchenette, took the sheets off the mattress and let it get some air. Then I remade the bed and lay in it for four entire days, a notepad by my side. Things were so quiet I thought I'd gone deaf. It was like being a baby again, and that's how I began to write my next script. It was about a young girl who has adventures in her daydreams. The daydreams begin to encroach upon and finally enter reality and she has to save the world by inventing new characters and overcoming her self-created enemies. I had in mind an eerie film, almost a chiller. Something hinging on how intense children could be.

I got into the swing of it. My sleeping patterns wrestled themselves back into shape and I woke up at ten instead of noon. The phone still didn't ring but I felt Louis was waiting for me to produce the script. It was like I'd cracked open all the hassle of my daily life and there was total peace and bliss underneath. Plus Marcia White had bored a hole in my brain and become my imaginary mother, prophet, mentor, line editor, spirit guide and agent. Every snappy line I typed out I'd think Marcia would like that. Every clever little nuance, every pithy description – Hey, Marcia, am I good or am I good? When I realised I'd eaten all the food in the house I went down for provisions. But on the street I had a kind of panic attack. I hadn't been out in weeks and the open air suddenly made me feel numb and invisible. Cars and people were swerving too close to me, I thought, and the King's Cross noise I'd always loved was scraping in my ears. I muttered something to myself and it felt like my voice was coming from very far away. The sky seemed both close and vast. Just two months' isolation had unhitched me from my city life. This was the danger: the city had demoted me. I ducked into the food shop: as soon as there were four walls around me I felt perfectly normal again.

"Leila!" the owner's son, Raphael, greeted me joyously from behind the counter, "I fourt you was dead."

"No, still here, sadly," I replied. That was the tone of our customary banter. We'd start on about how astonishing it was that neither of us had been maimed in a brutal accident since we'd last seen each other, move on to how the English were the most genetically narrow-minded race on earth, then inevitably conclude that humankind had finally destroyed itself with greed and ambition and was heading speedily towards another Ice Age.

The gobbling heat of the summer always made me go nuts. And the phone still didn't ring. For the most part I didn't mind: it was as if the sun had dragged out all my social zeal and laid it out to dry. The parameters of my world had shrunk to the bedsit's thin walls, warped boards and damp roof. I was happy: there was nothing I wanted. The days spent sitting at my desk making lists of things I desired – mansion, Jag, secret underground grotto filled with open treasure-chests housing great shining piles of miscellaneous jewels – were finished. I worked hard and I liked it. But occasionally, at around seven or eight some evenings, I couldn't get it out of my head that there were people all over London showering and picking out clothes to wear, making meals for dinner parties or having drinks somewhere nice. Doing the script was like walking a tightrope. The moment I stopped to actually think about what I was doing, I noticed my own absurd position and felt myself beginning to fall. There was no reason for the script to be any good: nothing I'd done previously had been. But even when I was asleep, the idea was turning around in my mind. Then I would wake up, eat breakfast and begin to write. At midnight, I would stop. And that was how the summer went.

The day the weather started to cool off was the day I typed THE END. I went down to the food shop to have a gloat-fest with Raphael.

"An idle mind is the devil's workshop, Raph," I said to him.

"Aint that the troof," he replied, flicking through a magazine. I took a

HER FEATURES REARRANGED THEMSELVES INTO A SEMBLANCE OF POLITE INTEREST — THE KIND OF INTEREST ONE MIGHT SHOW IN A COMICAL THOUGH SLIGHTLY GROTESQUE DOG

brief stroll around the shop: "I feel a bit strange, I've got nothing to do now." I did a few muscle stretches: "I haven't gone for a run in ages."

"Yeah, I thought you was looking a bit flabby – NDI," murmured Raphael, not raising his eyes from the mag.

"NDI" meant "no diss intended". That decided it. I went back up to my room and left a message on Louis's machine saying I'd got the script ready for him to see. Then I put on my running gear and went out. Twenty minutes later I was out on the street red-faced and bent double against a lamp-post, my heart contracting with pain, the blood boiling in my ears. An old woman made a big show of skirting around me. That was London behaviour for you: they'd never help you, not even if you were having a heart attack. Everyone in London thought they were on the brink of getting stabbed all the time. "Don't mind me," I called to the woman. "I'm just having a brain haemorrhage." I had a problem with old people from a certain generation. I was convinced they were hardwired with every prejudice going. It never failed to make me smile when I read about the latest attack on an old person.

I finally got back to my place and flopped on the bed, waiting for the room to stop spinning. The completed script sat innocuously upon my desk. As I lay down I realised how exhaustion was eating into my bones. I groggily closed the curtains and plummeted straight into a dense sleep. A couple of hours later, a beeping noise woke me up. Now the script was over, every sound was an intrusion, a disavowal of the silence I'd just enjoyed for so many weeks. The light on the answerphone was flashing. It was Louis, he was congratulating me, and I was to come to cocktails tonight: "It's very casual – you know – people are just piling over to my flat. I wanted something discreet. And don't bother about bringing wine either, I'm going to have a glass of something cold waiting for you anyway."

To someone like Louis, "casual" could mean wearing yellow gold as opposed to platinum. I had about an hour to get ready so I utilised every high-tech tool at my disposal, opening up the vast armoury of implements designed to enhance feminine beauty – and once my tooth brush, hair-brush and flannel had been rigorously deployed I spent the other fifty-four minutes soaking. My bath was so deep and hot I was inclined to dump Louis and spend the evening in there instead. But I dragged myself out and clambered into the only decent clothes I had – the Oxfam ensemble I'd worn to Dick's funeral.

My instincts had been right: Louis' do wasn't casual at all, it was a veritable gala. The little flat he'd mentioned was a galleried apartment where ancient brickwork sat uneasily alongside brushed-steel fittings, and his bathroom was so overdesigned that it was impossible to tell which feature was for which function. I had the manuscript in an old envelope, and when Louis opened the door he took it from me and punched me on the arm, which is what people like him do when they want to show affection. Before I knew what was going on I'd been absorbed into the party and a girl came and gave me some champagne, saying; "Are you Leila? Louis told me to give you this. If you want a top-up come and find me, cos everyone else is paying for theirs." Sure enough, I looked over to one side of the room and there, by the makeshift bar, were other young hirelings operating a nifty till system. Only Louis would have turned his "discreet" get-together into a lucrative operation. But it made sense. It wouldn't surprise me if he actually owned a few bars here and there, and this was his version of "taking one's work home".

There were a lot of people I knew at the party. Louis was obviously spreading his feelers out amongst the bohemian creative demimonde in his search for bankable talent. Roy was around but he couldn't bear to talk to me much, because Roy was the Grieving Abandoned Sibling. I stood at one of the huge windows and looked out across the city's skyline. As always I was stunned by its brutal, senseless unloveliness. London was a bric-a-brac yard – Dump Your Unwanted Buildings Here. I heard a certain laugh behind me and felt a stab of recognition slicing painfully right down through my head and chest and stomach. Marcia White. Marcia White my fantasy lifestyle guru and girlfriend – I hadn't yet come out of the closet (it was nice in the closet) – was here. She was talking to a man. "Oh, I won out in the end," she was saying. "Miramax bought the rights for a quarter-mil."

"Nice," said the young man.

"Yeah", replied Marcia, "Lucky fucky me." They laughed again.

During that brief exchange I had an odd sense of my life suddenly having a pattern to it, of it being fated and set in order – and if that scene with her in the church had been the beginning of a line, this party was the end. She had been my filter, my foil. The changer of my ways. I spun round and elbowed the man out of the way in one deft movement. "Marce!" I cried. Then I thrust myself forward and landed a kiss on her cheek. A tight smile was upon the face of Marcia White. I stood and watched while, as if in slow motion, her features rearranged themselves into a semblance of polite interest – the kind of interest one might show in a comical though slightly grotesque dog. But that was enough for me.

"Oh, hi. How's it going?" she asked, and I beamed:

"I'm glad I bumped into you. After I saw you last I really tried to follow what you said. I thought it was really inspiring."

"Right."

"It worked as well. Well, I mean, I hope it did. I just now handed some stuff to Louis."

"Great."

"Yeah, I'm pleased."

"Do you have any on you?"

"Any –? No, I didn't make any copies."

"No, I mean stuff. You know. You said you gave some to Louis. I just wondered if you kept any back for yourself. I could do with a smoke – or whatever you've got, really."

Slowly the penny dropped. Marcia was looking at me expectantly, and it was nice to be needed. I moved in a bit closer:

"You mean drugs. I don't have any drugs, I don't do that. I didn't think that you did either."

"How would you know what I do or don't do?"

Suddenly I was tongue-tied. This chance meeting was a thousand times worse and more intimate than any three-in-the-morning telephone freakout you could have with a lover. I practically couldn't get the words out of my mouth:

"Oh, you know. Your interest in humility and purity and whatever. Religion. God."

"God? God!"

Then she did a funny thing. She started to back away from me, saying:

"Are you sure you're meant to be at this party?"

"Yes, of course. I came to give something to Louis. But I'm glad you're here – I've been thinking about you."

"In what way, thinking about me?"

I reached forward and grasped her arm, and I felt her flinch. I said:

"About what you said, that you should make yourself into nothing, erase your ego. Don't you remember? That you should just work and not push for success, because material success doesn't mean anything anyway."

She shook her head:

"No. That's the opposite of what I believe."

I was still holding her arm. Her voice was going slightly high as she continued:

"Look, I've spent a long time in this industry and it's a dog-eat-dog world. You've got to eat or you get eaten. That is my advice to you. I wish you the very best of luck, I really do. Now take your hand off my arm, please, and don't come near me again."

She tried to walk away but I had yet more things to say to her:

"How can you say eat or be eaten? That's what I used to believe before I met you!"

"Before you met me? You never *met* me. You don't *know* me."

There was a look of horror on her pale little face. I finally, totally realised that she had no idea who I was. She thought I was a fan, a groupie. A loon. She must get a lot of those. But still my tongue wouldn't hush up:

"Yes I do. We met in the church in Highgate, how can you not remember? You were crying."

Her face changed a little, but I understood by then. She remembered the church, the altar, the Christian doo-dahs everywhere. But she didn't really remember me.

"Oh that," she said flatly, "That was nothing."

"No it wasn't."

"What d'you mean, 'no it wasn't'? I know my own mind. That was nothing, that was a wobble. I always have those when I'm negotiating the next deal. I signed the next day. Now, could you possibly get out of my space? I don't want any more hassle from you."

I looked at her for a moment, and my face felt very hot. The last thing I remember noticing before she walked away was a thick chain glinting around her neck, next to the tattoo, just visible under her shirt. The chain bore the waxy lustre of high-grade currency. I suppose she bought it with some of her deal cash.

When I went home after the party I thought I'd be awake for ages but I hadn't even taken off my suit before I hit the bed, comatose. I slept for around twelve hours, woke up, ate breakfast and grabbed another ninety minutes' deep rest. I woke up again for lunch and then crashed out once more, still wearing last night's clothes. Each time I opened my eyes I remembered Marcia White – her fear of me, the way I was (no doubt) practically sweating lust and desperation. She wasn't a visionary at all. She wasn't pure. She was just like all the others – all my competitors. I saw the reality of my life in sharp focus: the hard work, the loneliness, the failure and bitterness. The epiphany I'd had in the church was as phoney as a stage-set. I understood that now.

When I finally awoke again it was dark. I made myself a mug of herbal tea and sat on the bed in front of the telly, wrapped in the duvet. The phone rang and it was Louis: he was cleaning up after the party, actually his "people" were, it had gone down a storm, he was sorry he hadn't had more time to chat to me. But he'd spent the day today reading the script, because he was so keen to see what I'd come up with. Because I'd come so highly recommended from so many people (what people? I didn't know any people). It was nice, what I'd written. Nice, and poignant. He really liked it – he did. It was certainly original. But, the thing is, Louis was a business man. He wasn't a pioneer. There was such a thing as the market, and the market dictated what kinds of films people should be making. People like me should heed the market. Maybe I could have done something a little closer to the bone, was Louis's opinion, which he expressed most humbly. He'd thought from meeting me that I'd be into, oh, he didn't know, cop-killers and cyborgs and gangsters. But my screenplay – I could hear as he leafed through it delicately – it really was lovely, for its type. But wasn't it, you know, girls' stuff?

Louis thanked me and said he'd be in touch. He was planning a Christmas party; maybe I could come, and bring some friends, of course. He looked forward to seeing me there. I hung up and put the Christmas party into my diary. It was September. I slept all night. Even in my dreams a message hammered like relentless Morse code through my head: *I have no talent. It doesn't matter what I write about. I have no talent.* In the morning I went down to see Raphael who, I realised, was my only friend, even though I didn't know anything about him, not even his surname. But he was happy to see me:

"Leila! Party-girl. Was you asleep all of yesterday? Cos you was so caned and that?"

"Something like that. I gave him the script."

SUDDENLY I WAS TONGUE-TIED. THIS CHANCE MEETING WAS A THOUSAND TIMES WORSE AND MORE INTIMATE THAN ANY THREE-IN-THE-MORNING TELEPHONE FREAKOUT YOU COULD HAVE WITH A LOVER

"So, when're you leaving?"

"Leaving? I'm not leaving. Where for?"

"America. Hollywood."

And suddenly I was back in the business of hiding my pain. It was a mistake for me to have become a screenwriter: I would have done much better as an actor. I could be A-list; I'd been in rehearsal for a quarter-century. I gave a nonchalant shrug:

"The bloke I gave it to, he's thick as pig-shit. He didn't get it. He called me today for changes but I told him, I don't jump through hoops for anyone. He wanted such a dumb-down, like that was more important that anything else."

And then my only friend Raphael, shop-counter philosopher extraordinaire, gave one of his classic mighty shrugs, splaying out his fingers, his hands palm-upwards. He spoke to me like it was obvious, like he understood the entire sweep of human life and I was a tiny infant unschooled in the ways of man:

"Yeah, but money talks, innit?" ☻

THE SPIRIT IN THE WOOD

MARK MANNING recounts the terrifying tale of the time he and Eldritch Bill travelled to the dark heart of the Punch and Judy show, and found out a few things about their own dark hearts in the process. Illustrations by DAVID MITCHELL

There are few things in life that have sent a shiver up my spine more than when Bill was possessed by the Earth Spirit, Mr Punch: that terrifying wooden-headed puppet, that mad, murderous doll who has been committing acts of extreme violence for the entertainment of children and illiterate adults for over a hundred years.

Let me explain. For some serious reason we had decided to become the Punch and Judy Professors. It was all tied up with our hunt for the Devil. We figured that as Mr Punch was the only figure who regularly outwits the eternal trickster, we might find out some important information.

Our mission was of the utmost importance, as we were hunting old Nick to retrieve our mortal souls.

By guile if necessary.

Bill had signed us up for an intense week of training; we were to be educated in the ways of getting away with murder by one of the oldest and wisest professors in England, Professor Silas Montague.

I don't know how Bill had managed to get the old man to agree to teach us the arcane and mysterious secrets of that *petit guignol.*

But as I've mentioned more than once before, Eldritch Bill has connections.

It was raining when we set off into that dark and dreadful night. Bill had a strange map, definitely not an ordnance survey or an *A to Z.*

I thought I was pretty *au fait* with the East End of London. As an insomniac two am prowler down forgotten black alleys, it had chilled and thrilled in my secret gothic heart for more than twenty years. But this sinister map with its route through rat-spored gunnels and rickety bridges over those long lost rivers; The Hackney Brook, The Black Ditch, The Fleet, The Shoreditch. They're still there, of course, being used as sewers and buried beneath tarmac and the ever rising city. Snaking down from hidden springs on Hampstead Heath and Highgate.

It felt as if we were travelling through these grimy narrow streets into an older more lawless London.

We got lost several times, stuck up some winding, dead end, rat-black alley.

It was easy to see why that humorous old fellow saucy Jacky had plied his murderous trade here in these narrow spaces and gas lamps.

I thought everywhere these days was lit by electricity. Apparently not. The gas lamps flickered in the suffocating gloom, small pools of yellow like sick heartbeats in the dreadful darkness. Yet another ingredient in our rapidly rising anxiety. I've never seen as many gas lamps. Shimmering beneath the rain, casting broken rainbows.

Many's the time I had wandered these sinister streets simply grooving on the macabre tension that seems to hum with the thin ghosts of evil intent and evil deed.

But I recognised none of them.

There were names of passages and alleys that I'd never seen before, which is unusual, because I love the poetry of place names. But these? How could I have missed Grope Cunt Alley, Blood Row, Hangman's Yard?

One of my great pleasures is reading the list of all the streets in the *A to Z*, looking for simple little poems two or three words long. I have collected many beautiful place names, miniature epics like Horse and Dolphin Court, which fired my imagination for days on end.

But this litany of impending doom was starting to freak me out slightly. Bloody Murder Street, Plague Death Court, Rape Road, Arse Bandit Passage: there was no way I would have missed these grim jewels.

The rain stopped abruptly and the dripping rooves and gurgling drains seemed overly loud. It was only then that I remembered we had not seen another soul for the hour or so we had been wandering this black brick labyrinth.

I was surprised, to say the least, when we discovered a fairly large section of the old Fleet river. I thought that mephitic sewer had been buried years ago, along with all the other tributaries pouring down like poisonous snakes into the Thames.

A slight fog was building up, swirling like a yellow disease, slinking serpentine around our ankles, caressing the ground with its foul odour, licking the cracked windows of shabby tenements. Within ten minutes we found ourselves in a dense pea-souper. Another oddity from the past I thought had disappeared during the Sixties with the advent of electric heat and air pollution laws.

"It's over that bridge and up those stairs." The grimy slimed walls and rotten wet wood reminded me of a Gustave Doré engraving for Mayhew's study of the London poor, a particularly heartstopping view of St Paul's seen from the East.

The wooden stairs didn't feel safe, boards were missing here and there, I didn't like the way it squeaked.

We climbed the endless stairs, up higher than the fog. I looked down at the swirling yellow smoke, it felt as if we were high on some ominous Carpathian mountain looking down on the swirling poisonous clouds of a haunted planet.

I was reassured somewhat by the familiar dome of St Paul's Cathedral which dominated the black starless sky. I have a very special relationship with Wren's masterpiece that is far too complicated to go into here, save to say that the transcendence of that beautiful cathedral has saved my sanity on more than one occasion.

We came to an unremarkable wooden door, something you would imagine to see on an allotment shed, not a place where someone with the secret fame of Professor Silas Montague would live.

Bill lifted his hand to knock but it was opened by an ancient white haired skeleton of a man. "Ah, there you are," laughed the old man. "Come, come it's warm in here." God knows what I expected to see in this bizarre eyrie high above the squalor of the rat warren streets below, but Silas was wearing a red velvet smoking jacket that had seen better days and some eastern style hat, like a fez only more colourful. He was smoking an ornate pipe. His eyes danced brightly, iridescent and full of mischief, the eyes

"YOU'RE JUST IN TIME, IT'S NEARLY MIDNIGHT. HERE, LET ME TAKE YOUR COATS. WE HAVE TO MAKE OUR SWAZZLES." SWAZZLE? WHAT THE FUCK WAS THAT? THE OLD MAN RE-ENTERED THE ROOM WITH A BOTTLE OF BRANDY AND SOME PIECES OF METAL, COTTON AND BANDAGES

of a man far younger than this wily septuagenarian.

"You're just in time, it's nearly midnight. Here, let me take your coats, we have to make our Swazzles." Swazzle? What the fuck was that? The old man re-entered the room with a bottle of brandy and some pieces of metal, cotton and bandages.

That's all you need to know. As a proper professor of this ancient mystery cult I am forbidden to tell you how they are made. The Swazzle is the soul of Punch. It's his voice. That terrible squawking mayhem stoked scream;

"THAT'S THE WAY TO DO IT!!"

Swazzles can only be made during the witching hour.

I can tell you it involves a small but painful blood sacrifice, which connects you to the brotherhood of professors, but that's all. The knife was passed around, a simple carving knife, and we all made a small nick across our thumbs. The blood was mixed with a cup of lime tree

I PLACED THE OBJECT INTO A GLASS OF BRANDY, SILAS MADE A FEW STRANGE GESTURES OVER THE LIQUOR, AND THEN, NOT UNLIKE THE EUCHARIST, HE PLACED THE SACRED SWAZZLE IN MY MOUTH

sawdust, the wood the puppets are traditionally made from.

The puppets are available to buy, if you know where to look, but the more dedicated puppetmasters always carve their own.

There was no doubt about whether we would buy or carve our own dolls. We wanted – needed – to understand the soul of this mystery. We were determined and desperate men. We dearly desired the return of our souls. The Devil had shafted us big-time on the deal. A few baubles and pretty women. Pathetic. We were worth far more than that.

The Swazzles were completed fairly quickly, a few minor adjustments and we had the precious things that were to be our bond and covenant with the magical brotherhood of Punch and Judy professors the world over.

The information on the crafting of the Swazzle was read from an old leather-bound book in grave tones by the professor.

I placed the object into a glass of brandy, Silas made a few strange gestures over the liquor, and then,

not unlike the Eucharist, he placed the sacred Swazzle in my mouth. Nothing. I tried to speak. I just sounded as though I had coins in my mouth. He placed the other Swazzle in Bill's mouth. Bill spoke and scared the living shite out of me.

It was the fucking amplified voice of a devil. I fell back from my chair, knocking it over. What the fuck had happened? Bill, as scared as me, spat the thing out and jumped back. He was shaking like a leaf.

"You must not be afraid of the spirit in the wood or it will kill you or send you mad."

The old bastard could have told us that before all this shit-your-pants sorcery.

"The lot of a professor is a heavy one," he continued. "But the great Tree Spirit told me you were worthy, otherwise I would not have revealed the secret of the sacred Swazzle to you. Come, both of you, we have a little time, the Swazzle must be mastered by the time the clock strikes one."

There was something about his voice. I knew he wasn't lying. A shaft of silver moonlight revealed by the passing of a black cloud, it seemed like a good omen. Full and pregnant it was too, stars like the tears of angels.

I tried again. I too could feel the spirit of that little devil doll, he was in me, I knew with absolute certainty I was possessed by that Tree Spirit. Which, as we eventually found out, was as real as that beautiful moon and the generous, yet deadly, sea.

I had the power of the Tree Spirit's voice. I was exhilarated, yet wary and confused at the same time.

"You must sleep now," said Silas. "We have much work to do, rest and we will start when the cock crows."

When the cock crows?

Did he have a fucking chicken around here then somewhere, I wondered, as I climbed into a rickety old bed that smelt of damp.

In the next room I could hear Bill farting happily and opening his window.

I was tired and fell straight to sleep. My dreams, however, were troubled, stopping just this side of nightmare.

Of course it was the dolls I dreamt of.

Over a breakfast of kidneys, bacon, liver and fried eggs, the old man said that it was completely normal. It was the dolls visiting you.

"No doubt you were at some festivity. It is the same, but slightly different, in most professors who carry the Tree Spirit."

He was correct. I remembered being at some Bacchanal, but the puppets weren't doll-size. They were like real people, dancing and singing. That mad old professor was battering the shite out of everyone. Sausage machines squirted blood and gore all over the place, as an endless supply of babies were tossed into that infernal machine.

There were whole trees festooned with dead policemen, hanging by the neck. A skeleton dancing around with a huge jug of wine. Real crocodiles snapping at ankles. A massive hangman lynching all kinds of government officials. And poor old Judy, her face black and blue. Two black eyes, her nose dripping blood and all her teeth knocked out.

That's when I woke up.

Bill was tucking into his kidneys and bacon as if he hadn't eaten for a week.

The memory of my dream had severely worried my appetite away. Bill started in on my breakfast and asked old Silas if there was any more fried bread.

Apparently Bill had had a similar dream, only it was set under a railway bridge by a canal. There were lots of people hung from the girders and Pretty Polly was being raped by old Punchy. The rest of the dream cast were screaming blue murder and fighting. Joey the Clown was kicking the hell out of all the others, like a wooden Bruce Lee.

The dream didn't particularly worry Bill. Which didn't surprise me, as he is the only person I know who enjoys having nightmares. It makes him feel tough. Silas took us into another windowless room and turned on the gaslights, and there it was in all its dreadful majesty.

The red and white striped theatre. I've never seen a more elaborate puppet theatre in my life. It was topped with an ornate, baroque swirliness I've only ever seen in the awesome churches of Munich and Estonia.

It was the Vatican of puppet theatres. All manner of beasts and men writhed around in the gold leaf

extravaganza. The red velvet curtains were decorated with jewelled stars and moons. Beneath the stage in incredibly intricate needlework, stitched onto the red and white shining silk stripes, it said: "Professor Silas III's Magic Punch and Judy Show" in an elegant copperplate. My jaw dropped. Bill's arse was silent. It was a seriously beautiful work of art.

"Before we study the lore of this ancient and mysterious theatre, I will perform a shortened version of the play," said Silas. He lit two more gas-lamps beneath the small wooden stage which gave the uplit theatre a macabre limelight feeling.

He turned off the main gaslights and disappeared around the back of his theatre.

For some reason I was afraid. But it wasn't deep fear. It was more the delicious anticipation one feels whilst waiting to see a really scary movie. Some badly amplified music started, it was crackly and slid around your head, like that creepy fairground music you hear on old horror films after smoking too much grass. The music stopped abruptly as the little curtains opened. A hideous old woman with a baby was running around in a tizz, shouting like a panto dame about where that bad Mr Punch was. The background scenery was a beautifully painted but rather shabby-looking house. "Mr Punch! Oh you naughty-naughty man, where are you? I need to go to the shops."

The laughing, yet sinister, squawking voice of that red-nosed

rascal, started its mad braying offstage. Then, in a flash, up he leaps onto the slap board. He was truly, truly hideous to behold. A good four inches taller than Judy. His spindly, spasticated legs dangling over the front of the booth. The gas lamps flickering away gave him the appearance of some mad demon from hell. He was laughing wildly and saying bizarre things. I could feel my palms sweating. It was genuinely spooky.

"Oh, Mr Punch, you've been drinking again haven't you?" She admonished the wooden effigy from hell, who was squawking little nonsense songs and making bizarre noises.

"Where's my housekeeping money, Mr Punch?" she demanded.

But old Mr Punch, still squawking like a maniac, shouts back at her, "Spent it!"

He laughed at the ugly woman.

"You've spent it? Oh Mr Punch, how am I going to buy food for the baby? What did you spend all our money on, you wicked, wicked man?

Old Punch, he laughed and said, "A horse!" and started laughing again.

"A horse?" Judy looked out of the window. "Where is it? I can't see no horse!"

Punch was still laughing at the stupid Judy.

"Oh you rascal Mr Punch! You gambled all our money on some silly horse race." Judy thrust the baby into Punch's hands and exited crying and saying that she would have to go and pawn her coat again.

Mr Punch looked at the baby, "Oh what a lovely little baby," and started rocking the infant in his arms gently. The baby started crying. "Poor baby," razzles Punch. The crying grew louder and louder. Punch was losing his temper, rocking the baby faster and faster. His apoplectic rantings turned into furious rage. He threw the baby on the slap board and started battering it with a huge stick. "Naughty baby! Naughty baby!" he screamed, battering the poor infant all around the room. The baby's screaming grew louder and louder until the mad puppet could take no more and finally slung the baby out of the window.

"That's the way to do it! That's the way to do it!" Like some evil parrot.

Judy entered the room immediately and asked where her baby was. Punch pointed at the window. "Out the window," he chuckled.

"Oh no! Mr Punch, you've killed our baby," she started crying. Punch tried to comfort her, asking for kisses and saying that they could make another one, then started to sexually harass the distraught mother.

"Give us a kiss!" he squawked tirelessly, until, after a while, he finally lost his temper and started throwing her around the room. He eventually killed her.

"Oooh, Judy dead!" he said without the slightest remorse.

"Never mind, Punch go see Pretty Polly."

His beautiful mistress. This was the part that had Bill laughing his pants off. I was finding the whole thing terrifying. The red-nosed bastard had just battered his wife and child to death and was now about to go gallivanting off to Shepherd's Gate with his prostitute slapper.

Of course his journey to his floozy's flophouse was interspersed with all kinds of comic capers and various creepy, mad characters, each representing some sort of established authority, all of them outwitted by Punch's Zen-like riddles and mad spiel. The first to get brained was the oafish policeman who tried to arrest our hero for murdering his wife and child. Punch made short work of the dumb bobby and killed him with his stick. He carefully laid the dead cop at the side of the stage, muttering and laughing, carefully counting the bodies. "One, two, three," he laughed before squeaking his famous catchphrase, and set off to see Polly. Next was the Beagle, some kind of Victorian magistrate. He too was battered to death and carefully counted onto Punch's little pile of corpses.

A physic was next, a quack doctor of sorts. Punch joked with the physic, getting him to treat an imaginary pain in his bollocks. He got a dose of Punch's cheerful homicide: massive head injuries then slung onto the pile of dead bodies. Counted carefully again.

The counting of the bodies was laboured in preparation for an extremely adept demonstration of puppetry. Joey the Clown turned up, the only puppet that Punch does not murder. This was because Joey made no attempt to harm Punch and seemed to be even smarter than old banana nose himself.

This part of the show is called the body count. It is how fellow professors can judge their colleagues respective skill at pulling off all this exhilarating mayhem and is genuinely funny.

By this time I was lost in the magical performance and was laughing heartily along with Bill. The pair of us were like seven year old psychopaths urging Punch onto even more atrocities, "Kill the clown!", shouted Bill. "Kill the fucking clown!"

"Brain the bastard! Come on Punchy, kick his fucking head in!" I shouted.

An icicle of sweat melted down my back as the mad cartoon antics stopped abruptly. Oh my God! The fucking puppets have seen us. Both puppets silent, staring at us. Punch cocked his head, as if he'd just realised his *petit guignol* was being observed.

"Punch no kill Joey. Joey Punch's friend," said the demon doll, with all the menace of that infernal voice, that only a master puppeteer could summon. Then the two of them started singing and did a little dance, before Punch said goodbye to his mischievous mute friend.

The hangman Jack Ketch goes next. Only he is not beaten to death. Instead, the great ugly brute, dressed in an ominous hat with a skull and crossbones on it, tricks him into putting his own head in the noose, and is strangled to death on his own gallows. Punchy swung the dead hangman like something from William Burroughs' mad masterpiece *Naked Lunch.*

As this was a master professor, and the performance was not a watered down version of the original play, there is no crocodile or sausage machine. The grand finale – in a burst of smoke appears old Nick himself. Unfortunately, the crocodile has replaced the appearance of Satan in most of today's shows. I can see why. This terrible apparition would give our mollycoddled children nightmares for years. Punch, through his mad jokes and insane behaviour, completely baffles the sophisticated Devil that was on display here – a kind of diabolical Noel Coward. Punch got him in the noose, laughed insanely, and threw the dark one out over the stage swinging in Jack Ketch's authentic looking gallows.

The miniature velvet drapes were drawn, the voice of Punch fading, as he sang some long forgotten Victorian music hall hit. I recognised it as, "Only some violets for my mother's grave", the tune that Mary Kelly, Jack the Ripper's final victim, was heard singing before her death and horrific mutilation by that savage serial killer. It was a nice touch. I chuckled at the black humour.

Professor Silas emerged from behind the booth dripping perspiration, wiping his brow with a handkerchief, breathless, waving us to go into the adjacent room, unable to speak, so out of breath was he.

Both myself and Bill were speechless. In some strange way that tiny little puppet theatre had been as spectacular and emotionally draining as any Spielberg Hollywood blockbuster.

The fact that it was the performance of a single man with tiny wooden dolls added to our admiration. It was around this time that I started beginning to wonder if Bill and I were going to be up to a performance of our own. It seemed like a lifetime's work.

How the hell did he change glove puppets so fast? They were bouncing up and down with such speed and dexterity it seemed like there had been three or four puppets banging around on that mad slapboard, but of course that would have been impossible. The old man only had two hands. There was a whiff of real magic floating in the dust motes swinging in the single shaft of light coming through the skylight. The pair of us felt honoured to have witnessed this remarkable show.

It had touched something primal in us. That funny little man had got away with murder; even destroying the bogey man that the Church has been pedalling for centuries. It was as if he'd murdered his own conscience. There was deep shit in the symbolism of that insane theatre.

Silas must have read our minds.

The first thing he told us was that the only result of trying to dig deeper through the surface of the wooden world of the puppets was confusion and mockery. Punch himself would laugh at your foolish attempts to nail the little bastard down.

"He is inside you now," warned Silas seriously. "Start trying to peek inside the meaning of any thing, you end up with that same depressing abyss that lurks at the centre of all

"YOU READ THE BOOKS?" ASKED SILAS, WIPING HIS MOUTH WITH A NAPKIN. WE ANSWERED IN THE AFFIRMATIVE. WE WERE HOOKED. WE WANTED MORE

things," he continued. We both understood perfectly well what he was talking about. And decided not to probe any further.

"Besides, the Earth Spirit is fond of you, you wouldn't have been chosen otherwise."

In my guts I knew he was right. The spirits are powerful and all play a part in shaping our destinies. We had been chosen. That was all that counted.

We would enjoy this gift of reckless wisdom. To have the power to see through everything, without questioning why, was a deep, dark sacred thing and would truck no abuse.

How did we know?

We just did.

Silas took us to the study and told us to read a huge pile of books. He would speak to us the following morning, when the chicken crowed.

We were both keen students and immersed ourselves in all the mysteries and ways of the Punch and

Judy history, from elaborate theories to transcriptions of Victorian writers keen to explain the meaning of this fascinating little play. It was hard going but as the midnight hour arrived once more, we had all but finished our studies and retired. The dreams were still there, but somehow the darkness had faded, the players at the feast were less insane, charming almost. Judy was particularly foxy, as was Pretty Polly. The cop was off-duty, as was the hangman.

We ate our kidneys, liver, bacon and fried eggs keenly, realising we hadn't eaten at all the previous day.

"You read the books?" asked Silas, wiping his mouth with a napkin.

We answered in the affirmative. We were hooked. We wanted more.

"Now forget them." He answered cryptically. "All of it a crock of dogshit.

"A real professor does not disseminate his secrets for the world to see."

I was confused, what was he doing? Again Silas seemed to be reading my mind.

"I told you last night, you were chosen. The magic cannot be taught through this."

He picked up a garish book giving a concise history of the Punch and Judy Theatre.

"This? Rubbish!" He threw it disdainfully onto the rest of the books. "All of it, riddles and false trails left by the real professors. A real professor would never dream of revealing the secret of the sacred Swazzle to the unchosen. You are Neophyte, in one week's time you will be adepts of the first level. You will receive a silver Swazzle and will swear an oath to the Earth Spirit to reveal nothing of our ways. As a first level Adept, you will re-enter the world. You will be summoned when you have reached the second level. This you must achieve on your own. It is the law. Come, you have much to learn."

I knew that there was something of the hermetic in this anomaly from the last century. It just seemed to hit something inside of me, some atavistic weirdness that I couldn't understand. But never in my imagination had I imagined some magical obscure collection of occult scientists at work behind this children's entertainment thing, a seaside grotesquery, a Victorian predecessor of Tom and Jerry, Sooty and Sweep. Sweep, as you may remember, also had a Swazzled tongue.

Of course, we were to learn that all the major occultists worked under some form of disguise. News International, the secret school of Rupert Murdoch's black, black magic, beaming down evil propaganda from his satanic satellites. His intention? To destroy the world of ideas and cultural aspirations. A foul Satanist of the worst kind. Apparently, both myself and Bill had been under the careful scrutiny of the brotherhood of the Sacred Swazzle since we were four years old. Of course, even writing this could put me in danger. Silas said that we could write about their order, but with caution. The world will view you as an eccentric fool, which can only be of benefit to our order, more smoke to cover our

tracks with, another level of secrecy to this benevolent order whose sole intentions were to aid the people of planet Earth onto a higher level of evolution.

As long as I don't reveal any of the secrets of the brothers of the Sacred Swazzle I would probably be OK. But, he hastened to add, the Earth Spirit, whilst being generally a benign deity, was also capable of mad rages and mischievous pranks. A brother of the Norse god Loki, he was fond of drink and was fallible. Which basically I read as a warning not to piss him off.

We spent the following days working hard, learning the secrets and beliefs of this unique brotherhood. We learnt how to channel the Earth Spirit's supernatural powers. We studied hard and both Bill and myself learnt of invisibility. After five days we were both adept at becoming invisible. Flight would take longer, said Silas.

We were given severe reprimand when we started sneaking around in our invisibility to see naked women. After the chastisement of the Earth Spirit there was no way you would catch me perving around invisible ever again, believe me.

I feel I am not giving too much away to say that the play is within the play. A mystery, wrapped within a puzzle, inside an enigma.

But enough. I cannot reveal my interpretation, your interpretation will be completely different.

The work we put in to master our skills was intense and emotionally extremely taxing. We found out things that we'd probably rather we didn't know. Bill's cataclysmic misogyny, for example. There is no script for our red-nosed friend's violent frolic. Each tale is different. My detached cruelty, for instance, manifested itself in the amorality I gave the Devil towards the end of the drama. His charming sophistry I based on that wicked lord from *A Portrait of Dorian Gray*, Henry Wotton.

Our first attempts at performing this *petit guignol* would have been amusing if they weren't so revealing and indeed terrifying.

Bill crept nervously into a practice puppet theatre: there was no way Silas would allow us novices into his baroque puppet opera house.

No sooner than the curtains opened, Judy stood there with the baby. Then, with a strangled Swazzle straight out of hell, before Judy had said a word, Punch was swearing and punching the unholy shite out of the mother and child. I have never seen such violence, not even in the goriest gangster Hollywood Scorcese Robert de Niro crap.

Bill had spat out his Swazzle and was screaming a torrent of hatred at the wooden doll: "Bitch, fucking slag! Whore, CUNT!" All the time hammering away until Punch's stick splintered and broke. Bill threw off the Punch puppet and started hitting the puppet with his own fist, bloodying them and screaming insults as if he'd gone insane. The puppet theatre fell over onto its side. Bill emerged from the tent, his face a mask of demented rage, he was strangling Judy with both hands. The mad bastard pulled off Judy's head, threw it on the ground and started jumping up and down on it, till there was nothing left but splinters.

"Whore!" said Bill and spat on the broken pieces of wood. He looked around, he seemed dazed.

"Having problems at home, Bill?" said Silas, his hands held together, his two index fingers in front of his lips. "Because the play has no set text or script, it is very tempting to work out one's frustrations within the drama." He continued sagely: "But if you performed like that in front of children, or even adults come to that, not only would you give the children nightmares for the rest of their lives, but you probably would be lynched by a bunch of Butlin's redcoats or castrated by the children's decent, god-fearing *Sun* reading parents, calling you a paedophile, or something just as unkind."

"I don't know what came over me," said Bill, head hung low, staring at the destroyed puppet. "I just took one look at Judy up there with that fucking baby, and I wanted to kill her, no not kill her, destroy her, wipe her out of her very existence. I wanted to murder her and her ghost as well," added the Scotsman, trying to fathom out where all of this rage was coming from.

"You see," said Silas. "This is what happens, the Earth Spirit is guiding you, Punch himself is guiding you.

The wood knew of your silent rage, your secret loathing, the way you seethe in your unquiet bed. And like a dream, he confronted you with this deep anger and fear. It is not Judy you loathe, Acolyte.

"It's the whole fucking lot of them.

"That bitch with the forbidden fruit.

"That cunning sly orchard thief and all her scrumping bitch daughters.

"Woman, she is evil.

"This is a fact, even they themselves know this.

"Without this guile and capacity to destroy, to ruin a man through love, how would she feed her babies? Without some struck idiot toiling in the fields, digging holes in the road?

"For her.

"She who must be obeyed.

"While the cuntbitch eats chocolate biscuits, watches soap operas, smokes fags, drinks gin and dumps the brat on her poor suffering mother," lectured Silas.

Bill looked at the man, the muscles in his jaw twitching, frowning, trying to understand the old puppet master's words. "So what should I do Professor?" asked Bill respectfully, as if he were in the Dojo and Silas was his Sensei.

"You must kill your heart, son.

"Anger like the doll just showed you is wasted energy.

"Woman is a cunning thing, love her only weapon. If you allow those arrows she carries stuffed up her cunt to strike you in the heart, you are as good as done for.

"A slave.

"Kill your heart, friend.

"Be ice.

"I think those bald-headed idiots, what are they called? Ah yes, the Buddhists, they refer to this as a cessation of desire.

"They refer, of course, not just to the desire for profane love, but a cessation of desire for everything.

"Cars.

"Possessions.

"Status, vanity.

"They're right of course, but why do they have to be so fucking serious about the whole thing, with their stupid fucking robes and baldy haircuts, ringing little bells and sniffing effing joss -sticks.

"Meditation and all that serene smiling shit," ranted Silas. "Forgive me... as you can see I still have a few mountains to climb myself, one moment please..." Silas walked towards the corner of the room and started smashing up a piece of furniture with such violence I was more than a little concerned.

"I mean, it's not as if these fucking skinheads are the only fuckers to have come up with this shit, a bit of comparative religion study would have shown the same doctrine in Ecclesiastes, that bum vibe preacher with his 'everything is vanity' crap.

"All this dogmatic literal interpretation of the scriptures.

"Those fucking retard Jew-cats headbutting that stupid fucking wailing wall.

"Those moronic thugs of Islam.

"With their ridiculous Fatwas and Taliban Nazis.

"They may have read the Koran a thousand times.

"IF YOU ALLOW THOSE ARROWS SHE CARRIES STUFFED UP HER CUNT TO STRIKE YOU IN THE HEART, YOU ARE AS GOOD AS DONE FOR"

"Remember every word.

"But do any of them understand it?

"Or is the authority of their Ayatollahs based on the fact that they are the cleverest parrots?

"The word of God is everywhere.

"Not just in those dopey books.

"The words of God are in pop songs.

"In movies!"

Silas was on a roll. We listened intently to his inspired rant. He started singing. I thought he was about to do the speaking in tongues shit, but no, in a high-pitched voice he started singing that camp classic: "Somewhere over the rainbow, sky's are blue... What the fuck is poetry if it isn't the word of God? The holy spirit is everywhere, even in these stupid little dolls. Tell me Bill, that assault you made upon Judy, do you perceive now what I'm saying, preaching, or am I just like those bald-headed arsewipes and those ragheaded sand-niggers!" Silas, out of breath, sat down on a chair and wiped his brow with a silk handkerchief.

Bill narrowed his eyes and spoke hesitantly. "I, erm, well I think I know what you were talking about, errm, I don't mean to be impertinent sir, but, forgive me for being frank..." Bill's tone of voice altered from reverence to timid contradiction. "Shouldn't you, like, practice what you preach?"

Silas looked at Bill, his eyes seemed to burn black and red, like the embers of a fire. He picked up a book and threw it at Bill. It was the King James' Bible. A heavy one. It caught Bill full in the face and knocked him off his chair, "Get out!! Out now the pair of you! Fucking imbeciles! You know nothing!" He collapsed back into a chair and fell asleep, drunk as a motherfucker.

Bill walked over to the snoring Professor and stuck two fingers up at the brandy-stinking master. He turned to me. I shrugged.

"Instant arsehole, just add alcohol. Same as everybody else. Let him sleep it off. Come on, let's practice with these puppet fuckers."

We didn't see Silas until the following morning when that fucking chicken started doing its shit. I swore under my breath that I was going to kill that fucking useless bird, kill it and fucking eat it. What's the point in being a bird and not being able to fly?

I could hear that fucking irritating fucking Muzzein shit as well, some warbling, shoeless, fucking Islamic parrot at the top of his Whitechapel-mosque budgie cage. Come to the mosque everybody, pray to the east and fart at the west.

Silas ate his kidneys and liver and stuff in silence, you could tell he had a hangover and was more than a little embarrassed about his non-sage rambling.

We didn't give a shit. We just troughed down into that kidney, liver and fried eggs stuff. Like skinny hogs in a field full of shit and turnips. I was even getting a taste for this gruesome offal breakfast.

Silas grunted and nodded towards a small door I hadn't noticed before, "Up there," he whiskey-croaked. Silas took the lead, handing us a pair of candles. We followed him up the narrowest winding spiral staircase I'd ever had the discomfort of climbing. The walls were made of oak and worn down from the shoulders of countless climbers up this wooden mountain.

We arrived at a wonderfully sky-lit room, the whole ceiling made of glass. Bright blue sky, white clouds drifted slowly by. The room was clean and smelled of wood. Two immaculate teak benches with vices. A collection of fine sharp tools, chisels, files, saws, hung neatly on the wall. A Singer sewing machine, not electric. Silas unlocked a cupboard and started throwing lumps of lime wood onto the floor.

"Puppets," he mumbled as he tossed an assortment of rag scraps and buttons onto the floor. He farted loudly as he closed the door behind him.

We got to work.

I sketched out a rough drawing of our puppets. We had both decided that they were to be the most gruesome ugly fucking things in the world. I don't know why, maybe you can tell us.

Bill, who never goes anywhere

without his trusty carpenter's pencil, started drawing on the wood. I started in on the sewing machine. It was tricky, but I soon got the hang of it. I was lost to the world for hours, pricking my fingers and getting tangled in the cotton. Bill was hammering away behind me with his chisel, swearing and laughing.

All of a sudden he went silent, a chill ran down my spine, right to my arsehole. I farted. Whenever Bill is quiet, there's usually a reason. If he's not doing his Tourette's Syndrome swearing, or singing Black Sabbath riffs, there's something wrong.

I turned around with no uncertain amount of trepidation. Bill was sat on the floor, wood shavings and splinters all around him. He had a hunk of wood in his bloody-chisel-fucked-up hands. I walked over quietly and stood behind him, "Fucking hell," I said, "It's fucking him, isn't it?"

"Just came out of the wood," said Bill. "Just came out of the wood," he repeated. "I was just like knocking into the lime with the chisel, not really thinking about anything except splitting the wood. I wiped the sweat off my forehead and there he was, grinning at me." He handed me the bloodstained wood.

It was him all right.

Old Punchy.

I took him to the other bench and started in with the fine chisels and sandpaper. My job is always the icing. Bill hacks out the cake and with my soft woman's hands that have never seen a hard day's work in their life I sculpt the wrinkles and polish the chin. I could hear Bill battering away, singing traditional coal miners' songs. A bit like sea shanties but all about coal stuff instead of sea stuff.

Quite beautiful in a brutal ugly kind of way. Dead canaries, Aberfan, slag heaps, the boss is a bastard, being the main themes. I started to work, painting the devil doll's faces, choosing the scariest palette I could imagine. I didn't want this pantheon of the world's most secret mystery cult to be charming. I wanted to put the fear of God into anyone who ever saw it. I wanted fellow professors to be too scared to place their hands up their little wooden arses. By the end of the day we were exhausted. There was no sign of Silas, so we kipped on the benches, beneath the starlit sky, beaming silver down through the glass ceiling.

We didn't see or hear from Silas for two whole days. We would awake from dreams of puppets and an offal and fried egg breakfast would be steaming away by the door amongst the wood-shavings and scattered pieces of cloth.

On the third day we had finished. We had a basic cast. The Skeleton, the ghost of Judy, Pretty Polly, Jim Crow, Crocodile and Hobby the Horse we could carve at our leisure.

But there they were, magnificent and truly terrifying: a hideous Punch, a truly ugly Judy, Joey the Clown – who for some reason had turned into some kind of psychedelic preacher – monstrous Jack Ketch, and of course that suave old devil – The Devil.

We descended the narrow spiral staircase, clutching our gruesome work to show to Professor Silas.

The mad bastard had hung himself.

We found him dangling from one of the gaslights.

He'd left an envelope on the fireplace, addressed to the pair of us.

Bill gingerly opened it while I took a closer look at he dangling corpse.

Of course he'd shat and pissed himself, you could smell that halfway up the stairs.

His snout was red, his hair mad and white. Not unlike a lot of professors: they all tend to take on the appearance of their wooden Bacchus.

He had Punch in one hand and the Devil in the other. Weird.

"Go," said Bill.

"What?" I replied.

"The note," he said. "It just says go."

"That's it?"

"Yeah. Just go. Fucking cryptic tosser. Is there any kidneys and liver anywhere? I'm just fucking starving," said Bill, throwing the note on the ground.

"We have to be near Brick Lane. I heard that fucking Muzzein crap this morning, just after that fucking chicken started doing its crap. We could get some breakfast curry or something," I offered.

"Yeah." said Bill.

"What about Silas?" I asked, not really bothered. Bill looked at the swinging corpse and frowned, his lips

WHENEVER BILL IS QUIET, THERE'S USUALLY A REASON. IF HE'S NOT DOING HIS TOURETTE'S SYNDROME SWEARING, OR SINGING BLACK SABBATH RIFFS, THERE'S SOMETHING WRONG

pursed, pondering.

"Fuck him," said the rotter finally. Bad Jocko opened the front door. "He's fucking nuts anyway."

Brick Lane.

The Happy Shitter Tandoori House.

Keema curry and Kingfisher lager for breakfast.

Excellent. ☻

Mark Manning's first collection of memoirs, Crucify Me Again *(Codex) is now available to purchase on our website,* idler.co.uk. *And if you want to find out what Mark has been up to musically, go to* www.zodiac-mindwarp.com

THE BIG QUIT

**The story of a man who becomes addicted to giving up
by MATTHEW DE ABAITUA. Illustrations by EDWIN MARNEY**

I met Leavitt by the small bandstand on the east side of Victoria Park, as arranged. He was early, I saw him from afar as I drove up Grove Road, a hulking man with a slight stoop, self-consciously smoking beneath the Victorian pagoda.

Although it was July, blue sky had not been glimpsed over London for a month, a lid of dour, interlocking clouds sat low upon the city confirming the suspicion that we were all locked in here together until the bitter end.

Leavitt was my closest friend. He'd rang that afternoon.

"I've got to see you. I've decided to quit."

"You're leaving your job?" I was astonished.

"Yes. No. It's bigger than that. I'm quitting everything. The whole show is over. I'm going for the Big Quit."

I was worried. Leavitt often spoke of his life in such catastrophic terms.

In fact, he spoke of his life as if it were a phantasmagoria of disturbing and malign images, but as he worked as a researcher on *Kilroy*, this was understandable. But this Big Quit sounded serious and final. I feared the worst.

"Please," I said. "Let's talk about this. Let's meet up for lunch in Clerkenwell."

"Clerkenwell is too small," he replied. "Besides, I'm at home. It's already begun. I'll meet you at the park."

Leavitt had recently developed claustrophobia. He gave up travelling by Tube after an incident in which he stepped onto the platform at Highbury and Islington and hallucinated that it was no bigger than his living room. Increasingly, he talked of London as his prison, its offices and bars a multitude of holding pens, the M25 an impassable wall of traffic.

So we met in Victoria Park, the green lung of the East End. I had hoped that its wide open spaces would relax him. No such luck. When I arrived, Leavitt pointed directly at two teenage boys loitering over by the duck pond.

"Look at those two bastards. I've just seen them wrestle a Canadian Goose to the ground. One held it down while the other flopped a string of phlegm onto its struggling beak." I squinted at the boys, but I could see no sign of the bird. I turned back to Leavitt.

"What happened to the goose?"

"It struggled onto its feet. Shook itself down. Its wife and goslings emerged from behind the bush, it even couldn't look at them, it was so humiliated."

Leavitt looked awful. When he raised his washed-out blue eyes to me, I could see where life had pressed its thumbs into those hollow orbits. Where it had taken him in hand and branded his flanks. A lost animal, he even moped about with the sulk and the size of a beast of burden. As we walked along the path, I noted how a genetic kink had left him pigeon-toed, his right foot would curve inward, giving him the shuffle of a weary ox. It was clear that he was a man out of time, better suited for the Middle Ages perhaps, where someone could always find a use for a great bearded lummox. In the twenty-first century, where money is invisible, information intangible, power just a cons-piratorial whisper, great big Leavitt

was just in everybody's way.

And he knew it.

Our walk took us beside the skate park where we paused to watch a young boy flip up and roll down the ramps on his board.

"Kids," said Leavitt. "They scare the shit out of me."

I motioned toward a bench. We sat down together. Even though my first child, Leanna, had been born only two months earlier, Leavitt remained uninhibited about his loathing of children.

"But I'm not afraid of babies," he said, pausing to ensure I was not offended. "It's when they become little adults that I have problems – you have to realise how completely different their upbringing is compared to ours. They are the post-paedophile paranoia generation – the first generation to be raised entirely within earshot.

"You can see it in the way they play – half amongst themselves, and half for the audience. That's why I can book them for *Kilroy* without fear – they've been on TV all their lives.

"There is nothing more depressing than the sight of seven adults who have ran out of things to say to one another, sitting around a toddler like its a television. Then they go off and have another kid because they need another channel."

Now he was working himself into a rant. Thoughts that had been pacing his mind all week leapt at the chance to propagate. When anxiety was upon him, he could be incorrigibly self-obsessed, and monologue unselfconsciously for an entire evening.

"I've seen obese seven year old boys cocooned in prams the size of sedan chairs – pampered, Game Boy-punching Buddhas borne through the streets by their harassed bearers. And I've seen scrawny six year old girls with dog leads tied around their wrists, being dragged down Kentish Town Road by their junkie mothers, late for their next appointment with the needle. Either way, you can't hope to raise a sane child anymore – I tell you, you're going to have a fight saving your daughter from all this. I respect you for trying. I wish you the very best, but I can't face it anymore."

Clearly, I had been right to worry about my friend's state of mind. Leavitt had suffered breakdowns before – in his Mancunian youth, he had been found tearing the heads off pigeons in the Arndale Centre. When the police pulled him over in Didsbury, he was carrying a plastic bag half-inched from Dixons. The arresting officer peered into it, and saw a dozen pigeon heads arranged in blood-soaked cotton wool.

I inquired after what had triggered this latest excess.

"I was putting together a youth of today special for Wednesday's show. The producer's been keen on delinquency horror stories ever since he had his ThinkPad snatched outside the Oval. He told me to find the worst kids in London. I turned up three little monsters."

Despite his bulk, Leavitt was

"ONE ELEVEN YEAR OLD BOY, TWO TEN YEAR OLDS – HE'S BLACK, THEY'RE WHITE. ALL CRACK DEALERS. NOT RUNNERS, OR LOOK OUTS OR BAG BOYS. DEALERS. PLAYAS"

nimble with Rizlas. He slipped a briskly composed fag between his lips, lit it, and ushered the smoke from his mouth with a flick of his tongue.

"One eleven year old boy, two ten year olds – he's black, they're white. All crack dealers. Not runners, or look outs or bag boys. Dealers. Playas. As far as the Met can ascertain, they've been supplying an entire girl's school in Hampstead.

"It took me nearly a week to track down them down. I found them walking away from a blazing BMW in an underground car park in the Elephant and Castle. I asked them if they wanted to be on *Kilroy*, and of course they did.

In the car, I glanced nervously at them in the rear view mirror. They were blowing cones and passing around a digicam, which was showing MPEGS of gangbangs they'd thrown with their underage girls' school clients. They turned the volume up so I could hear them fucking away, non-consensual three on one by the sound of it."

The two geese tormentors pushed by us. Leavitt slowed to a dawdle to let them by, his face hitched up in disgust.

"TURNED OUT THE BLACK KID WAS THEIR LEADER. HIS NAME WAS BUDD. BUDD WAS LEAN AND PRECOCIOUSLY-MUSCLED, WHEREAS THE TWO WHITE KIDS WERE JUST JUNK-FOOD HONEY MONSTERS"

"With these kids, it's like some trigger has been sprung in the gene pool – nature has accepted that they will die young and so it has put them on an accelerated life plan, just so they can pass on their wad of DNA before they cark it at thirty, dead by crack-induced cardiac arrest. I tell you, if you ever doubted that man is a nasty creature, innately depraved, born twisted by Original Sin, then half an hour with these ungodly brats would soon turn you into a birch-wielding Calvinist. If the devil sold Corn Flakes, these kids would be the free gift.

"Turned out the black kid was their leader. His name was Budd. Budd was lean and precociously-muscled, whereas the two white kids were just junk-food Honey Monsters. Budd's skull was a dark duodecahedron of angular planes, he wore his white top unzipped to expose his six-pack. You could have played noughts and crosses on it. It made me feel so pathetic."

Leavitt took a long blink, sank his head into his hands and exhaled. I was worried he might start to cry. But he mopped up his spilt emotions, shook himself together and continued:

"Anyway. So I bundle Budd and his little henchmen into my office and all three of them slouch there in their giant trousers, communicating – as far as I could tell – in a series of clicks and whistles.

I sit behind my desk and ask them the first question:

"Do you think crack dealing is wrong?" Budd fixes me with a flinty stare and says something, I can't

understand what exactly as he's speaking in a hybrid of patois and sarf London slang. So I ask him again: "do you think crack dealing is wrong", and again he answers me, and again I can't understand what he's saying. I ask the two white kids and they're exactly the same – I can just about make out the words but they're words I've never heard of. "Cotching w'ma beanie." "S'touch na s'rank." Now I'm thinking: shit. I took all that time tracking this lot down but there is no way I can put them on *Kilroy*. They're completely unintelligible. So I say, "look, forget it boys. It's over. You're not coming on the show. I can't understand a word you're saying."

They look furious, murderous, and these two ten year old white boys reach inside their puffas and each pulls out a pair of Glock pistols. They hold the guns flat, pointed in an X toward me."

I was appalled. "They pulled a gun on you?"

"Guns. Four of them. In my office. I thought, Christ, these kids are going to plug a cap in my ass just because I won't put them on *Kilroy*. I'm just sitting there not knowing what the fuck to do, when Budd tires of the efforts of his two fat little henchman, leans over to me, and says:

"I'm going down the pub. I'd like a pint of bitter please. Would you like a drink? It's my round." And the two little heaps of dough either side of him start creasing up, hissing with laughter, the muzzle of their pistols chuckling up and down.

Budd continues: "I'll have a pint please and a packet of peanuts. Do you have any crisps? Smoky Bacon." My first thought was that he was being suddenly nice to me, perhaps even offering a bribe. But then I looked at the way he had fashioned his features into a slack, gormless expression and realised he was doing an impression of me. I mean, my liking for pubs is written all over my waist. And these young kids obviously found the idea of going to a pub fucking hilarious. As if them with their gold, and their Adidas and their crack and their guns and their underage girlfriends would ever stoop to going to a fucking pub. He's taking the piss out of me, but that doesn't matter, because I realise I can finally understand what he is saying. This revelation would have made me leap into the air, if I hadn't been so terrified of making any sudden movements.

"So I booked them for the show, on the proviso that Budd answered all of Kilroy's questions in his imitation of my gormless accent. He signed the release forms, and on the way out, he sold me some very high quality cocaine."

Leavitt lived on the fourteenth floor of a tower block off Daling Way. It was a short walk from the park. We ascended in the lift, a metallic coffin with a tang of Tennents and urine.

"I put up a notice, saying 'please do not piss in the lift'."

Leavitt held his index finger to the pulse in his throat.

"But someone took it down and pissed on it."

His flat was in a terrible state. On entering, I was stung by the high-pitched odour of the sodden and unwashed. The hallway carpet was waterlogged, the pile retained Leavitt's footsteps as I followed him into the lounge, the heart of the devastation. The carpet had been torn back from the floorboards, which clung onto wet, black clumps of underlay. A small assault course of chairs were piled on a table which in turn was balancing on the sofa. The stereo and TV looked like someone had put the boot in – they consoled one another around the drinks cabinet, which was upturned, its spirit leaking out. The carpet was heaped up on the balcony, its malformed swells resembling a spontaneous formation of igneous rock. Had someone hosed down the room?

"Did you have a fire?"

"No, quite the opposite. I had a flood."

"On the fourteenth floor?"

"Yes. I was surprised too. The water tank on the roof burst. A wave washed down the side of the block until it hit my balcony, and then it broke in here." Leavitt held his hands up, helpless before fate. "So that's that."

We set about mopping up the puddles and stripping away the rest of the carpet. Years of grime were tangled up in its pile, a gum of ash, wine and dead skin that came away on my hands. Together, we hefted

be.
Gon
the c
realised
lounge, s
shelf to sco
into a cardb   n
ashtrays, bottle   vodka,
even framed p   s, Leavitt
and family, Leav   d ex, Leavitt
and friends. When the box was full, he laid it down, snapped a piece of A4 from a notepad, scrawled on it

"Please Do Not Steal This, You Little Shits" and then sellotaped it to the lid. Half-protesting I followed him out to the lift.

"You can't throw these away," I said, pulling out his collection of *Godfather* videos, then waving a photograph of Leavitt with his last serious girlfriend.

"She was last century. I carried a torch for her. But now it's just a match."

The lift doors chunked aside.

With a slow shunt of his foot, he shifted the box into the lift. "I don't want any of it anymore."

He reached in, pressed for the Ground Floor, and stepped back as the doors closed.

"There. Gone."

The purge of the flat exhilarated him. His great frame skipped from room to room, he tore files from shelves and chucked them without a second glance. He ransacked his paperwork: proposals, agendas,

...mulated ...is office life ...om their paper ...patched in a minute. ...d and bagged his record ...ction. I unplugged his Playstation and his video. I hauled the telly out to the landing. But the task of loading them onto the lift I left to Leavitt. He went about the Big Quit with the focus and vision of an artist. The clear-out was his self-expression, and his catharsis. He gave everything the final push, while I merely followed him around with a bin bag, a dutiful amanuensis.

The kids made it easy. They nicked everything we sent down.

Only once did I raise an objection, when he held a wedge of bank statements, tax forms and council tax remittances over the maw of the black bag. It was one thing to dispose of a lifetime of faded memories and a decade of boyish consumerism. Quite another to throw away the official documentation of his citizenship. I looked him at him intently.

"Are you sure about this?"

"No". A grin streaked with sulphur and stained with tannin. "But what choice do I have? I have no job. I have no home. Did I tell you I've informed the council that I am vacating the property?"

He hadn't. The image of Leavitt crashing on my sofa for a year flashed through my mind.

"I have a month and then that's it. Gone."

"Where will you go?"

By now, the bin bag contained his birth certificate, his degree certificates, both BA and MA, and an entire anthology of debt with submissions from Visa, American Express and Barclaycard. Leavitt flashed me the one thing he had preserved: his passport.

"I don't know where exactly. But I'm leaving this fucking city, that's for sure. It's a boom-time madhouse on the turn. In fact, the whole society has become just a waste of everybody's time. This isn't a new beginning. This isn't a quest for a better quality of life. The Big Quit is survival. It's my medicine. My chemotherapy."

So we continued the clear-out of his life. Although it was the irresponsible, palpably wrong thing to do, it also felt unquestionably right – an afternoon epiphany, a moment of clarity for us both that had to be acted upon immediately lest he slip back into the habitual addiction of the day-to-day.

Perhaps it was my recently acquired fatherhood that made me so sympathetic to the Big Quit. The idea of turning my back on little Leanna and the whole mediocrity makeover my own life had undergone since the wedding was a tempting one. Responsibility had me by the throat. And if I was too much of a New Age Coward to act on this instinct to flee – if I had made my peace with compromise – then I was keen to live out the fantasy vicariously. Yes, I dreamt of joining Leavitt in the Big Quit. We all have our Plan A – a life of successful artistic expression conducted in a gradual migration across the continents punctuated by tumultuous affairs with equally artistic but respectfully less successful women.

Yes, I would like to mark my remaining years on an axis of broadminded, big-breasted and brief encounters. But Plan B suits me. I have dallied with stretching the boundaries of my experience. Now it is time to snap back into shape. As much as I recoil from the choices I have made, I still walk Spitalfields market with Leanna strapped to my back, flush with genial virility. That makes up for the fact that our cluttered lounge has taken on the air of a waiting room; the two of us flicking through the channels in search of stimuli, distraction, escape; alighting from advert to gameshow rerun; bored and in a loop, waiting for sleep, waiting for the baby to wake up, waiting for work to begin again. But that's Plan B for you. The Long Game, played according to a strategy of patience and diligence. I can do it. I am doing it. But Leavitt couldn't. He had lost the suspension of disbelief required for Plan B. I understood that. What I didn't understand was how one bad encounter with Budd had convinced him to undertake The Big Quit. Leavitt had a sensational temperament, he could tease out an impending apocalypse from any given edition of the Daily Mail. But there was also inertia to him, a considerable mass of apathy hung on his heavy bones that weighed against any snap decisions. I decided that there must be more to this momentous decision than he had let slip.

We drank Earl Grey on the balcony and watched the sunset, diffused by the pollution, spill unchecked across the cloudscape.

"THIS ISN'T A NEW BEGINNING. THIS ISN'T A QUEST FOR A BETTER QUALITY OF LIFE. THE BIG QUIT IS SURVIVAL. IT'S MY MEDICINE. MY CHEMOTHERAPY"

Down below, the estate kids were dividing Leavitt's possessions between them – big brothers had been summoned to haul away the white goods, little brothers scuttled away with mattresses on their backs while baby sisters thumbed and discarded his library of modern classics. The only possession that caused any friction was his collection of rare Nineties Trance twelve inches. Everyone wanted them.

Once it was clear that the mysterious owner of these things was not about to call the police, the pillage took on the leisurely pace of a car boot sale. Even the crack heads joined in, abandoning their patch in the underground car park to root away for something that could be swapped for a rock. Leavitt watched them all with amused detachment – smoking the last of his Golden Virginia, toddling out to brew another pot. We smoked and drank in silence until the clear-out was complete, the last bin bag emptied, the last cardboard box filleted and flung aside. Then Leavitt spoke.

"Do you see that kid over there?" On the playground, a fat boy sat weighing down one end of a seesaw.

"He's been there all afternoon, just watching them. Not once did he join in. I admire that boy, content to sit on his fat ass while everyone else scrabbles for their piece of the pie." He leant over the balcony.

"Oi. You. Yes, you. Fat boy on a seesaw. What's your name?"

The kid looked sullenly upwards, slid from the seesaw and walked off into the dusk. There. Gone.

As the last of the daylight faded, halogen lights ebbed over the walkways and car parks of the estate. The sirens struck up – the balcony thrummed with the thump-thump-thump of the police helicopter. The air turned chill. It was going to be another tense, threatening evening out there, and I had my family to think about. Leavitt thanked me for my help, but I couldn't look him in the eye. An almost post-coital awkwardness and guilt lay between us. He showed me to the lift and I was still putting my coat on as the doors slid shut.

It was to be a month before I saw Leavitt again.

It all started again with another phone call.

"Is there a television near you?" Leavitt's voice was deep and urgent, it rumbled near and far as if being hunted along the lower registers.

"Leavitt!" I exclaimed. "How the hell are you?" I swivelled away from the monitor and leant into the receiver.

"I'm outside Dixons. You have to see this. Is there a television in your office?"

"There's one in reception. Wait there, I'm transferring you." I put the phone down and jogged through the cubicles. There was an immense plasma screen in the company's cavernous reception. I flicked it on and picked up Leavitt's call.

"Channel 4. Look, there he is. That's Budd."

On the screen, a black lad, with his shirt open to reveal the force of his six-pack, was slouched on a green sofa, one lazy hand resting on the thigh of Gail Porter. I fiddled at the volume. Gail was saying,

"…this is the latest mobile from Ericsson, WAP-enabled, full Internet access, FM radio and it's so small it will barely make a bulge in your Calvins. This is top of the range Street Stuff. Budd?"

I had never seen anyone present a TV show with their shirt open before. You could see the kid had style. Leavitt had made him out to be a monster but dropped in the cheery, low budget world of half-term TV, Budd looked no more threatening than the "wild one" in a boy band.

"On the street, this'll get you high ratings innit."

Gail nodded sagely. "After the break on Street Stuff, I'll be looking at the Nintendo Game Cube." Turns to Budd.

"An' I'll be chillin' on the street, checkin' aht the brothers scorin' high ratings with their in-car MP3." Then, in jaunty unison, Gail and Budd leapt off the sofa to deliver the show's catchphrase into the hastily tilted camera.

"Street Stuff. Louder. Faster. Cooler. Yeah."

I didn't know what to say. A month passes by briskly in the metropolis. September had been a smear of sleepless nights and strategy meetings. I had called Leavitt to check in on how The Big Quit was progressing but all I had dialled into was the dead tone of a disconnected line. After that exhilarating afternoon clearing out the flood-damaged debris of his life, a sense of fear and guilt overcame me – fear that he would become my burden, guilt that I had allowed my own longing for freedom to encourage him in this great irresponsibility. These feelings, combined with the inconvenience of his being incommunicado, made it easy to put Leavitt on the back burner. Out of sight, out of conscience. But now he was back. What state was he in?

"I need to see you." He spoke briskly with the air of one who is closing a pressing business deal. "I've borrowed this phone off… sorry, I didn't catch your name… off Lucinda and she needs it back now so I'll meet you for lunch. Can you do lunch?"

I could.

We met outside Jack Straw's Castle before lighting off into Hampstead Heath. The slab of cloud that had oppressed the Summer had darkened to a rain-bearing sulk for the Autumn. In fact, it had been raining all month. The flood in Leavitt's flat had been a premonition of the Great Floods that now lay over Hampshire, Kent and Yorkshire while the city itself had acquired the humid, saturated stench of a Caribbean rain forest.

Leavitt showed up wearing a fake fur coat that accentuated his doleful bearishness, it steamed as we walked

"FOOD REPRESENTS AN ENTIRE BUFFET OF ANXIETY, AS YOU WELL KNOW. STEROID-ENHANCED BSE-RIDDLED BEEF WITH GENETICALLY-MODIFIED POTATOES AND A SIDE ORDER OF VEGETABLES MARINATED IN INSECTICIDES. NO, FOOD IS NOT FOR ME. I LIMIT MYSELF TO BISCUITS. HOB NOBS, ACTUALLY"

through the mulch of a tree-lined path. I tried to cadge a cigarette off him, confident that I'd be able to scrub the smell off by the time I got home.

"Sorry, I've quit. No more draw, pills, fags or booze. No coffee, no tea. No uppers, no downers. No earning, no spending. I'm clean."

He looked better for it. The hollows beneath his eyes had filled out, his jawline had tightened, his stride was boisterous and robust. Clearly, The Big Quit had its benefits.

"My aim has been to preserve an equilibrium. I attend to natural rhythms, get plenty of sunlight, go to bed early, and avoid unnecessary stress, which isn't easy as there's a lot of it about."

He shrugged and walked on. Physically and psychically, he seemed much improved. He was now prone to exuberant gestures – as we spoke, he would pluck conkers from the path, or leaves from a tree. However, his self-obsession was total as ever. It was as if he had an internal timer that clocked off the minutes he was talking and then, when it ran out, an alarm would sound to remind him to talk about me. Then he would inquire about my family and nod though my brief reply with feigned interest. Even as I was talking I knew the timer was being reset for another twenty-five minutes of Leavitt. It was hopeless to talk about anything other than his latest theories or encounters. So I gave up on my account of Leanna's bout of croup and asked him if the sight of Budd co-presenting a TV show had upset him.

"Well, this is my last day. I'm already out of here. If anything, Budd's success only affirms my decision. I knew as soon as I met Budd that – if I could persuade him to speak English – he was made for television. He's a charismatic kid, smart, with a puffa stuffed with street cred. Did you see the item he did after the break: 'How Buff is Your Mum?' Genius. You know, Gail doesn't let just anyone put a hand on her thigh."

"I couldn't understand what he was talking about. I guess I'm too old."

A drizzle fell upon the Heath. Our fellow strollers manoeuvred for cover. Tucked beneath the canopy of an oak, Hampstead nannies were working yellow kagouls briskly over the thick duffel coats of their infant charges. The joggers plunged by us regardless. Leavitt smiled and wriggled deeper into his fur coat.

"Did you catch what Budd was saying about ratings? You can't tell me that isn't genius. Ratings are going to be his gimmick. I can feel it. Not that he invented them. I first heard about ratings when I was researching the Youth of Today show. It's a system kids in South London have for calculating the exact status of you and your peers. You get points for how good you are at football, how sexually precocious you are, what brands you wear. What aftershave. Your ratings go up if you fuck two girls at once or if your parents buy you a top of the range mobile. Your ratings go down if you put on weight or do well in class. Children have always had a keen eye for a hierarchy. In the past, it was just about who was the hardest, who was the cock of the school. Today there are many more factors that go into determining status, hence the need for a complex system of measurement like ratings."

Whenever Leavitt talked about the culture of children, a numb sense of helplessness came over me. My whole parenting plan B seemed delusional. As soon as Leanna could watch TV, Leavitt insisted she would be lost to me. She would roll her eyes with contempt at my out-dated notions, and take her guidance from people like Budd.

"He's going to roll ratings right out across the country. I know it. Children have always competed for attention. Now, they are learning to attract it in the same way as the media does. With sensational content. They will look great, and they will sell themselves with the same hyperbole of drugs, sex, glamour, money. You're not raising a daughter – you're raising a TV show."

I couldn't tell if he was just baiting me. But when it came to kids, Leavitt knew his stuff. The extensive consultancy files on pre teen demographics had been the first to go during our clear-out of the flat. Although I was the one who had a child of my own, I knew nothing beyond feeding times and teething. I had the pride and fear of first-hand experience but he had hard facts.

"That was why those kids were so adamant they were going to be on Kilroy. Have you any idea what actually appearing on television can do for your ratings? Maybe I should have stuck it out and offered to become Budd's agent. That would have been the smart thing to do."

Rueful, momentarily so, Leavitt halted his stride and I noted – as he adjusted his coat – that he was thinner.

I gestured to his ghost of a gut. "Have you given up food too?"

"Food represents an entire buffet of anxiety, as you well know. Steroid-enhanced BSE-riddled beef with genetically-modified potatoes and a side order of vegetables marinated in insecticides. No, food is not for me. I limit myself to biscuits. Hob Nobs, actually."

We walked on past the Highgate Ponds, the rain pricking their surface. It was my turn to speak. I updated him on gossip, although little of it interested him, which I respected. He never had much time for anyone else. Most found Leavitt insufferable because of his egotism. Yet I always indulged him. He existed at a right-angle to the rest of my life. He was my Fool, and all I asked from him was entertainment.

Inevitably, he interrupted me:

"I am also celibate now," he announced.

That was no sacrifice. For the last year, rubbing people up the wrong way was the closest he came to sex.

"You'd be surprised. There have been several encounters. The ironic thing is, now that I've quit my vices, I have all this excess energy. I am actually horny. Last week, I cracked and went to a singles bar."

"You went to a pick-up joint?"

"Well, it was more of a put-down joint. My ratings are very low right now. It wasn't a great success."

We were interrupted by my mobile. The office calling. One of my various chains jerked tight.

"I have to go. Do you have any plans for your last night?"

"I don't know. Getting pissed is out of the question. But I fancy something decadent."

"I could take you out for a meal," I suggested.

"Actually, I was thinking more of a tittie bar."

It was a slow night at Carnal. The girls outnumbered the punters two-to-one. As my eyes adjusted to the low light, I was surprised by how small the place was. Beside two yards of bar, a sales team bonded with their line manager. On the stage, a black woman in white lingerie gently abraded herself against a pole, her lips mouthing the lyrics to the Puff Daddy number playing on the big screen. After sustained lobbying from the sales team, the barman changed the channel from MTV Base to Sky Sports One. Then she swayed alluringly to the commentary of the Fulham vs Blackburn game.

The dancers stood around in their underwear, mostly huddled together for warmth, their ethnicity as contrived as the staff photograph on the cover of an annual report. I expected the pervasive air of desperation to depress Leavitt. It was quite the opposite. With his fake fur and exaggerated manners, he took on the persona of a liberal pimp, diligently asking the first two women to sidle over where they were from ("Rio." "California.") what they would like to drink ("Red Bull." "Water.") and how they were feeling ("Great!" "Great!"). To move things along, the Californian insisted with can-do candour that she loved to dance. "Like, show off my butt and stuff?" I gave Leavitt twenty quid. I was paired off with the Brazilian who informed me, solemnly, that London was nothing like she had expected it to be.

The basement was divided into a number of wooden stalls. We took our coats off and sat a yard apart on a low bench.

The dance was softcore, referencing every trick in the repertoire. The two girls pinched their nipples, cooed in delight, dropped to their knees and flicked their hair in unison across our respective crotches. The Californian threw herself onto all fours and then reached behind her to tighten the gag of her g-string.

Leavitt turned to me.

"The appeal of beautiful naked young women playing with themselves never wanes, does it?"

He took a Hob Nob from his pocket and nipped off a bite.

After the third dance, we tired of the girls and returned to the bar. It was buckling under the weight of a gang of city boys. They launched themselves unselfconsciously upon the stilted atmosphere of lust and desperation, wisecracking from behind the mouths of their bottles of Becks. The music was back.

Yet, the arrival of these virile men with the gung-ho hedonism of sailors on shore leave could not blind us to the rest of the punters. The tables were occupied by the shabby, the obese, the old and – in one case – a man who had ticks in every box of that unfortunate checklist. Leavitt picked him out, waving his glass of sparkling mineral water rakishly in his general direction.

"Look at that dirty fucker. Look at the ears on him. Like someone has practised origami on two slices of processed ham. You could play table tennis with those lobes. Promise me you'll tell me when my ears go like that. I shall have them cropped."

The tables were definitely second class. The dancers who serviced them catered to niche tastes – brazen slappers for the old boys or nimble miniatures for the nascent paedophiles.

"I feel weird here," I confessed.

Leavitt nodded. "Our fellow punters do take some of the sheen off the evening. But if you're worried that this isn't much of a last night on the town, then relax. The women are almost naked. That'll do for me."

There was an awkward frisson as the Brazilian and the Californian returned to the bar, studiously ignoring us to canvas for the attention of the city boys. We watched them smile and laugh the same way they had smiled and laughed for us. Leavitt sipped his mineral water and winced out of habit, forgetting he was no longer drinking neat scotch.

A feeling of fondness for my old friend passed over me, a tender, drunken emotion. I grinned at him, expecting a reflection of my camaraderie but saw only distraction, his mind elsewhere and considering his future, which was still unclear to us both.

"What's your plan?" I asked, finally.

"I have enough money to do some travelling. Since I refuse to drive now, I am attracted to islands. Small ones, obviously. Beyond that, I haven't given it much thought. I have quit worrying."

But Leavitt, I thought, where will you stay? What will you do? What about money? Will you ever come back?

"Where are you going first?"

"Lundy Island, off the coast of North Devon. Three miles long and half a mile wide. I shall walk it every morning. I read a leaflet about it. Apparently the island has very interesting flora and fauna. I intend to start with the fauna."

I was disappointed. The Big Quit had promised to be a big adventure. How bathetic it would seem if it ended with Leavitt communing with mountain goats. I began to regret

encouraging him out of my life.

"It's not too late to stay. You've picked yourself up. You look great. All you'd need to do is get another job and you could be back on top again. Are you going to abandon everything just because of one bad kid?"

Leavitt deposited a freshly shredded beer mat into the ashtray. "I might look fine now, but I'm still just delicately floating on the meniscus. It wouldn't take much to pull me under again. Besides it wasn't just Budd. There was something else, although I don't know whether it's any more of a justification. It was an incident on the Silverlink Overground train between Hackney Central and Camden Town."

I waved away the attention of a brace of diminutive Peruvian girls in lacy slips. Leavitt leant in and told me the story of the final straw.

"It all began with a hangover on a humid Monday morning in July. Increasingly, my hangovers were manifesting themselves as an agitated or anxious state. I woke abruptly at six, as if an alarm had sounded the instant the alcohol left my system. I could feel my internal organs bucking and writhing. My heart was going like a snare. I bolted out of bed and it was as if I was peering at reality from behind a broken window. The dividing glass was gone. The wind grated across the tissue of my brain.

"I marched out to catch the 9.15.

Sirens pursued me. On Mare Street, I was a ghost. The cacophony of a bus would pass right through me, its exhaust billowing out of my mouth. Everyone was carrying a knife or a can. I winced at every face I saw. Other people were an onslaught: with my left hand, I took the pulse in my throat and with my right hand I took the pulse on my left wrist, and locked in that contorted pose I staggered down the street. I remember walking by two homeless people, a scrawny teenager with his mate, who was face down, not moving, clearly dead. The kid asked me if I could spare change for a drink. I turned on him.

"'Don't you think you've had enough? Don't you think you should cut down a bit?' It was embarrassing. It just leapt out of me. The inside and the outside were becoming confused.

"It was the day after my encounter with Budd. I was still nervy about the incident with the guns. Also, my producer had issued us with some new guidelines for selecting guests. It wasn't just a matter of picking interesting people anymore. They had to push various buttons amongst the audience profile of the show, which is stay-at-home Middle England empty nesters, Estate Mums, Dole Dads, students, pensioners. The consultant had defined each of these groups according to their anxieties and we were to select guests who triggered them. Anxiety was to be the hook to ensure repeat viewing. Fear can be awfully compulsive. That was when I

"IT WASN'T A GOOD-TIME SCREAM. IT WAS AN UNEQUIVOCAL, INVOLUNTARY, INCESSANT SCREAM. IT WAS THE SCREAM OF A MAN, UNMANNED. SCREAMING LIKE A BOY, LIKE A GIRL, LIKE A BABY"

realised I would be seeing Budd again. In the Venn diagram of contemporary anxiety, Budd – young, male, black, poor, strong, criminal, virile – is the shaded intersection where each of the circles overlap.

"So in the jittery fug of the hangover, I was glancing at my fellow passengers and the full import of the consultant's theories hit me. In an age of peace and prosperity, we have no hope. We know things can't get any better than this. We only have hope during war time or depression. In peacetime, the only way is down. That's why we look on the future with fear, and that's why we stopped defining people according to their aspirations and switched to their anxieties.

"So I was sat there wringing the handle of my briefcase when the train pulled in to Dalston Junction. The doors opened, and I heard screaming.

"It wasn't a good-time scream. It was an unequivocal, involuntary, incessant scream. It was the scream of a man, unmanned. Screaming like a boy, like a girl, like a baby. Screaming like the soldiers at the Somme. I looked out of the window and saw him writhing on a crowded platform, his fellow passengers had huddled back a few yards to give him some space. Some quarantine.

"He had the same pale complexion, cheap suit and briefcase as the rest of us. His thinning hair was stuck to his scalp with sweat, the knees of his trousers scuffed and torn where he had been scything his legs across the concrete, trying to get up, trying to get away.

"In the carriage, we all exchanged glances, searching for a consensus as to what we should do next. The doors hung open. I felt a hot flush rise within me, my fingers flew to my pulse and confirmed my worst fears. Cardiac trauma, surely. Or some primal response. The urge for fight or flight, supressed by the etiquette of urban life.

"I risked another look. Whenever his scream failed him, he gasped 'no', 'no', 'no'. In that brief silence, I felt another lurch within me, a loss of control of my own consciousness. The instincts that had been kicking away within me now raised a full revolt at my refusal to act. My mind boiled over. I had to bite back the urge to get out onto the platform and start screaming myself.

"To steady myself against the yaw and pitch of my anxiety, I put my hand on the shoulder of the woman next to me.

"'Sorry,' I said. 'I find it unsettling.'

"'Why won't they shut the fucking doors?' she hissed.

"I discovered that I was now rocking on my legs with the uncertainty of a new-born foal, space contracting about me. The carriage was the length of a coffin.

"The screaming man crawled up to the open doors, leaving behind a slick stain of urine upon the platform. I made my way toward him, unsure of whether to help him onto the train or kick him back onto the station.

His terror was infectious. A surging, black-backed thing was rising within me. I could keep it down no longer. It ascended catastrophically, so quickly it could not decompress in time and when it broke the surface, waves of sweat slunk off its sides, pitching reality into a dizzying carousel.

"I fell upon the filthy floor of the carriage.

"I must have blacked out briefly. When I looked up, the doors had closed and the train was easing out of Dalston Junction. But I could still hear the screaming.

"When I got into the office, I settled down to work but found that I was still locked in the indecision of the anxiety. I couldn't do anything. The phone seemed to weigh a couple of kilos. I had to use two hands to move the mouse. Even clicking on icons was laborious. Windows opened leaden-footed, disgorging information I could no longer decipher. Voicemail and email quickly stacked up but I had lost my will to work through it. I opened the nearest thing to hand, the presentation on anxiety. Its charts mocked the catastrophic – but also essentially inconsequential – experience I had just gone through. A phantom breakdown, a panic attack about panic. Happens all the time. Get over it.

"I muddled through the day and when I got home, I discovered the flood in my flat. I took off my shoes and paddled. That was when it occurred to me. The Big Quit. I

would wash it all away and start again. I would turn my back on the daily anxiety and fear of the future. I phoned a polite resignation speech into the office answering machine. It gave me no pleasure – it was not cathartic. My job was just the first habit that had to go. But as I quit each thing in turn, I found myself becoming addicted to abstinence. Each stage of the Big Quit has given me back more of my old self. As I brush away each habit, I discover more and more of Anthony Leavitt. The man I used to be, and the man I could be again.

"But I never did find out why that man was screaming."

We didn't go down to the basement for any more dances. As the club filled up, we fell into silence. Leavitt watched me get progressively drunker and smiled weakly at each of my attempts to whip up a sense of celebration.

I began to worry about the questions I would face when I got home. Where have you been? Why are you so drunk? Why do you reek of muscular perfume?

On our walk home, I insisted we duck into a pub so that I could scrub myself down. I undid the cuffs on my shirt and lathered myself with the tiny soap. Under the harsh light, I noticed the mottled skein of capillaries breaking out across my cheeks, a web of dissolution and stress. I was caught in it.

Even after scrubbing myself down,

I could still smell the perfume in my hair and my shirt. I flicked the excess moisture from my hands and turned my face under the hot breath of the dryer. From left to right.

When I came out of the bathroom, Leavitt had gone.

Dear Matthew,
I am writing to you from my caravan on the Isle of Skye. It is exactly one hundred and fifty days since I left you in the toilets of the Blue Dolphin. You must forgive me for running out on you like that, but you were very drunk and I was afraid you might try to hug me when we finally said goodbye.

Anyway, I thought I'd let you know that the Big Quit is nearly over. I have travelled continents in search of the perfect place to live. From Lundy, I went to Gomera, off the coast of Tenerife. From Gomera, I tried the Greek islands, of Paros and Naxos, before heading off in search of more vigorous conditions. I journeyed out to the Inuit islands of the Arctic where I settled finally on Baffin Island. I had to learn to shoot, as there are polar bears there. Life on the ice wasn't too bad. The threat of predators meant that my fear and anxiety was at last in its natural habitat. I became extremely fit, hardy and self-contained. You would think that I would finally be happy.

Regretfully not. I am alone. I have been alone for quite some time. It is easy to travel the Earth and fail to strike up a single decent conversation. The heroic aura of asceticism soon waned. I was not prepared for the utter lack of attention one receives after cutting oneself off from society. As much as I wished to reinvent myself as a self-sufficient man, I have to concede that I crave others. One ceases to exist when one is no longer reflected in the eyes of a friend or a lover. I have even found myself thinking fondly of children.

I came to Skye with the last of my savings. It was a compromise, an attempt to live both in isolation yet amongst a people with whom I have some common ground.

I live in Glendale, on the western coast of the island. There is a small community of English ex-pats here. Yet none of them have gone out of their way to make friends with the mad man living in the caravan in the bay. I have made some overtures but all my small talk muscles have atrophied. I bring such intensity to bear on each encounter that I despair of ever becoming friendly with another human being again.

The winter has been unremitting. I write to you while wearing a pair of wellies. You see, I awoke this morning to discover that the caravan has flooded. It is a sign.

I walk every morning across the Glen to the deserted village of Lorgill. It was abandoned during the clearances. There are sparse ruins, a waterfall, and the echoes of life. Even though the village was gutted over a hundred and seventy years ago, the peat retains the presence of the lost community. The past feels closer here.

Lorgill is the nearest I get to company, these days.

Then, I walk along the coast to Neist Point, where some enterprising scousers have bought a lighthouse. I eat my breakfast on the sea cliff, watching the turmoil break on the rocks below. You can see the other Western Isles from here, and I have thought of heading out to the remoter islands. But I don't have the strength anymore. After eating, I get up and walk to the edge. My waterproof snaps in the wind, and the rage of the rain and the sea wipes me clean of all thoughts except one. Suicide.

Every day, I step back and trudge home to Glendale. Before I reach the caravan, there is a ruined watermill just on the way down to the bay. It bears the marks of a failed restoration. I think that about a decade ago they tried to turn it into a tourist attraction. But the roof of the visitors centre has caved in. The Welcome sign lies face down in the peat. I sit there and catch my breath and think about coming back. But that's not going to happen. Not all new starts work out. Sometimes, things are so far gone that no matter how hard you try you can't bring them back to life.

Enough.

I was in Portree yesterday. I was considering buying a newspaper again, just to see how it felt. The *Guardian* had a photograph of the Mobo Awards above its masthead,

and there was Budd. I read about his TV Show, "Ratings", and his debut album, "Chow Mein", which I found pleasingly obscure until the journalist explained it was the South London pronunciation of the phrase, "do you know what I mean?'

When I think of Budd, driving forward to success, I feel better. There is a lesson in the way he has gone about his life. He has stepped over the fearful and the anxious to get exactly what he wants. If I was still drinking, I would raise my glass to him.

On my walk this morning, I noticed a woman move into a house on the other side of the bay. I watched her possessions being unloaded. There were numerous canvases, indicating that she is either an artist or an accountant who has had a breakdown and taken up watercolours. She is attractive, a little older than me, and endearingly nervous in the way she hovered around the removal men as they hauled her life into its new home.

Tomorrow, I will take my walk again. I will post this letter, head out to the deserted village, return up the coast to Neist Point and stand there and decide, once and for all, if I am going to take the final step of the Big Quit.

And if I can't do it, then I will call on my new neighbour, say hello, and ask to borrow a mop and a bucket to clear up the caravan.

Yours,
A. Leavitt.

STEWART ENQUIRY

JOCK SCOT picks up the tale of Stewart Enquiry, the Idler's racing correspondent. Stewart has at last made it to Punchestown, and finds himself in the company of Mr Ronnie Wood and other high livers. Illustration by CHRIS WATSON

Stewart stood swaying gently, a pint of champagne in hand, and gazed out over the multitude of punters as the runners went to post for the second race, *The Ron Wood Fender Telecaster Challenge Trophy Steeplechase*. Ron had talked the chaps at Fender guitars into sponsoring the race and they had also donated one of their latest models as a raffle prize. Splendid stuff, very rock 'n'roll, very Ronnie. Stewart attempted to suppress a smug grin, his hurried selection of Helen's Nest in the opener had seemed strange, stupid even, but was in fact sentimental. A lass of that name had given him his first "proper" kiss, on the occasion of his eleventh birthday, so £50 to win it was. When Suicide Commission, the hot favourite, fell at the last, bringing down two other fancied runners, Stewart's sentimental selection was handed the race on a plate and jockey Brendan Powell booted his mount home in fine style, to Stewart's delighted disbelief and mad cheering.

Helen's starting price of 33-1 meant that he was already £1,700 up. He caressed the lovely wad in the left-hand pocket of his trouserings and slipped the nail of his pinkie under the elastic band which bound the notes and had a dual-realisation. One, that the wad wouldn't be there for very long, whatever happened, and secondly, he had the raging horn! The grin that threatened his usual urbane racecourse cool was aided and abetted by the growing effects of the five Es he had necked en-route to the course. He had come over all spongey, time to get a grip. He extinguished the grin with a long pull on his bevvy, lit up a Major and nodded his way from the balcony back into the box. People from Fender were attempting to mingle with Ron's guests. Off in one corner slouched the leather and leopardskin-clad figure of Keef, who had somehow acquired a black greyhound pup! He sat swigging from a bottle of Jack Daniel's as he fed the hound chipolatas from the buffet. Junior towered over them and waved to Stewart, indicating a freshly–rolled spliff and grinning as only a very–happy, very stoned Rastaman can. Stewart joined them and Keef informed him that he had purchased the whelp from the fabled tipster Turbo Tracey in the carpark where he was also vending religious artefacts, chocolate bars and apples and oranges!

Junior passed the reeking reefer, he was having the time of his life and had really hit it off with Keef. There was no sign of Shane. Stewart asked if the dog had a name yet. "Beezlebub," quoth Keef from behind his aviator shades. A bemused Stewart then collared Ron and asked him what he fancied in "his" race. The Rock Legend whispered out of the side of his mouth, "Squirrel In A Dress." Stewart spluttered on the spliff and consulted his racecard. Sure enough, there it was! Number seven, green and white quarters, gold cap, pilot of Danoli and Istabraq, Stewart's favourite jockey, was in semi-retirement, riding only in the occasional race. The fact he was on Squirrel In A Dress today was a trip in itself.

Ron raised his voice a semi-tone and, leaning lip-smackingly close to Stewart's shell-like, uttered the old gambler's mantra. "Get on it Stewart, fill yer boots!"

No more was said, there was no need.

Passing the lethal spliff to the tipping Rock God, Stewart left the box and headed for the betting ring. As he perused the bookies betting boards his eyes lit up, (sparkled rather, they were already bloodshot). Squirrel In A Dress was freely available at sevens and eight to one, nine in a place! He showed daylight to his slumbering wad and elbowed his way to Paddy Power's patch. Paddy shouted his usual greeting to Stewart, "Here comes lunch!" Stewart realised he was shaking and, swallowing hard, peeled off his winning wad and proffered it at Paddy. "£1,500 win about the Squirrel, number seven, and make sure you bootleg it." Paddy was currently driving a top of the range Mercedes which Stewart's heavy losses at Cheltenham, six weeks previously, had helped pay for. He studied Stewart for all of one and a half seconds before greedily shepherding the large denomination notes into the gaping satchel at his elbow. His clerk noted the bet and as he handed Stewart his ticket Paddy guffawed, "Tea, Dinner and Supper!" Our hero trousered the ticket and turned on his heels. Apart from his own personal bookmaker, Victor Chandler, who was also a close personal friend and confidante, Stewart could not find it in his heart actually to like bookmakers. The only time he could bear to be in their company was when they were handing him large sums of money. His last wife had nursed similar feelings about Stewart throughout the last two years of their violent, drunken sham of a marriage.

Stewart felt the need to stretch his legs and decided to walk down to the last fence while he still could and watch the race from there. Keeping an eye out for Shane he floated away from the Ring down towards the race course.

"£1,500 down the pan," was the thought which lurked at the back of his drug addled mind. He quickly flushed that negative vibe and struggled to regain some composure. The deed was done, the money was down, all was now in the hands of the Gods of Racing and those of Charlie Swan. As he neared the final fence the nags were beginning to go down to the start and he watched them with an expert eye. The confident favourite, Black Brando looked, much to his dismay, trained to the minute and had been laid out especially for the race. A magnificent animal, jet-black with three white socks and a large triangular star on his forehead. He fairly ate up the ground and the jockey had to take a sharp tug to prevent him from running away. Next down were the joint second favourites, Decent Flange and Dirty Old Farmer, who also looked like they would give their backers a run for their money. Stewart was beginning to doubt the veracity of Ronnie's information, but dismissed the thought on sighting Squirrel In A Dress. He really filled the eye, and he slowly cantered by. Jockey Charlie Swan recognised Stewart and pulled him up. With a toothy grin and a cheery "Hullo there Stewart! How's the Craic? Are you on?" Stewart admitted he had "A small interest." Whilst swelling with pride that his hero had stopped for a blether, Charlie asked after Shane's health and, saying he'd see them for a livener after racing, gave

Squirrel In A Dress a slap across the withers and was off down to the tape.

The runners were now all down at the start, a medium-sized field of ten, all of whom were in with a chance. The overnight rain had affected the going, it was now officially Good to Soft and this change was reflected in the betting. Black Brando was still attracting punters who were snapping up the last of the 5 –2. He acted on any surface, so the softer ground put him at no disadvantage. Also attracting good support were Dirty Old Farmer and Decent Flange, now joint second favourites at 4–1. Dirty Old Farmer had won well over course and distance just three weeks previously, while Decent Flange was a running-on third in the same race, after being caught flat-footed at the start. Word had gone round about Squirrel In A Dress as the Wood/Fender party got on and the bookies were shortening the price accordingly. It was now impossible to find any price longer than 5–1. Stewart had a last look round for Shane as he heard the commentator say, "They're under starter's orders, and they're off!"

He reached the fence just as the field were approaching. The 16–1 shot Beyond The Pale had taken a keen hold and sent the birch flying as he put in a short one. The field was well grouped, with no more than ten lengths between the leader and the backmarker whose green and white colours and gold cap caught Stewart's eye. With an audible sigh he raised his binos to his bloodshot eyes and brought the runners into focus as they turned left after the stands and headed out into the country. ◉

GET YOUR LOVELY BACK ISSUES HERE

Go to idler.co.uk, or make a cheque out to "The Idler" and send to: The Idler, Studio 20, 24-28A Hatton Wall, London EC1N 8JH. £1 per item P£P

1: August '93
SOLD OUT
Dr Johnson

2: Nov~Dec '93
SOLD OUT
Homer & Will Self

3: Jan~Feb '94
£5.00
Bertrand Russell

4: April~May '94
SOLD OUT
Kurt & Matt Black

5: July~Aug '94
SOLD OUT
Douglas Coupland

6: Sept~Oct '94
SOLD OUT
Easy Listening

7: Dec~Jan '95
SOLD OUT
Sleep

8: Feb~Mar '95
SOLD OUT
Jeffrey Bernard

9: May~June '95
SOLD OUT
Suzanne Moore

10: July~Aug '95
SOLD OUT
Damien Hirst

11: Sept~Oct '95
£4.00
Keith Allen

12: Nov~Dec '95
£4.00
Bruce Robinson

13: Jan~Feb '96
SOLD OUT
Stan Lee

14: Mar~Apr '96
£4.00
Bruce Reynolds

15: May~Jun '96
SOLD OUT
Hashish Killers

16: Aug~Sept '96
SOLD OUT
John Michel

17: Nov~Dec '96
£4.00
John Cooper Clarke

18: Spring '97
£4.00
Thomas Pynchon

19: Summer '97
£3.00
Psychogeography

20: Winter '97
£3.00
Howard Marks

21: Feb~March '98
£3.00
The Gambler

22: April~May '98
SOLD OUT
Alan Moore

23: June~July '98
SOLD OUT
Summer Special

24: Aug~Sep '98
SOLD OUT
Krazy Golf

25: Winter '99
£10.00
Man's Ruin:
Louis Theroux,
Howard Marks,
Pirates
(320 page
book format)

26: Summer '00
£10.00
Paradise:
Reggie Perrin,
Jeremy Dyson,
Uri Geller
(290 page
book format)

WORLD OF PAIN
SPILL THE BLOOD
Story by JAMES JARVIS Poem by HANNAH DYSON

THE OLD ONE SOARS O'ER CITY SKY
WHEN HAIRY MUTT-MAN HE DOTH SPY.
SUCH FEARSOME WRATH THIS FOP INSPIRES,
THE OLD ONE IS CONSUMED BY FIRES.

TRANSFORMED IS HE TO WINSOME CAT
THE OLD ONE PROFFERS MUTT A PAT.
FOOLISH MUTT RESPONDS IN KIND;
BIG MISTAKE HE DULY FINDS.

RISING UP WITH MIGHTY PAWS
DUMB-MUTT'S FACE HE MADLY CLAWS.
A FIGHT ENSUES TWIXT MUTT AND CAT,
EQUALLY MATCHED IN HAIR AND FAT.

"WHAT PASSES HERE?" A POLICEMAN CALLS
AS SCRATCHED AND BLEEDING POOR MUTT FALLS.
"ABUSE OF ANIMALS! YOU MILKSOP FOOL!
"HOW COULD YOU BE SO GOD-DAMN CRUEL?"

"LISTEN MAN, I'M NOT TO BLAME.
"THAT CRAZY CAT HAS GONE INSANE."
BUT GOD AND COP EXCHANGE A LOOK:
AND HEATHEN FOOL IS BROUGHT TO BOOK

STILL LIVES

By KARL ABRAMOVIC

La Fée
ABSINTHE

**Distilled in France
from wormwood
and other aromatic herbs**

ORDER ONLINE:
eAbsinthe.com

THE DIRECTORS'
ANNUAL GENERAL MEETING ABOARD
THE LA FÉE ABSINTHE BUS

THE IDIOCY OF IDEAS

An excerpt from a novel in progress
by BILLY CHILDISH. Illustrations by JOHN MACHON

What's wrong with me being ignorant? We at Walderslade Secondary School for Boys pride ourselves on our ignorance! And anyway, if us Walderslade kids weren't ignorant then some other poor sap would have to be, and, if you think about it that wouldn't change things one single jot, would it? No, it's best that life stays exactly as it is, the way that God himself intended, with us Walderslade kids getting it in the neck from above and below. In short – carrying the can for all our parents and lousy teachers' inadequacies.

Our masters grimace down at us through the stubs of their yellowing teeth and can scarcely conceal their contempt for us. They pace up and down the empty corridors, grinding their back molers, making sure that none of us boys has secretly sneaked in here before morning bell has rung, to have a crafty fag, or to warm our skinny arses on these clapped out old radiators of theirs. Apparently, the fresh air is just what we need – then why do we have to come to school? Actually, they grind their gnashers together so hard it sounds as if they are eating their own teeth!

Mister Shawd gets down on his hands and knees and peers under the desks looking for hidden children. As he stands and straightens up, his steel kneecap cracks back into place like a pistol shot. It reverberates around the empty classroom and he marches back out into the corridor. You think that he has gone, but then sneakily he sticks his head back round the door and sniffs at the air like a horrible rat, tip-toes up to the store cupboard, throws the door back and catches Wallace in there having a snout.

We in the B stream like to think of ourselves as the bane of our teacher's lives.

Although it is important that we remain forever ignorant, mediocre and unimpressive, we have heard rumours about some pupils in this school, (notably in the "A" stream) who are clever and will apparently be allowed to sit their exams and make something of themselves in life. But we don't meet or talk with them, they are something like a myth that nobody is sure even really exists.

It is in deference to these chosen few that we step aside, doff our caps and generally make nuisances of ourselves, thereby creating room for the more intelligent and deserving pupils amongst us to fulfil their glorious destinies!

I stand freezing in the centre of the tarmac playground. There is nothing very friendly about forcing children to go to school. I have been sent here on account of my laziness and backwardness and it's true to say that I can't read or write and everybody agrees that I am disruptive and have some rough corners that urgently need smashing off! Yes, I can assure you that I didn't come here of my own free will, none of us kids do, though our instructors assure us that we are here for our sole benefit and certainly not their's – which is all hogwash!

During the week my father lives in London, or somewhere, and is an Edwardian spook. He has another woman he lives with called Anne, who my mother mysteriously refers to as "his mistress".

Although my father has supposedly left the family home, he still comes home some weekends to boss us about. He tells me that I am not to play with the kids from over the council estate as they are a bunch of bloody hooligans! In turn the kids over the council estate refer to him as "creeping Jesus", because in the summer he used to float mysteriously around the garden in his beard and sandals. Most times he doesn't show up at all, which, all in all I think is for the best.

Even when my father is in London he keeps us on our toes by making violent telephone calls to my mother in the middle of the night, threatening to turn up on one of his surprise visits. In this way we are constantly reminded not to step out of line and that we are still very much his property! It is through his caustic remarks and indelible presence that my Mother keeps the house spotlessly clean and is trying to force me to learn to speak the Queen's English. When my father does come home I am drilled for my grammatical inadequacies, told to stand up straight, tidy myself up, to not run around like a bloody savage and for Christ's sake, to talk bloody properly!

"You've been hanging around those damned yobs again, haven't you?"

I look at him. "Do you mean those bloody hooligans?" I correct him, and I have to conceal my naughty smile. Apparently, he can tell who I've been playing with just by my accent.

"Where on earth did you learn such an uncouth tongue!?"

"It's Chathamese," I explain.

"Chathamese? – There's no such damn language!"

Although I am obedient by nature I have to turn and walk away. My father calls me back and tells me that I slump my shoulders, my teeth are appalling, I need a haircut, I should clean out my ears, I am bloody thick, my feet are too large and that I wear out my shoes and scuff them because I am arrogant! Also, I should pick my feet up properly!

Really, to start trying to teach me manners, respect and how to talk properly now, is a little bit late. Anyway, our parents and teachers don't have any manners and all of us kids at Walderslade school already talk like a bunch of dockyard chavies. Which is handy 'cos that's just where our destiny lies, the dockyard or the dole queue.

I, for one, will aim for the dole queue with all my heart! I see myself as less than everybody else, yet somehow superior. People tell me that it's my face that is going to get my head smashed in for me, because it is petulant and sarcastic. It would seem that I have already failed in life.

In my bedside cabinet I have some of my father's stolen pornography books. Most mornings I like to lay in my warm pit playing with myself until the last possible second. My mother even brings me a cup of tea in bed, but I still refuse to get up, and instead hide under the sheets and let her stupid tea go cold. Then, from

IT SEEMS THAT I AM GETTING MORE AND MORE VILE AND DISAGREEABLE BY THE SECOND. IN FACT, I HAVE NEVER FELT SO SPITEFUL IN MY ENTIRE LIFE

the school field I hear Mister Shawd blowing his whistle and I'm happy to know that I'm late for school yet again. Then my mother comes in and shouts at me to get dressed. Quickly, I scurry out  from under the covers, step into my unpolished shoes and am ready for school. The quickest way to school is illegal and I have been put on detention for my flagrant and repeated disregard for authority!

Me, and my worthless companions stare forlornly out through the rain-flecked windows at the distant road which lies beyond the perimeter fence. There is a continuous stream of cars going past and a lady with thick, elephantine legs is putting up her yellow umbrella.

It seems that I am getting more and more vile and disagreeable by the second. In fact, I have never felt so spiteful in my entire life. I can positively feel the hatred oozing out through the pores of my skin and crawling over the backs of my hands like poisonous insects. I look up to the blackboard and the clicking clock. It seems that I can't even stand to see a perfectly ordinary woman putting up a yellow umbrella without foaming at the mouth.

My mother says that I am sarcastic and argumentative, "you're just like your bloody father!" Mister Shawd says that I am a prize specimen, then he beats me.

Every day at least a dozen of us boys are singled out for correction at his hands. No act of cruelty is a surprise to us anymore, already we have been humiliated in every possible way and actually believe that we deserve to be beaten. Any of us who are chosen for punishment, whether it be for our disobedient natures, or perhaps merely at the whim of one of our glorious masters, refuses to cry out in pain, and are even a little proud as our heroes' names are entered into the punishment book.

One of the funnier aspects of our situation is that if we are indeed rejects, then what does that make our teachers? This thought cheers me up no end. Really, I have to stop myself chuckling sometimes at their "so called" intelligence. It seems that we are going to be made to pay not only for our own faults but also for those of our parents and our teachers.

All of our masters, with the exception of Miss Heart, the assistant music teacher, has a special "little friend", either a vicious bamboo, or perhaps an especially ancient and pliable slipper, which is kept within easy reach, on their desk in front of them, or sometimes, if they are a little more shy, they keep he, or she, (for all of their weapons have sexes,) in the drawer, or perhaps in the store cupboard, which often doubles as a punishment room.

When I first came to this glorious school, I stood timid and alone in the cold, harsh playground all morning break, toeing the busted tarmac. The poor weeds pushed up into the cold September sunlight, the skin of my cheeks smarted and I put my hands numbly in my short pockets. My blue blazer, which my mother had bought for me two sizes too big as an economy measure, drew a gang of elder boys round me. They mocked me for being a rich kid. One of them asked me where my mummy was and then another one gave me a dead leg.

When I picked myself up from the tarmac they had gone. I looked down at my bruised, goose-fleshed leg, trying to comfort myself against the cold. There was already a tear in my new blazer and lots of little pieces of black grit stuck into my bare, white knees.

What I really needed was to take a shit. I walked over to the outside bogs. A little river of piss trickled out through the open door and I could hear the cat calls of the fifth formers echoing out into the playground. The entrance to the bogs was surrounded by fourth years who gobbed on any of us who dared pass between them. As I entered the place, the stench of urine and disinfectant stung my eyes. I peered into the piss-stinking bogs, trying to find one with paper and where somebody hadn't shitted all over the seat. There is only hard-skinny bog-paper in those toilets, that skids off your arse and the big boys will swing between the cubicles like monkeys and kick the bog door in whilst I'm sat here hovering over the busted seat and expose my small, nude penis.

After school we saw Mister Goldsmith, the deputy head master, being chased around the front field by a fifth year waving a flick knife. Mister Goldsmith is old and slow and could only just manage to trot along in front of the boy like a tired old donkey. A large crowd gathered and we all cheered as Mister Goldsmith did several laps of the silver birch tree.

Every Tuesday we have Biology with Mister Swain and he has to beat me across the buttocks with his rubber slipper on account of my cheekiness. Mister Swain is small with a rat-like moustache and a Canadian accent. He thinks that all of us pupils are pathetically stupid with me being the king of the pile! On the other hand he believes himself to be incredibly smart, which is why he is our teacher.

Who knows if he gets a "hard-on" as he beats us poor wretches in his care?

Mister Shawd, on the other hand, has no need of such pathetic means of correction as canes or slippers, because he is a military man and has a military knee-cap, made of British steel! Which is his main weapon against us children.

When Shawd is standing next to you (and in truth he really is nothing but a bald midget) with his toad-like tongue whispering threateningly into your schoolboy ear, then you know for sure that you are about to be shown the error of your childish ways. Yes, when Shawd starts making love to you like that, it means that very soon, in the not too distant future, he is going to bring his steel knee-cap smashing up into your school-boy thigh and deliver one of his famous dead-legs... Whereupon the happy recipient falls howling to the feet of his Lord and Master.

"Am I hurting you boy?" he whispers.

"No, sir!" I reply most truthfully and honestly.

"Well I should be boy, because I'm standing on your hair!"

This is one of Shawd's little jokes, and really, in some ways, I think that I am supposed to laugh, but I'm not sure which will bring me the most pain; to smile with him or to stand rigidly to attention, in the military fashion, as he has taught us all to do.

"Do you think I am hurting the boy?" Shawd turns to Dog-jaw. Dog-jaw, who stands head and shoulders above Shawd, is his constant shadow. He smiles down at me from his big benevolent face and shakes his jowls at me.

"Aowe down't know wroughtly, boot Aowe fink der lad's in nead off un hair coot!" Dog-jaw has two pink plastic hearing aids wired to his huge dome-like head and speaks like a barking dog.

Shawd smiles with anticipation and licks his thin lips.

"AOWE DOWN'T KNOW WROUGHTLY, BOOT AOWE FINK DER LAD'S IN NEAD OFF UN HAIR COOT!" DOG-JAW HAS TWO PINK PLASTIC HEARING AIDS WIRED TO HIS HUGE DOME-LIKE HEAD AND SPEAKS LIKE A BARKING DOG

The point is, that I have long beautiful blond hair and the exquisite face of a cherub and Shawd hates my beauty. I glance into his hard little eyes and smile hopefully, looking for some warmth and compassion that might be lying there and thereby spare myself the pain of his steel knee-cap crashing up into the muscle of my left thigh. But there is none. I bite my tongue and go down.

"Did I tell you that you could lie about on the floor, Loveday? What do you think this is, a holiday camp?" He turns to Dog-jaw and he delivers another one of his hilarious jokes. Dog-jaw smiles bemused so Shawd turns instead to the class. The class goes boggle-eyed with laughter, everybody busting a gut to show their appreciation. And even I have to laugh, lying there on the floor, my feet kicking on the tarmac, my face contorted by the terrible sharp throbbing that runs burning up and down my paralysed leg.

"Say 'thankyou', Loveday."

Shawd leans his little face over mine and I wriggle in the grit grimacing.

"Fuck you, sir!" I say. I whisper it through clenched teeth, my eyes smarting on account of the cold. But

he hasn't heard me properly, I say my naughty word in secret.

"Speak up Loveday, so everybody can hear you." And he licks his thin lips again. "Say 'thank you very much, my dear teacher, Sir!' Say 'thank you' Loveday."

I try to get up, but he easily pushes me back down onto the cold ground before I can find my balance.

"You want to decide whether you want to get up or lie down Loveday!" he shouts triumphantly, which hands everybody a good laugh. And they stand around puffing out their stupid cheeks, and they're grateful for it, because in truth, they love Shawd and his brutality. Then he suddenly turns on them.

"So you think that Master Loveday is a comedian?" Shawd scans the little circle of youthful faces. "Well do you? Is Master Loveday an endless source of amusement for you? Would anyone like to come out here and swap places with him?" I grimace up at them from my resting place at Shawd's feet.

A hush falls over the little group and they look demurely down at their scuffed shoes. Shawd holds them with his sharp eyes and re-pastes the little strands of hair that flap insolently in the icy wind above his bald head. He glues it back in place as if he's a small kitten fixing its whiskers. It really is comical to see that idiot trying to arrange his pathetic strands in that defiant wind. Finally he slaps them down with a thick lick of his disgusting spit and defies us all once more with his rodent-like eyes.

I climb from the tarmac and hobble over to stand with my classmates. I turn and look back at him, really quite small, even compared to a school boy. And Dog-jaw stood behind him, like a big stupid shadow. It is comforting and reassuring for us to be reminded of our station in life by our masters, and to know that we should expect nothing from the future other than a good duffing.

No, we students at the Walderslade Secondary School for Boys are noted for our ignorance, it is handed down to us in hushed and reverent tones, we learn it off by heart from the blackboard and are only allowed to come to this school on the condition that we promise, most solemnly, to remain ignorant and to never amount to anything in this world, so help us God. ☻

THE FINAL RAKE

The last instalment in the troubled tale of Clive D'Arcy
By ANDREW COPEMAN. Illustration by RAYMOND WEEKES

This view. This view from this window. Ah, still it soothes me. Street lights bleed Lucozade over the stricken neon facades of clip joints, lap dancing clubs and mini-cab ranks. The pedestrian flotsam and jetsam take their unswerving course. The corners shield then disclose bent creatures stumbling deep nightward; wrecked ramblers searching for whatever it is that drives them on. Sirens detonate. Plastic moons fluctuate. Good sense and logic dissipate.

Christine's downstairs. Hard at work, bless her. This room, our room, just partly functions without her. Check the Rolex. Forty five mins till she knocks off and we can sleep, safe in each others arms. I smile, so content.

So content.

Even the crusty slug trail of dried toothpaste over the crotch of my C&A jogging bottoms doesn't concern me. Scratch my armpits through the white acrylic of my England shirt. Beckham of course. Style still matters in the world of Clive.

Out on the street below, someone gets flattened. Like me.

When I met she. Those many months ago...

I had reached an impasse of snowdrift proportions. Nothing sparked me any more. A perfect Savile Row double breasted blazer, hung off my carcass like a cheap kagool. A Thomas Pink blue double-cuffed gingham, offset with a silk Pierre Cardin tie, was a big "So What?" Even my alcoholic refuge The Throat and Cancer had lost what little sordid appeal it had once held.

Hobson, the Landlord, although thick as the proverbial two-short, spotted the change. "Oi, D'Arcy," he scowled at me whilst buffing a pump. "You don't 'alf look moody son. What's up?" How could I explain inner torment to a cretin who'd think it was the name of a nag running in the 4:15 at Chepstow? "Not that I give a flying fuck D'Arcy. It's just that long faces make for a shit atmosphere; a shit atmosphere makes for an empty pub; an empty pub means I ain't making no smash; I ain't making no smash means I get the right hump; I get the right hump, I go get me sawn-off and do a Paki post-office; I do a Paki post-office,

I get nicked; I get nicked I get sent down and have to spend X amount of years surrounded by nonces 'n' assorted filth; I get out, I kill you. See? So, it's worth your fuckin' while to cheer up, you miserable cunt. 'Ere, have a snifter on me." The Landlord places a triple Glenfiddich and soda on the bar.

"Take it" he snarls. I do. I take eight more.

Hobson's right. I cheer up. I cheer up so bloody much that I giggle insanely, fall into walls and offer Werewolf, Hells Angel, founder, leader and only member of the "Army of One" local Chapter to a bout of arm wrestling. This is an individual who throttles rotweillers for relaxation. He dislocates my shoulder. I'm too ruddy anaesthetised to feel it as he matter of factly pops the joint back into place. I buy him a drink. I buy everyone a drink. Happy Jelly the Exploding Clown shows the assembled his new scar, a milky river snaking up from the V of his crotch to his chin. "Semtex'll do it! Ha, ha, ha, ha, haaaa!!!" he screams. Royston at the jukebox drops "My Generation". "Charlie Richardson." He toasts. Happy starts dancing like an epileptic. Werewolf decks him. As the song's coda implodes, feedback, crashing drums and Daltrey sneering, The Throat and Cancer kicks off. In a blink of a red eye, Happy lights a cherry bomb which he shoves in the

Angel's ZZ Top beard. For three seconds his facial hair smoulders.

Everyone hits the floor.

Werewolf's chin explodes.

Enraged, the plasma-dripping biker puts a table through the nearest window. Suddenly, we're Saturday night Dodge City. I crawl to the exit as the regulars take our local apart.

I sleep in the park.

Dishevelled and distraught I awaken. It is late. I walk.

Time has been reprogrammed by Professor Stephen Hawking, tripped out on serious DMT. Dusk is dripping over the trees, though it feels like 11am. Drains whisper, roads quiver and faces appear from the shadows. I'm disintegrating. I need to anchor, to find a safe harbour.

The caf is tucked between an alleyway and a used car lot. Like Edward Hopper has just signed Nighthawks and lobbed the canvas to earth. Christ, I need a cup of Earl Grey. Slip inside.

Oldsters tuck into all day breakfasts, a crew of petty louts sip orange Tangos and check their mobiles incessantly. I scratch to the counter and order. Take the tea (they don't serve Twinings, but I feel it would be churlish to complain) and collapse at a window table far-side.

It is welling up inside me. Grief, indefinable yet wholly REAL. I should cry, weep like a lost child but I can't physically find the strength. Sip the cuppa. Tart.

"Hey. Mind if I join you?" The voice is a nightingale's. At this precise moment, it is the sweetest thing I have ever heard. "I–" before completion, she is sitting opposite me and my life will never be the same. "Christine" she offers her hand.

"Clive" I croak, reciprocating.

"Saw you. Look really quite forlorn. Snap." She is five foot nine. Her red hair cascades to her shoulders like a young Jane Fonda. That's a lot of Little Red Riding Hood. The tight black collared shirt is see-through and snug. Her tits strain the buttons. "Cigarette?" She proffers a nail. I decline.

"Don't." I reply.

"Go on." She shrugs, inserting a filter between slick pink lips. "You look like you could use it." What the hell. She sparks it. I inhale deeply, exhale and feel the surge. "This isn't all bad." I stare at the bonfire tip. "What do you do Clive?" Of all the questions to ask. My first fag, the girl of my wet dreams and a crisis of self.

"I am Clive D'Arcy, Dashing Young Blade About Town." She pisses herself.

"Sorry," she convulses, hand over her grin, "But that is the biggest load of crap I've ever heard." She drags. "Seriously though. A handsome chap like you has got to be successful. Own firm? Broker?" She leans tantalisingly close. "Gangster?" She arches a cute eyebrow. I am now in possession of a raging hard-on.

"I'm… I'm…" I can't find the words. It all sounds so false. "I'm just Clive D'Arcy." My reflection in the tea-cup is speckled with limescale. She touches my cheek.

"Do you want to spend the night?" I snap erect like I've just had 50,000 volts passed through me.

"Pardon?" I splutter.

"No strings. I need someone to hold me. That's all. We both need someone to hold." My fag is a stump of ash. "Yes." I respond. Christine tosses her hair and winks.

"C'mon. S'not far."

Her flat is spacious and clean. Stripped floorboards and Philippe Starck in the en-suite kitchenette. She has taste. And cash. Perhaps there is a supreme being after all. "Take the sofa" Christine motions to a Conran in a corner. I sit. "Toilet," she purrs. I track her beautiful rump in the short black skirt. The brown knee-high boots, the sheer glisten of her black pantyhose. Out of sight. I unzip my fly and pet the python. Flush. I stuff my weapon back and re-zip. Attempt to appear composed. "So," she sits close, "Can I…" I read her thoughts.

Our tongues fence, feint, counter-feint, parry, riposte. She caresses my chest. I unbutton her, feeling the swell of her cleavage. She moans. I nip her earlobes, neck. She gasps, tugging my strides.

I'm free.

"Oooohhh…" she sighs. Her tongue traces my throbbing shaft, circumnavigates my head and flicks my Jap's Eye. "Please…" I flip, grabbing a fistful of her locks. She consumes. Adrift on a sea of ecstasy, my dinghy has sprung a leak. My nuts tighten. I'm bailing like Billy-O to no avail.

"I'm coming. Oh ruddy shit, I'm coming!" She sucks like a famished ant-eater and I explode; a torrent of hot bollock bouill-abaisse deep in her throat. She swallows it all. "Yum, yum," she pants, surfacing.

"Fuck!" I yell, throwing her back on the sofa, tearing her shirt asunder and munching those pert mammaries. My hands stroke her legs. I'm aflame. A blue haze descends. Tonight, Matthew, I will be Emperor Nero. Off comes the skirt. Tank the pantyhose, advance downtown. Her knickers soon follow. I freeze. Staring at me is a diminutive meat and two veg. Christine is gripping my head.

"Clive," she pleads, "Oh, Clive." Her/His knackers are two Tic-Tacs, cock the size of a chippolata. Erect. It feels like a bison has climbed into my gob and died. I suck.

I suck and it's incredible. My premier erotic moment. Christine doesn't last long. Within two minutes I'm receiving a mouthful of cuckoo spit. Gulp. Not unpleasant; tastes like pecan nuts. Been

and gone and done it now. Christine proffers me her behind. "Fuck me Clive. Fuck my tight arse!" I nudge my knob to her puckered brown opening and press. She screams. I sink it in to the hilt. Burning fingers grip the old fella and I pump like a madman. I'm splitting this randy bitch in two. She's tossing her petite piss-whip in time. I maul her breasts, distend her nipples. She wails like a banshee and I unload my genetic payload, right up her colon.

Plane crash.

Reeking of sweat and sex , we uncouple and fall to the floor. Sweet coma follows.

The mourning after. I wear a funeral face. Why? I am blissfully happy, yet I know that I shall never see Christine again. She serves coffee and croissants. Fresh slices of orange sprinkled with demerera. We showered together. I held her tight and confessed my love. She cried into my shoulder. Her hair is still wet. I stroke a damp fringe frond from her eyes. We talk, we talk about nonsense mainly. She snuggles up close and I plant butterfly kisses on her temples. God, I just want to shoot the day and stay but I remember I have to sign on at three. Don't know where I am. Christine calls a cab and begs me to see her tonight. "You just try and stop me" I hiss, squeezing her butt. "Just try sweetie." We kiss wetly. She breaks away. "Got five minutes darling." She smirks. "In five Clive…" She unzips and eats me.

The Moldavia Towers Job Centre looks like fucking Disneyland. I'm whacked up on love drug and flying. Happy Jelly's in a wheelchair and neckbrace. I grab the malignant midget's chariot and waltz him about the floor a bit. "Go on Clive son!" he yells, like a tartrazined six year old, "I am cuntin' Ben Hur! Yesss!!!" We career past a flinty bitch in glasses and heels. Happy gooses her. She drops her clipboard. "Saveloy!" Happy growls. Unfortunately, Mustapha the security guard doesn't appreciate the finer points of gladiatorial combat. He stops the wheelchair with a size 11 steel cap in Happy's chest.

"Calm down," he monotones.

"Get your friggin' foot offa my chest camel shagga!" Happy windmills his arms. "I'm fuckin' veteran burke! I was blowin' meself up in fuckin' Burma Gangshows when you were floating in old man Achmed's cobblers!"

Mustafa raises his eyes. "Calm down," the security guard reiterates, brooking no alternative.

"C'mon Happy," I slap his shoulder. "Let's donate our autographs." I wheel him away.

"You're on my fuckin list Mustapha," the Exploding Clown rails, "Remember cuntin' Kuwait! Oh fuck…" He heaves and deposits a ton of puke on the scratchy green linoleum.

I arrive at Christine's just after

THE MOURNING AFTER. I WEAR A FUNERAL FACE. WHY? I AM BLISSFULLY HAPPY, YET I KNOW THAT I SHALL NEVER SEE CHRISTINE AGAIN. SHE SERVES COFFEE AND CROISSANTS

seven. She's prepared pasta and the Muscadet is chilled. The dress is Pam Hogg, the heels 'n' hose Agent Provocateur but the beauty is all her own. "Hello." She smiles and kisses. "My, my, Mr D'Arcy. Your breeches are exceedingly tight." That's something of an understatement. My cock is on a course of horse steroids and if the angel continues stroking me , Hi-Ho Silver's gonna charge through her prairie. "Away!!!"

"You can always re-heat it baby." I nod at our food in the Heals bowls on the Habitat table.

"Actually," she unzips me, "You're absolutely right."

"Come here," I demand, ripping her designer and releasing her orbs. Christine sucks sex breath over clenched teeth.

I go to work.

One week transpires. The two, three, four and a bit and it's exactly the same as the first time. I single handedly redefine the concept of smitten.

I-am-in-love.

And then Christine asks me to co-habit. Ordinarily this would be a massive no-no. I'm a bachelor, a player. I've got my rep to maintain. But this situation is different: She is part of me and I of she. So, I hire Russell; man with a white van and decamp Saturday.

Some say love is a hunger in your sinking need. I say love is a flower and you its only seed.

Christ it blossoms.

I actually begin to take pride taking household chores through to successful conclusions. Washing up does not phase me. On the contrary, I find it Zen-like in its soap bubble monotony. Me and Mr. Muscle develop a close bond and it seems that sometimes Sundays I am never happier than when I'm scraping windows with Christine painting her toenails on the couch.

I loosen up under her guidance: Out go the whistles, in come sweat shirts, T-shirts and short sleeves. Christine buys me a pair of Reeboks. I wear jogging bottoms habitually. Even cultivate stubble. The new Clive; scruffy yet wholly ecstatic.

Then fucking disaster.

I come back to our flat early evening after a day spent feeding ducks in the park and reading Ezra Pound stanzas. My darling is crying.

"What's wrong? Baby. Hey... Hey..." I hold her and rock my Princess gently.

"It's not you honey." Christine snorts, clears her throat. "It's my past Clive. A part of my past has caught up with me. And... And..." She breaks into tears. "I'm scared." I let her ride the convulsions. She calms. We kiss. I make her laugh. We share a fag or two. And then she tells me everything.

"I was a misguided girl in my youth. In and out of care homes, foster homes. Abused by my stepfather. I was a poor sad boy called Keith. But I knew, Clive, I fucking knew deep down inside that I was a woman. Then one day as a sweet little seventeen year old, I dolled myself up, stuffed bog roll down my black lace Gossard and me and my girlfriend Janice, a proper shitkicker from Glasgow, hit Soho. Janice was a clippy. She introduced me around. So, one thing to led another and very soon I was working Walkers Court. Bloody good too. Natural born hustler. I was pulling down a monkey a week. In time, I could afford operations. Harley Street. Painful, protracted but eventually I shed Keith and the Christine you see, the Christine who adores you, was born. Then I met Kit-Kat." Christine gulps, shakes her head, sparks up and continues. "Kit-Kat was a pimp. Five foot black dude. Sharp as a Stanley, who packed nine and a half inches. 'Fact, he got his nickname 'cos he used to shove four fingers up punters' pussies. He became my protector, my mentor, my lover. Then after years and years of graft, I got bored. Janice had the offer of a dungeon in High Street Ken. All through the Nash's. Anyway, she wanted me to manage it, to be the Mistress. I loved her and leapt at the chance. Wrong. Kit-Kat freaked. I told him where to get off. He decked me. I stumbled away but he found me. He and a mate Costa, a fucking Maltese shit cunt convicted nonce, abducted me, drove me out to Battersea Power Station and raped me for three days solid. Then Costa hamstrung me with a machete. I was found, near dead, by some kids on skateboards. Hospital. Recovery. Moved out of town. Still hustled but this time as an escort. Personal Services columns in local rags. Got this place. Dated nice guys occasionally. Then you fell from Heaven." Christine strokes my face. "Don't ask me how but the bastard's tracked me. He was waiting in his Beemer for me outside Tesco's. Followed me all the way home, all the way to our front door. Then split." Christine quakes, holds me close. "Jesus baby, what are we going to do?"

Times like this, I wish I was John Gotti.

I decide to stay at home the following day.

We both do.

It's like we're under some weird house-arrest: The psychic atmosphere is gangrenous and there's not a maggot in sight. Any motor that slows below is a potential threat. Our intercom buzzes. We ignore it. Finally, the night falls and we watch "It's a Wonderful Life" on DVD. This singularly fails to lift the depressive mood.

Fitful sleep.

Christine and I decide to venture out the next day. I clutch her hand and keep my eyes peeled. We have lunch. Table at the back, chairs against the wall with a clear view of the restaurant's open doors. Nothing. We start to relax. Snog. My angel seems happier than ever. I caress her red-hair. Encased in a force-field of love we wend our way flatward.

Then the wasp in the dry Martini.

We're about a block from home, arms entwined around each other's waists, laughing.

A screech of brakes. A black BMW mounts the pavement and blocks us. "Run!" Christine screams. I yank her close. "No. The time for running's over." I let her go. Square up.

What cockroaches from the car is a five foot excuse for humanity. I thought Happy Jelly was messed up. Imagine a Nigerian Kojak with Marty Feldman bug eyes and you're half way there. It's backed up by a black bomber jacketed Maltese bouncer wielding a bike chain.

"Alright cunt," the midget spits at Christine. "This your new wanker? Christ Costa," he turns to the Maltese who gobs. "Bitch don't 'alf cuntin' pick 'em." He laughs. "Name's Kit-Kat, prick. The no-womb sick freak might've informed you of me. Well, just to let you no-marks know, that tonight, I said tonight, you die." Kit-Kat stares straight into my eyes and licks his lips. "Bye-bye dickhead." The animals turn, return to their Krautmobile and tear away. Christine vomits and falls. I scoop her up in my arms and pull her home.

"Stop Christine. Stop." She's a whirling dervish, lobbing clothes into a suitcase. "Stop, stop!" she yells, choking on her tears, "Clive, you have no comprehension of what you're dealing with. We have to go. Clive, my darling, darling Clive, we have to go. Now!" I grab her. She drums her fists on my chest hysterically. "I know a little village in Cumbria. They'll never find us."

"Cumbria?"

"Um. Called 'Royston'. It's so..."

Eureka!

"Say that again babe." She blinks through saline. "Royston."

I kiss her. "You're a genius." I call a cab. "Keep everything locked. Don't answer the phone or the intercom. Sit tight. I'll be half an hour, tops."

I'm out the door.

"Clive..."

The Throat and Cancer looks like Colonel Kurtz's compound. I push through the saloon door which droops off its hinges. Hobson's behind the bar, strangely quiet. Probably because of the upper bodycast he's sporting.

Silence.

And then, oh sweet joy, The Small Faces' "Rollin' Over" comes kicking out from the CD jukebox. "Tune!" Oh dulcet tones!

I run to the sound. It's early, he's only been in here an hour I'd deduce. Nowhere near loaded. Blue blazer, Smedley, rings, ID bracelet, swept back platinum quiff, scar on face, bullet hole scar in the middle of left hand. Hamlet, large vodka and tonic, no lemon, plenty of ice. "Royston!" I yell. He stares at me. "Fuckin' 'ell D'Arcy. You scared the shit out of me. I've got a poxy heart condition remember. Oy!"

"Listen Sir, I really need your help."

Royston sips. "You all right son?"

I shake my head and give him the story. Royston finishes his drink and reaches for his Nokia. " Solly? Roy. Listen up. Dezzy about? What? Yeah, yeah, okay. Chap in a spot of bother. Got a stain that needs removing. Pick us up in ten. The boozer. Yes come heavy. All right, all right. Shalom me son." He puts the mobile away. "Pleasure D'Arcy." I fall onto his shoulder sobbing. He pats the back of my head. The Litter's apocalyptic version of "I'm a Man" detonates.

We're outside the flat; side

street. Jag. Royston and Solly up front. Dezzy smoking next to me. "Get out, D'Arcy and wait." Royston gives me the thumbs up. I exit and cross the road.

Christine knows not to come down. It's all been explained. She is packed and waiting. The sky is darkening, street lights trip sodium and I am close to shitting my pants. What if Royston and the boys are too slow? What if I'm caught off guard; BANG! Dead to rights? What if Kit-Kat and Costa are too much to contain? What if... Forget it.

Don't even have time to light my cigarette.

The black BMW piles round a corner and pulls up alongside.

I can't swallow. Doors click.

Kit-Kat, wearing a dwarfy bespoke and black Kangol pork pie hat, approaches. Costa backs him. The Maltese wields a steel baseball bat. "In exactly ten seconds, you sorry piece of shit, you will cease to exist." Kit-Kat grins and points at the flat. " Now, as for fuck-face above, well..." the evil midget nods at Costa, "My man's got a real bull's cock on 'im and a taste for blood." The Maltese swings his club and blows me a kiss. "End of." Kit-Kat sweeps a hand over his face.

Shit.

It sounds like an explosion at a stock-car track. Royston's motor ploughs straight in to the BMW, crumpling its side. The following does not, contrary to popular mis-conception, happen in slow-motion. Neither is it real time. It's all pixelated; fast motion, like a bad Benny Hill sketch.

Kit-Kat is frozen to the spot.

Costa charges.

Royston sidesteps the swing and spiked knuckle duster on fist, takes out the lug's temple.

Kill shot.

The Maltese collapses. Solly picks him up, tosses him onto the mashed bonnet and using a hammer, proceeds to make dog food of the guy's face.

Dezzy leaps at Kit-Kat. The black midget's too stunned to dodge. They crash to the floor. Dezzy yanks off Kit-Kat's Kangol and frisbees it into the road. He smashes Kit-Kat's face repeatedly into the pavement. Royston wades in now, kicking the shit out of Kit-Kat's kidneys. "Up!" yells Royston. Dezzy grabs the collar and hauls the black midget vertical. Royston eyeballs the destroyed visage.

He clicks his fingers. "Cut 'im."

In one clean, precise movement, Dezzy produces a cut-throat razor and slices. The jugular blood explodes. It arcs high and fast and hits me square on the shoulder. I black out.

Come to in a different flat. Night. Street noise. Lots of. Neon pastes the walls. I'm wearing a shell suit. Christine appears. "Hey. We're safe. In Soho." She kneels and kisses me.

And I know we are. ◉

THE DOWN BEAT

A story by STEWART HOME
Illustration by WOODROW PHOENIX

I'd made a few records and enjoyed a small reputation. No chart hits you understand, I am a musician's musician. My modest success was enough to enable me to dine out on my reputation. I'd been to enough fancy restaurants to know that good service was more expensive than good food. The service at Granita's was acceptable, the menu a little restricted. The interior showed more restraint than one finds in a Conran diner. I am rather too fond of damning with faint praise. Typical, of course, that Granita's was the New Labour eatery, since its wine and whisky selection left more than a little to be desired. However, the puddings were superb, an English obsession. I've always enjoyed flirting over spotted dick and custard.

The girl, I shall call her a girl since she was a few years younger than me, had once been a supermodel but the pressures of fame had led to her hitting the bottle. Leslie hadn't entirely lost her looks but I could see that more than a visit to a health farm was required if she wished to resume her old line of work. Still, there was a seedy glamour about the old girl and she'd managed to maintain a friendship with our host – who, incidentally, was celebrating a successful comeback to the pop scene. Brenda was better known by her stage name Electra, but close friends called her Brenda. Electra's current boyfriend sat beside her.

I CAME AFTER ABOUT TWO MINUTES, NOT WORRYING IN THE LEAST ABOUT THE OLD GIRL, SINCE SHE WAS STILL TOO DRUNK TO HAVE AN ORGASM

Brenda's boyfriends had an identikit quality -- short, bland, fashionably dressed, disposable – they were replaced with insipid regularity each spring. Brenda's manager Stan, and Leslie's friend Susan, made up the rest of our party.

Leslie and Stan had a lot in common, ranging from drink problems to resentment about being perceived as uncreative. All I shared with Stan was a desire to get my end away. Susan was out of the running, she was too bookish. Brenda was spoken for. This left Leslie, who was drunk. Stan didn't stand a chance. I caught the former supermodel glaring at his dirty finger nails. These would have disadvantaged him even if he'd dressed down, but Stan had the effrontery to sport a white suit and black open-necked shirt. There were standards of cleanliness I thought he sometimes missed. However, that evening I only declared to him that he never missed an opportunity for kindness. It would have been impolite to mention to Electra that she was foolish to give twenty percent of her earnings to a man who was incapable of negotiating his way out of a paper bag. Given this and the fact that Brenda couldn't carry a tune in a bucket, she'd done remarkably well to have a number one single five years on from her last hit record. I put it down to the marketing skill of her label – Verging Records. I should perhaps mention that Susan's sister Bevin was head of A & R at this august company.

Having finished my pudding, there was almost rapture in hearing Leslie propose that I might like to go back to her place for coffee. I was sober enough to realise that Leslie had been speaking figuratively when she uncorked a bottle of Chianti and poured two glasses of wine. I was seated on a sofa in Leslie's cosy Islington flat. There were two tiny rooms, and off them a kitchenette, toilet and shower, but no bath. Being drunk made Leslie argumentative and after nearly an hour of strained conversation I rather hoped she would pass out. Having returned from the kitchenette with a freshly opened bottle of wine, Leslie seemed in a fair way to oblige me; after a grim rally she suddenly collapsed on the sofa. I walked through to the bedroom and lay down. I was woken by Leslie some time later. She'd removed her own clothes and was in the process of dislodging mine. Once I was naked, Leslie lay back like a beached whale and I fucked her. I came after about two minutes, not worrying in the least about the old girl, since she was still too drunk to have an orgasm.

"You know about Susan," Leslie

said in an alcoholic `haze after I'd rolled off her. "We went to school together."

"Why, what do I ever find Susan but awfully clever?" I replied breezily.

"Well, what's that but silly? What on earth does awfully clever mean? She's having an affair with Maurice London."

"Maurice London, never? He's been born again. If news of an affair reached the papers it would ruin his career. A committed Christian with a string of gospel hits doesn't keep a mistress – especially if, as in Maurice's case, he claims to be celibate."

Leslie didn't reply. She was snoring drunkenly. I didn't have a lot of time for Maurice London. He sang like a drowned kitten suffering from the effects of rigor mortis. However, an inability to sing had never harmed any other pop star's career and Verging Records had done a good job of building London's fan base through promotional appearances at

bucolic churches and on cable television. Maurice was a reformed career criminal who'd done time for both pimping and drug dealing. His Christian revivalism shifted units even if his voice left much to be desired. London getting his end away with the sister of a top executive at his record company? It sounded unlikely but I decided to sleep on it. I didn't get to doze for long. Leslie woke me a couple of hours later and this time I made sure that her livelier desire didn't remain in ignorance of the peculiar homage I was wont to pay women tormented by carnal lusts.

After we'd both come, a simultaneous orgasm, Leslie was determined that I should find out at last how clever she was. To ensure the fog of obscurity surrounding her cerebral accomplishments was dispelled once and for all, she bent my ear for several hours. Leslie told me about growing up in Eltham in south-east London. About the scholarship she'd won to a private school, strangely failing to mention it was a sports scholarship – my brother Kevin, who is an expert on burnt out B-list celebrities, filled in this missing detail. About her friendship with Susan. About Susan and Maurice London. Each of these anecdotes was interlaced with Leslie's constant refrain – that she was very intelligent and nobody ever took her seriously because she'd once been a model.

While such candour is often a mistake in a man, it can be a felicity in a woman but unfortunately probity wasn't alluring on Leslie's

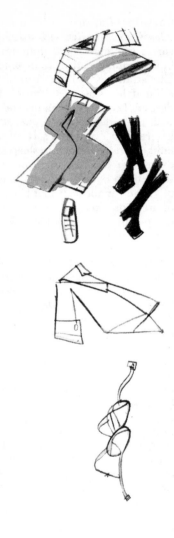

part. Rather than resembling a portmanteau, her personality was a simple dualism conjured up on the flat surface of a mirror. Sober, Leslie was shy and submissive. Drunk, she was self-righteous and passive-aggressive. I had on my tongue's end, for my own part, a phrase or two about the right word at the right time; but later on I was glad not to have spoken, for I may have prolonged the indecent amount of caterwauling Leslie indulged in. Eventually she fell asleep and I was able to nod off. The next thing I knew it was past ten in the morning. I stirred and Leslie failed to move. She obviously needed to sleep off her hangover. I scribbled a note which ended with my mobile number and the suggestion that Leslie call me sometime – since I omitted to include the word soon, I figured a social drink together might be put off agreeably until such time as Leslie had found herself a regular boyfriend. I didn't want to suffer her company too often.

I let myself out of Leslie's flat and marched along to Alfredo's on Essex Road. While I was eating a fry up, my mobile rang. I checked the caller's number and recognised it. I'd almost panicked, thinking that Leslie had woken and was attempting to summon me back to her lair. I greeted my brother Kevin and told him Leslie's story about Susan having an affair with Maurice London. He asked me to meet him for a drink in The City Of York pub on Fleet Street, where I might run the tale by him again. I agreed. Kevin loved hearsay. He worked as a picture editor on a national newspaper where he'd befriended innumerable journalists. Kevin liked gossip. Kevin liked dirt. Kevin relished providing me with the explicit details of any story his employer's libel lawyers suppressed.

When I arrived at the pub I found Kevin in the company of an older man. He was introduced as a staff reporter named Joseph Coogan. Joseph got me to repeat the gossip that Leslie had palmed off as pillow talk. He pushed a magazine article about Maurice London across the table. I glanced at it. The piece was nothing special, a clippings job spiced up with a couple of quotes culled from a Verging Records press release. From career criminal to celibate white gospel singer, that was London's story – or at least this fable was the highly sanitised version of his life disseminated to the media by a publicist who favoured Prada-style power dressing and believed her own bullshit. Personally, I didn't buy into this hype – and neither did Kevin or Joseph. The reporter laughed out loud, and I was happy to be able to do the same.

"It's a charming article," the newspaperman said.

"Oh, you're so deep!" I drove home.

"As deep as the ocean! All I'm saying is that the writer doesn't see anything."

"Dear me – how very stupid!"

"Not a bit," the reporter laughed. "Nobody does."

"Nobody sees anything!" Kevin cheerfully announced; to which I replied that I had often thought so too, but had somehow taken the thought for a proof on my own part

HER PERSONALITY WAS A SIMPLE DUALISM CONJURED UP ON THE FLAT SURFACE OF A MIRROR. SOBER, LESLIE WAS SHY AND SUBMISSIVE. DRUNK, SHE WAS SELF-RIGHTEOUS AND PASSIVE-AGGRESSIVE

of a tremendous eye.

Joseph laid out his own version of Leslie's story, amending it to include the one extra fact I had provided for him. He'd been under the impression that Susan had grown up in south-west London but I assured him it must have been south-east if Leslie had been her school friend. Coogan told me that Maurice London had four mistresses. He named them and he intended to shame them in an exposé. He ran through their penchants and proclivities, their sexual warps and kinks and bents. Then he pulled a sheet of paper from his pocket and went through a list of twenty-four prostitutes Maurice had screwed over the past three months. The reporter had been investigating the singer for more than a week. I pulled a face. I thought I'd uncovered a scandal which would excite the most jaded hack and it was plain that what I'd unearthed wasn't news to Joseph. He already had tomorrow's headlines laid out on his office computer. The chink in Maurice London's armour was the

HE BOUGHT ME A DRINK. IT WAS PLAIN HE REALLY FEARED MY FEELINGS WERE HURT, AND THE SENSE OF HIS SOLICITUDE SUDDENLY MADE ALL THE DIFFERENCE TO ME

way in which he treated the various bodyguards and prostitutes who worked for him. They resented his holier-than-thou attitude and at least one of them was prepared to sell London down the River Thames for a five figure sum.

I must have looked crestfallen, since Joseph reassured me that what I'd told him was really interesting. It provided him with confirmation of details from an independent source. He bought me a drink. It was plain he really feared my feelings were hurt, and the sense of his solicitude suddenly made all the difference to me. My chatter fluttered off into space, and the unsubstantiated rumour I had relayed to him became flat enough beside the brilliancy of his being there with solid evidence and witnesses to back him up. I can see him there still, his spotted jacket, his fine clear face all bright with the desire to be tender to my feelings. I don't know what he had at first meant to say, but I think the sight of

my relief touched him, excited him, brought up words to his lips from far within. I wanted to do justice to the generous impulse that made him speak; it appeared as simple compunction for a snub unconsciously administered to another man. To make the thing right he talked to me exactly as an equal and on the ground of what was no longer mere tittle-tattle but a solid piece of journalistic research that would blow the lid off some sordid pop secrets. The hour, the place, the unexpectedness deepened the impression. He couldn't have done anything more intensely effective.

After a couple more drinks I went home and listened to the rough mixes of Electra's new album. I'd been brought in to spice up the songs with my multi-instrumental and production skills. I can't say the music was good – but since Verging Records had agreed there was no reason why they should insist I be credited for my work when I preferred to remain anonymous, I could see no reason not to accept their money. I was, after all, in desperate need of some ready cash. My own records did not exactly rake in the ackers. So, as I got on with my work, I forgot all about Leslie, Susan and Maurice London. That is, until my mobile rang.

"You bastard!" It was Leslie. "You sold the story I told you about Susan and Maurice London to the press. She's just been doorstepped by a tabloid newspaper. They know everything about her but got one detail wrong, which is how she knew the information came via me but not from me. I may have grown up in south-east London but Susan comes from south-west London. I got a scholarship to go to school in Wimbledon which is where we met. You're just such a cunt. I can't believe you're such a cunt."

Leslie was drunk and wouldn't listen when I told her the story had come from one of Maurice London's bodyguards, or a whore who was disgruntled about the way she'd been treated by the singer. Joseph Coogan had the whole story, I'd not said a thing to him that he didn't already know. Leslie wouldn't believe that London had four different mistresses. She insisted that everything was my fault. After twenty minutes of arguing and abuse I hung up. Moments later, the mobile rang again. This time it was Susan's sister Bevin, the head of A & R at Verging Records. My boss couldn't believe I'd sold a story about her sister to the press. According to Bevin I was a complete bastard. I was sacked. I was finished. Every last one of my contributions to Electra's new album would be removed. Bevin concluded by calling me a complete and utter cunt.

At first I imagined the injustice I'd suffered would be redressed once millions of newspaper readers saw the headlines proclaiming Maurice London to be a love rat. However, as the weeks passed and the report failed to appear, I made a few discreet enquires. My brother Kevin had the whole story. Maurice had persuaded Susan that what I'd told Leslie about him having four different mistresses was a complete fabrication. Having swallowed this bald lie, Susan agreed that the best thing to do was deny she'd been Maurice's lover and let the paper know she'd sue if they ran this slander. Maurice also got his other mistresses to threaten Kevin's employer with legal action. Fancy lawyers were phoning the newspaper and threatening libel suits if the tale was printed. After the dirt about Maurice London's love affairs failed to get a public airing, I found it increasingly difficult to secure work as a session musician. I tried belling Electra to talk to her about the imbroglio but she wouldn't return my calls. Eventually I defaulted on my mortgage and lost my home. At the moment I'm sleeping on the sofa in my brother Kevin's flat, and I can't see my situation improving until Bevin retires in about twenty years time. ☻

Stewart Home's latest novel, Sixty-Nine Things To Do With a Dead Princess, *will be published next year by Canongate*

BOOKS

A FEW GOOD BOOKS
TONY WHITE and JJ CONNOLLY select the best reads around

MY ELVIS BLACKOUT
Simon Crump
Bloomsbury, £9.99

Taking a leaf out of J.G.Ballard's book, well, his short story, "Jane Fonda's Augmentation Mammoplasty" to be precise, in which Ballard substitutes "Jane Fonda" for "Patient X" in a medical report on a breast enlargement op (collected in the excellent *Semiotext(e) SF* anthology, Semiotexte, 1986), Crump has taken a selection of short texts, ranging from a paragraph to several pages, and inserted the King in to (almost) every one: "Country Song" is a selection of path-lab suicide reports – no Elvis here, but it does sort of set the scene. Bank jobs, cannibalism, murder, religion, and redneck insanity with guns 'n' girls, it's all here, making *My Elvis Blackout* read like literary manna for anyone who thought that Albert Goldman's seminal *Elvis: The Last 24 Hours* (Pan, 1991) was not exploitative enough. Originally published in pamphlet form by Scotland's Clocktower Press, this is one of the most unusual books of the autumn – those Harry Potter dollars must be going to Bloomsbury's head. Lucky for us.

THE EROTIC REVIEW BEDSIDE COMPANION
Edited by Rowan Pelling
Headline £10

If your tastes run more to the *Teenage Arsefuckers* school of wank fodder then you may find this book altogether too polite. But the *Erotic Review* has achieved something in its short life thus far in that it's made the genre respectable enough that well-known literary types are practically queueing up to get their fingers dirty, instead of churning out their porn anonymously as was once the case. With contributors as diverse as Damien Hirst and Alain de Botton, there's plenty here to grab your attention, and given ER's loyal and expanding (ho ho ho) readership, this volume will probably be filling a few stockings on Christmas morning. (As well as one or two pairs of cavalry twill trousers).

VOX 'N' ROLL Ed. Richard Thomas
Serpent's Tail, £7.99

It's hard to believe that the infamous Vox 'n' Roll events, held weekly at Filthy McNasty's pub near the Angel, London, have only been going for four or five years – so ingrained are they in the collective psyche. Vox 'n' Roll is the apotheosis of the "readings" scene: writers read, writers choose the music that's played, and, of course, people drink. The subtitle of the book is "Hot sauce with everything", but the only hot sauce I've seen in Filthy's environs was steaming on the pavement outside. Some of the illustrious authors who have told the tale and survived are collected together in this book – from Nicholas Blincoe to John Williams, by way of Stella (appropriately enough) Duffy, Ben Richards, Will Self and Irvine Welsh to name but a few. The only one that's missing is Shane McGowan – who for a time was practically the patron saint of the place. Good book. Same again, please.

'This is exactly the book you've been waiting for'
Michael Moorcock

ATOM Steve Aylett
Phoenix House, £9.99

Steve Aylett's latest is set in the fictional town (or state of mind) of Beerlight. As with all his other novels, Aylett here proves himself one of the most inventive users of the English Language around, and the most flagrant abuser of the laws of physics since Tex Avery. *Atom* begins with a heist, but what's been half-inched is nothing less than Franz Kafka's brain. There's a sort of nod to *The Maltese Falcon* in here somewhere, and a bomb that can convert everything within range "into a living Updike novel, the subtext containing information everyone already knew – the end result was a shallow reality in which every move was a statement of the obvious." Furiously unhinged, Aylett is the anti-Updike. Buy his books now, otherwise in years to come you'll have to pretend you were always into them, and dodgy book dealers will charge you the Earth for first editions.

THE DECADENT TRAVELLER
Medlar Lucan and Durian Grey
Dedalus, £9.99

The long awaited return of the depraved villains who brought you *The Decadent Cookbook* and *The Decadent Gardener*. This corrupt compendium of effluvia and excess is wrapped up in a pornographic narrative of parodic gentility which belies the playful degeneracy that our deviant duo inevitably encounter on their travels. The only thing that's missing here is a bibliography, because enjoyable as *The Decadent Traveller* is, the act of quotation – the indenting and italicisation of decadence – does slightly take the edge off it. A handy and diverting pocket primer, then, but it could be an encyclopaedia – or a library. Yours. Explore.

DIAMOND DOGS Alan Watt
Duck Editions, £9.99

From the title you'd think that Watt's
debut novel is a paen to Bowie Boys, or a
reiteration of that inevitable Burroughs
reference, but there's no cut-up in sight,
and in fact the title is a form of dedication
to the true king of, well not exactly rock
and roll, but certainly of Tin Pan Alley. The
narrator's dad is an alienated (by
definition, it is implied) Neil Diamond fan,
and a cop. There's a body. There's lots of
driving. No-one talks to anyone else.
There's a kind of euro art-house vibe going
on here, but it's written by an American,
so there's no need for subtitles. Good? It's
unputdownable. Just don't get me started
on the man who wrote "Red Red Wine" and
"I'm a Believer"– that guy's a fucking
genius.

THE AUTOBIOGRAPHY OF A THIEF
Bruce Reynolds
Virgin Publishing, £7.99

On the eighth of August 1963, a beautiful,
moonlit night by all accounts, Bruce
Reynolds and his accomplices halted the
Glasgow to London mail train and stole
over two and a half million pounds, worth
about twenty-six million today. The
robbery catapulted Reynolds from being an
anonymous thief into a celebrity fugitive.
His life, and the lives of his wife and young
son, would never be the same again.

After five years on the run Reynolds
was captured and sentenced to a mind-
boggling twenty five years imprisonment.
Many suspect, both now and then, that the
true crime was humiliating and an affront
to the already disrespected establishment,
although, that's obviously not what it said
on the charge-sheet. Too many MPs had
been caught with their trousers down, and
the mood of the nation was bordering on
admiration of the robbers. Prime Minister
Wilson nearly reprinted the whole
currency to scupper the thieves, but that
would have nobbled all the tax-evading
magistrates with their mattressfuls of
readies as well, so instead Bruce got his
twenty five years, of which he did ten.

The robbery and the sentence marked
the time when crime stopped being a fuck-
about, a game of cops and robbers, and
started to become a whole new serious
ballgame. The Bruce Reynolds of today are
suited and booted by Gucci and Prada,
seriously low-profile, understand money
laundering better than most certified
accountants, and are into white powders –
shifting during the week, sniffing at the
weekend. But in the late Fifties and early
Sixties Reynolds wanted to eat well, drive
race-track motors, dress from Jermyn
Street, and spend as much time as possible

SALON
Daily Mirror
1963

" Ah, the green fields of England, swinging London, dear old British Rail, those lovely strikes . . ."

CONTEMPORARY CARTOONS. TAKEN FROM THE GREAT TRAIN ROBBERY FILES BY BRUCE REYNOLDS, NICK REYNOLDS AND ALAN PARKER (ABSTRACT)

away from bleak, smoggy London, living-extra-large on the Cote d'Azur. All this took a lotta money. Working for a living was too much like hard work, too time consuming, so Reynolds stole what he needed to finance the jet-set life he was living.

But Reynolds also knows both sides of the coin, the two sides of the swindle, and his honesty in describing the struggles, head-fuck, and consequences of a long sentence are courageous and moving. He dispels myths rather than bolsters them. After getting out having done his ten, the lifestyle contrast could not have been greater. Depressed, suicidal, struggling with day-to-day relationships, wondering if he wouldn't be better off topping himself or deliberately fucking up to get put back inside, Bruce finally gets back on track when he's reunited with his wife Angela, although this relationship is not without it's own fair share of heartache.

This biography first came out in 1995. Since then, an industry within an industry has emerged chronicling and in some cases celebrating retired and semi-retired criminals, most of which are ghost written. The difference is Reynolds' great ability to articulate – his charm and criminal charisma come shining through. He's also thankfully short of self-pity and cod-psychological, we-woz-very-poor-guv, justifications for his criminality.

As a teenager, a bright and suggestible Bruce Reynolds was searching for adventure, something to excel at, to prove his mettle, and he found it in crime. He climbed Everest when he did that train. On another day fate might have had him bump into a pal who took him down a jazz club rather than out thieving. Reynolds could have ended up as the old-school jazz maestro he now resembles, as it is this autobiography is moving, at times funny but always truthful and beautifully crafted.

JJ CONNOLLY

COMIC BOOKS

As THE LEAGUE OF GENTLEMEN publish their first TV tie-in – A Local Book For Local People – we ask them to choose their favourite comedy books of all time

INK BLOT AND MAIN PIC BY RONALD SEARLE, FROM MOLESWORTH (PENGUIN)

THE BRAND NEW MONTY PYTHON PAPPERBOK *(Methuen, £12.99)*

The godfather of all comedy books – so startling in its design and conception that it still looks fresh now, despite all the jokes about Richard Nixon. Spawned countless imitations, all out of print, whilst it remains available to this day.

MONTY PYTHON AND THE HOLY GRAIL SCRIPT BOOK *(out of print)*

Revolutionary presentation brings the filmmaking process to life. Facsimile first draft bound with reproduction of the actual script together with lobby-cards and a break down of the budget – the 1977 equivalent of a fully loaded DVD.

BACK IN THE JUG AGANE
Geoffery Willans and Ronald Searle (Collected in Molesworth, Penguin, £8.99)

By rights Geoffery Willan's episodic diary cum sketchbook detailing the trials of public schoolboy Nigel Molesworth should seem irrelevant and outmoded – a relic of a bygone age. Yet thanks to Searle's viscious cartooning and to the truthfulness of Willan's creation these books remain timeless and above all very funny.

THE RUTLAND DIRTY WEEKEND BOOK
Eric Idle (out of print)

The baroque inventiveness of the Python books taken to its limit by their editor in chief in his first full solo project. Fake dust jackets, different sizes and textures of paper and uncannily accurate parodies of various periodical publications (chiefly the *TV Times*) combine to make this delightful artefact something to treasure.

THE GOODIES BOOK OF CRIMINAL RECORDS *(out of print)*

Poor old Goodies – they always seemed to suffer from appearing to be one step behind the Pythons (there's even a bitchy joke about it in the *Rutland Dirty Weekend Book* – a reference to The Goodies and the Holy Grail). Their second book however takes on a delightful life of its own with a bizarre narrative concerning the tandem-riding trio's political ambitions.

THE ONION PRESENTS OUR DUMB CENTURY
Ed Scott Dikkers (Boxtree, £9.99)

One of the finest pieces of satire of the twentieth century and that's no hyperbole. American history retold in a series of immaculately faked front pages with devastating wit and piercing veracity. Check out "Holy Shit, Man Walks on Fucking Moon" on page 113 for a truthful account of human reaction to that extraordinary event.

A Local Book For Local People,
4th Estate, £12.99

EDEN BY DANIEL ALLINGTON.
FROM JEFF NOON'S FORTHCOMING BOOK,
COBRALINGUS (CODEX, FEB 2001)

UNDER THE INFLUENCE: JEFF NOON

**Jeff Noon's debut novel Vurt seemed to land from outer space.
But the reality was very different, as he tells TONY WHITE**

Well, it all started, now let's see, with me discovering this book called *Torture Garden* by a guy called Octave Mirbeau. I suppose you'd call it a kind of "anti-establishment satire"; very extreme, a bit like de Sade. It was about this enormous, circular prison with a beautiful Oriental garden in the centre of it, and they'd let the bourgeoisie in to this garden, they'd charge them to come in and watch the prisoners being tortured. One other thing about it is that it was the only precedent I've found for some of JG Ballard's stuff – you could just imagine Ballard writing some of the sentences, but this was written in 1899. It's very cool, very distanced, and yet very extreme.

I was writing plays at the time, I was also working in Waterstones bookshop in Manchester, and I'd had a few plays on, but I was getting a lot of rejection slips back from theatres – I didn't really know what to do next. And then this guy started working at the shop and he wanted me to do a new play. He was a producer on the Manchester Fringe scene. I said that I was maybe interested, but the only thing I could think to do was an adaptation of this *Torture Garden* book – but set in, like, 1999 instead of 1899, and I couldn't think how you'd do that. Then this other guy in the shop came back from the US with a copy of this new magazine, and said, "Here, Jeff, have a look at this." It was called *Mondo 2000*, and I thought, "Oh right, some kind of porn mag," but I looked at it and I was amazed. If anyone doesn't remember, *Mondo 2000* was kind of the beginnings of cyber culture and "alt.science", but these guys weren't wearing lab coats, they had dreadlocks and names like "RU Sirius", and it was all that next-generation hippy, "science-is-the-new-drug" kind of thing. At that time, not many people in the UK were really aware of virtual reality – I mean, we'd all read William Gibson – but through seeing this magazine I started thinking about science as something that could be hip and sexy. And I can remember thinking that somebody really needed to write about this stuff in a fictional form. Around that time we also started getting lots of very technical books about VR into the shop, all coming from the US. This particular one came in – I can't remember what it was called, but it was a big book, with a prologue by William Gibson, which is very much Gibson doing his usual stuff, but there was one sentence in it about these kids playing a virtual game called "The Torture Garden". And I saw this and thought, "Yes!", and almost immediately started thinking about a play in which people were taking this virtual drug. Now, *Torture Garden* itself has no real plot, it's just like a series of scenes. But I really needed a plot for the play, an emotional structure if you like, so I started thinking about it and came up with a story about a guy who's lost his sister to this torture garden. Well, that's what he thinks; he thinks she's in there being tortured, but in fact she's in there doing the torturing. So I started writing this play, but then the theatre guy got a job teaching golf in Hong Kong! No, really.

So, basically I'd written half a play and there was nowhere for it to go. I mean,

novels are different, they exist in their own right, kind of, but it's pointless writing a play for yourself – there's got to be someone putting it on. So there was this real feeling of, well, what do I do now? It was an anti-climax. But then another guy in the Waterstones bookshop in Manchester (I mean, in those days Waterstones was a really happening place; they employed people who had a life, not who'd just left college), whose name was Steve Powell, ended up as Assistant Manager. But we were both a bit tired, a bit bored with what our lives were becoming; we were, like, 35, and working in this bookshop... And he just came up to me one day and said "Right, that's it, I'm starting a publishing company! Can you write me a novel?" And I just went home that night and started. I thought to myself, right, I've got this guy and his sister, the virtual drugs, I dropped the *Torture Garden* stuff, and thought I'd start where Gibson left off at the end of his cyberspace trilogy. In other words, I didn't want it to be about technology, I was writing about a place where all that had become invisible. And you know, setting something like that in Manchester was a bit unusual, but that was *Vurt*. It more or less wrote itself, with me writing every night after work, and into the early hours of the morning. The only thing that wasn't in place was the drug-filled feathers. They came about through sheer mental hard work. Sometimes things just come to you; other times you have to sit down and really work at it. ◕

Torture Garden, by Octave Mirbeau (trans. Michael Richardson), Dedalus Ltd, £6.99
Vurt by Jeff Noon
is still available from Pan, £6.99
Needle in the Groove
by Jeff Noon, Anchor, £9.99

DEAR TONY...

Literary movements make MICHAEL MOORCOCK nervous. So what would he think of the All Hail The New Puritans anthology? Idler lit ed and Puritan contributor Tony White sent him a copy. Here's the letter he got back. Illustration by MARK REEVE

All hail the do what? Hang about. Manifestos is it? New Puritanism is it? Prescriptions is it? Looks like low church shenanigans to me, matey. And we all know where that leads. Slaughter in Ireland and bigots backing the NRA. Got the book, but movements and manifestos make my feet start doing their stuff so I'm inclined to growl and sniff around it more than I usually would. Makes me very edgy.

I understand there's a slight tongue in cheek element to the whole thing, but as someone whom you might call an old catholic, I really do believe in using the full orchestra, and if necessary (as with that great English musical genius Havercall Brown, who didn't have a single symphony performed in his lifetime – similar to Charles Ives, his US equivalent) several fucking orchestras. The New Puritan Manifesto itself, if not some of the excellent stuff inside the covers, smacks of the Eighties miserabilists all over again – a sort of yearning backwards, really.

Which, I suspect, drives a lot of innovation in the end, so it doesn't really matter. I just hate labels.

Back in the late Sixties, early Seventies, I refused all attempts to make me describe the New Worlds stuff as a movement – lots of people, including contributors like Chris Priest and Co wanted to – but that already moves it into a political arena and I prefer to preach to people by example, not address the existing authority. These young buffers have had too much uni if you ask me. They want lordy's approval too much. They understand the politics too well. I always think it's best to avoid such ambitions. Reminds me of the disaffected Oxbridgers who turned up at the alternative papers and eventually took them over (Rosie Boycott included). Something Tony Blair did to the Labour Party, too, really. Anyway, movements, especially in these aggressive times, seem to have a smell of careerism, which, don't get me wrong, wouldn't make me think ill of anyone flogging a story wherever they could. I've been associated with at least half a dozen movements I've never heard of and Steve Beard could probably associate me with a dozen more! Which reminds me, I had a short correspondence with Matthew De Abaitua [Idler Dep Ed, soon presenting sci-fi documentary SFUK on 4Later] about his Sci-Fi TV thing. I hope he didn't think I was being rude. It's just that the story I remember has little to do with the story that's told. Still your "Purity League" ain't as arrogant as the new Celtic fukyoo movement which claims to have reintroduced character and landscape to literature along American lines. "Rejecting the English novel of character and society, we embrace the American novel of character and landscape", said one of them on the radio the other day. Then before that someone told how Martin Amis had introduced American method to English fiction. Tell that to James Hadley Chase, Gerald Kersh or Jack Trevor Story. The Sci-Fi story tells how English writers, tired of American methods, reinvented English science fiction. It's a story that only works if you forget that half of the writers doing that were Americans... New Worlds published a more or less equal number of UK and US contributors. We were rejecting modernism of all kinds, not casting around for a dialectic that would let us hang on to it. And tell that to Hank Janson.

Too many movements, too many loose stools. Oops! When all's said and done, it comes down to the individual writer and the use they make of their own enthusiasms. As I don't have to tell you, I don't feel fiercely about this. I never did. I even joined a movement once – Writers Reading, it was called – though I refused to read myself. I just subscribed. It was a self-promotion exercise by a group of writers whose work I liked anyway and in those days my name was useful to them. But unless there's really a weight to be shifted, the movements are usually marriages of convenience which then waste years in pointless dispute. I think of that drab movement – The Movement – that Amis and Co put together, with the express intention of overthrowing the old guard. It probably did overthrow the old guard, but oddly it didn't seem to sway public taste one way or the other (they still put in for John Masefield or even Mervyn Peake for their faves of the century), just what was respectable for a narrow section of the middle class to read. Even the broad middle class didn't know Larkin was better than, say, Treece, because they didn't buy either. You can only change attitudes and tastes through example and that's all New Worlds ever set out to show. Trying to reunite popular and, if you like, intellectual fiction – we had a fairly large part in helping that shift. To be honest, I wrote King of the City partly in reaction to books which use nothing but real places and products – I was among the writers who started using real places, people and stuff and after a while you start yearning for invention. A sort of back-to-fiction movement, I suppose... The New Puritan Manifesto, if taken too literally, would produce at best the minor Edwardian realists like Pett Ridge, whom I happen to value as much for their reportage as their literary gifts. The thing is, writers are liars. Trying to tell the truth on the page turns you into a liar, just as going to court makes you a liar. The advantage of writing over the law is that you can afford to admit you're a liar and start from there. As long as you keep it contained on the page and in letters to authorities, you grow to feel more at one with yourself. Mark Twain knew that. I just read a report of him accepting an honorary donship at Oxford – his train was met by cheering crowds wherever he stopped and the newspaper reported that after Edward VII he was the most popular man in England. That's what we're missing these days, pard – being film stars. And you have to work really hard, like Amis and Rushdie and Dennis Potter (god rot him) to get people to understand that you're a star. Sometimes you have to go to America (where celebrity is properly honoured in its own right) or die of some dreadful illness. Amis simply bonded with an even older fart than his pa – but a proper authentic old establishment ikon, Saul Bellow, whose star was in decline on his home turf. Like George Michael doing a record with Aretha Franklin, but unlike Tony Blair speaking sentimentally of Tom Paine who would have had a pamphlet out about him in two minutes (and still made you a serviceable corset in his spare time).

Reading a lot of Paine at the moment, and Thoreau – two great Americans who were declared "unpatriotic" and shunned by their fellow democrats... If Paine is an American. He was sort of in the middle. I ought to write a science fiction story about a USA that actually was run on Paine's principles (which were fucking sophisticated – he even understood the

THE THING IS, WRITERS ARE LIARS. TRYING TO TELL THE TRUTH ON THE PAGE TURNS YOU INTO A LIAR, JUST AS GOING TO COURT MAKES YOU A LIAR

things wrong with populist democracy – like right-wing demos against petrol prices...). Since my favourite cat died and I'm down to about one intimate old friend, I'm not making the plans I was, but if I cheer up I might do an historical fantasy on Paine. Outsold the Bible, died a pauper. That's the way to do it.

Hope all's well with you, pards.
Very best,
Mike ☙

All Hail The New Puritans is published by 4th Estate and costs £10. Michael Moorcock's King of the City *is published by Scribners UK for £9.99*

SOUND OF THE SUBURBS

**JG Ballard held an audience at the Globe Theatre in Southwark.
STEVE BEARD was there. Illustration by MARK REEVE**

It's pleasing that venerable British surrealist and original avant pop novelist JG Ballard should have stayed the course long enough to see the beginning of his own cultural rehabilitation. It's just over a quarter of a century ago that the manuscript of his conceptual techno-porn novel *Crash* was famously rejected by one publisher with an outraged message scrawled in the margin: "this author is beyond psychiatric help." Now it's autumn in a new century and Ballard is seated on-stage in one of the rotundas of the Shakespeare's Globe Theatre complex as part of the London Festival of Literature. Recipient of a national newspaper prize, routine media comparisons to Graham Greene and the eager attentions of a smart new readership switched on to his existence by his last novel *Cocaine Nights*, Ballard is here this evening to plug the new one.

Super-Cannes (Flamingo) narrates the investigation of a spree killing in an international corporate business park on the Cote d'Azur. Like its predecessor, it sees Ballard using the genre of crime fiction just as he once used science fiction to give a popular shape to his obsession with mapping the terrain of an eroded collective unconscious. It's all there in *Terminal Beach* really. Like many of his novels *Super-Cannes* works as an evolved short story where plot and character are

developed as a baroque exoskeleton for the protection of the internally secreted concepts (e.g. on hardcore pornography: "People watched, but in a nostalgic way, as if they were seeing a documentary about morris dancing or roof-thatching").

The blue ceiling tiles of the rotunda are painted with retro-Elizabethan zodiac signs and a phoney tree seems to grow through the floor. It's a hyperreal environment whose vertiginous restyling of history fits in with the larger effort to regenerate the local economy with the engines of culture. Southwark is shrugging off the wastage of its smokestack industrial past and is now apparently tipped by the Corporation of London as the

ON HARDCORE PORNOGRAPHY, BALLARD SAYS: "PEOPLE WATCHED, BUT IN A NOSTALGIC WAY, AS IF THEY WERE SEEING A DOCUMENTARY ABOUT MORRIS DANCING OR ROOF-THATCHING"

third hot capital investment zone after the City of London and Docklands. To wander through this riverside redevelopment strip with its dinky art galleries, wine bars, studios, theme pubs and other symptoms of hypertrophic late industrial renewal is to exit the dirty cosmopolitan mix of London and enter a protected zone of simulation, pre-programmed experience and boredom. It is in short to enter the suburbs.

The suburban landscape has always been Ballard's great theme, from his early disaster novels to the more recent run of novels, which deal with the psychopathology of the gated community. Ever since he made the move to the Thameside development zone of Shepperton in 1960 Ballard has closely mapped the psychogeography of the abject non-place. His own imaginative departure from the London imperium coincided with a larger generational ex-urban flight which went on to manufacture a range of consumer society lifestyles in the interzones between the cities. Ballard offers a glimpse of this late industrial landscape from the stage of the Globe Theatre complex when he shifts into obsessive mythopoetic mode and drones on about Shepperton as a place "full of people who work in vast industries and live in the M4 corridor" where they are surrounded by "film studios, marinas and windowless sheds".

There are dutiful titters from the metropolitan audience (who make an interesting change from Ballard's old *Atrocity Exhibition*-era readership of boffins, fanboys and sick fucks) who refuse to believe Ballard's key line from *Super-*

Cannes: "The Adolf Hitlers and Pol Pots of the future won't walk out of the desert: they'll emerge from shopping malls and corporate business parks." Ballard is often tempted to engage in ritual clowning at those moments when the concealing power of England's past prevents it from seeing the history of its own ruthless modernity. But here he resists using the old laugh line about Shepperton being the "Malibu of the Thames Valley" and contents himself with a glancing reference to St George's Hill near Weybridge in Surrey as the ultimate gated community. He mentions that it's the place "where the Beatles used to live" but is too canny to state that its history of secession dates back to the English Civil War period when the gentrification and enclosure of common land there was most fiercely resisted by the Diggers.

Instead he outlines his position in general terms: "People in whom our society has invested the most – doctors, lawyers and architects – decamp into these gated communities and then lock the doors. They secede from the rest of the population. Now this is bad for the health of our society as a whole. It leads to an internalised civil war." In *Super-Cannes* as in *High Rise* and *Concrete Island* the secession of the middle-class subject – whether voluntary or accidental – triggers episodes of psychosis that for Ballard are highly ambivalent. The spree killings of *Super-Cannes* are the psychotic waste product of a society whose health is endangered. But they are also the privileged expression of a society which is truly and directly psychotic.

Ballard has often stated that the history of the twentieth century consumer society is the history of the "normalisation of the psychopathic". The dark truth of this insight acknowledged by his fiction is that beyond a certain ever-moving limit society is compelled to manufacture increasingly extreme acts of psychosis in order to satisfy the demands of its normalisation machinery. Crucial to this ritual demarcation is a process of social remaindering to which the English class system has proved ingeniously adaptive. When the English aesthete Michael Bracewell praises Ballard as the laureate of motorway service station culture and a John Betjeman for the blank generation, he is avoiding the crime scenes which Ballard's forensic imaginings expose and substituting a fantasy of lost arcadia for the real and continuing trauma of war.

The end of the English Civil War saw the victory of the enclosure movement and the invention of the world's first theme park in the shape of the English countryside with its hedgerows and arable fields. That this is a manufactured landscape has been long forgotten. It's now inextricably tangled up with fantasies of Peter Pan and hobbits and wildlife and other genteel cover stories. Is the same thing about to happen to the English suburbs? Can we expect a whole nostalgic mythology of temperament to begin to settle on this scarified landscape like an Orwellian cloak? Ballard gets the biggest laugh of the evening when he refers to Weybridge as "a deeply sinister place". It seems that even when he is in imminent danger of being buried by his own well-earned success, Ballard is still capable of being dishonoured in his own land. ☙

Super Cannes by JG Ballard is published by Flamingo, £16.99

THE END OF THE ENGLISH CIVIL WAR SAW THE VICTORY OF THE ENCLOSURE MOVEMENT AND THE INVENTION OF THE WORLD'S FIRST THEME PARK IN THE SHAPE OF THE ENGLISH COUNTRYSIDE

HOSPITALISED

STEWART HOME catches up with Dennis Cooper, the notorious chronicler of the Californian underworld at a rare public appearance in the UK. Illustration by TONY WHITE

Long established as the most extreme voice in the normally staid world of literary publishing, Dennis Cooper's sperm 'n'blood-sodden scribblings make Bret Easton Ellis read like a self-indulgent flake desperately trying to sound hard. Until now LA-based Cooper has been published by the fiercely independent Grove Press in the US and Serpent's Tail here in the UK. However, he's just signed on with corporate publisher Harper and Row, so his latest book *Period* looks like being his last cult production. It's patently obvious to even the most jaded observers that Cooper is about to go supernova.

Period is a no-holds-barred exploration of sex and death, youth culture and the search for the perfect object of desire. *Period* centres on a mysterious writer called Walker whose novel – also called *Period* – concerns an older man's sexual obsession with a dead boy. *Period* is also about a satanic rock band called The Omen, black magick, illegal websites, sexual murder and murderous sex. No one knows what's true and what's fantasy in the unbelievably fucked-up world of Cooper's Californian teenage gross-outs. However, there's one thing we can be certain about, this is the most important novel thrown up by the counterculture since Louis Ferdinand Céline's *Journey To The End Of The Night* was first published before the last world war.

Period isn't just a book, it's a manifesto of what both small independents like Serpent's Tail and massive conglomerates ought to be publishing. *Period* isn't a novel – it's an incredibly tight, dense and totally wigged-out non-linear tour-de-force. You can forget about plot, Cooper gives you poetry instead. This is William Carlos Williams meets Georges Bataille at a down home fetish club operating out of a claustrophobic cellar close to Venice beach. *Period* demonstrates that corporate publishers can stuff the idea that a "novel" needs to be between sixty and a hundred thousand words long with a beginning, a middle and an end – Cooper's book can be read in an hour but stays with you for days. Length doesn't matter, quality is what counts.

Cooper's recent reading at The Horse Hospital in snooty Bloomsbury to promote *Period* attracted the cream of London's hippest and most intelligent journalists – including Billy "The Hack In Black" Chainsaw and Ken "Motormouth" Hollings. Underground film legend Nick Abrahams put in an appearance, as did David McGillivray (the man who scripted a slew of British trash classics including *The House Of Whipcord*). Indeed, there were even a couple of luscious librarians from the BFI archives present.

After his reading, a total stormer, I asked Cooper how his publishers reacted to being handed *Period* and discovering it was fearlessly non-linear and very short: "Pete Ayrton of Serpent's Tail didn't blink. Grove Press don't care, they're just like fine, whatever. It wasn't a problem. They just let me do whatever I want to do, and then they just put it out and don't give me any support whatever, so they don't care what I do. They're not going to help me out, so it wasn't a problem."

Next I asked Cooper what had prodded him into writing *Period*: "Just like getting it tight is the inspiration. Sometimes it's hard to get started but it just seemed that there would be these different strains running through the book, one is like missing time, things missing and just combining that with like different kinds of communication, like e-mail and instant messaging, transcripts of recordings or talk radio and stuff."

Finally, I asked Cooper why he'd called the Satanic rock band in his book The Omen: "I just thought that was the stupidest name. I was researching death metal, that Swedish stuff. There was no band called The Omen and I couldn't believe it. I thought if I use The Omen it's great because it sounds like a band that would have had to have been around since the Seventies. There is no The Omen as far as I know. Maybe there will be now."

That's where I had to leave it as far as an interview went. Dennis was catching a Eurostar train to Paris at eight o'clock the following morning, and it was already well past midnight. I had plenty to ponder as I clambered into the back of a waiting cab. For example, what was the relationship between Cooper's speaking voice and the LA demotic of his prose? Rather like the various strands of *Period*, at times the two seemed to merge, then they'd separate out and become quite distinct. I could conclude by saying this state of affairs epitomises our post-modern condition, on the other hand I might just as plausibly opine "that's showbiz folks". If you only read one work of fiction this year, make sure it's *Period*. It won't take you long to gobble down and what you get is likely to blow your head right off. Dennis Cooper is Dog (that's God backwards, schmuck). ◉

Period by Dennis Cooper
Serpent's Tail, £8.99

MUSIC

STOP THE MUSIC

The sign of a musical genius is a long, torturous period of inactivity. Miles Davis, Brian Wilson and Kevin Shields compete for the Idler's Greatest Creative Block In Music. By WILL HODGKINSON Illustration by JONATHAN BURTON

There is no greater sign of true artistic intent than a creative block. It separates the visionaries from the grafters; it tells the world that your inspiration is not on call. In the notoriously undisciplined world of music, however, creative blocks are often used as an excuse when the musician or the band in question can't be bothered to do anything anymore, have given themselves over to hedonism, or, in most cases, have realised that the one good album they made was something of a fluke and that they're never going to do anything very good again, so they'd better stall the record company for a while before they knock out some inferior product. But there are rules to creative blocks.

Session musicians, particularly those working on theme tunes for daytime television, are rarely allowed to have them; the highly accomplished musicians of James Brown's rhythm section certainly weren't allowed them. And a block that isn't marked by output at either end of it isn't a block at all.

Truly great blocks are not allowed to be enjoyable, either. The Canadian classical pianist Glenn Gould's long periods of inactivity between his Variations were not spent on the golf course, but alone in his obsessively dust-free home, furiously scrubbing the telephone for fear of catching germs from his caller after saying no to another potential commission to score a major Hollywood movie. The

Italian composer Scarlatti did not go wenching during the long years inbetween writing his sweepingly beautiful symphonies, but spent a good hour a day bashing his head against a brick wall as punishment for not being more productive. Scott Walker, whose late Sixties period of intense activity produced two of the best albums of that decade, *Scott 3* and *Scott 4*, spent the Eighties in pubs in Chiswick, not drinking or even socialising, but watching people play darts. Anyone who has heard the 1995 album *Tilt* would agree that this didn't seem this helped Scott to find peace.

The problem with so many creative blocks is that they mark the beginning of the end: after producing a great piece of work, the artist cannot cope with the pressure of coming up with something that articulates what they are trying to say as well as that did, and an indulgent record company and too much money means that there is nothing to reign in their talents and make them hungry. The Stone Roses seemed like they might be one of the world's great bands after their 1999 debut album, and the five years they spent supposedly recording the follow-up helped fuel that myth of a great band. But *The Second Coming* was awful. Given too much freedom, the chippy northerners had been allowed to have create a block that probably wasn't there, and too many dope-fuelled late-night Led Zeppelin sessions had far more influence on the albums than any dark nights of the soul ever did.

Proud possessor of one of the greatest creative blocks of all time is Brian Wilson. Given freedom from the rest of the Beach Boys in 1965, Wilson worked all-hours with a group of session musicians to make *Pet Sounds*, one of the most perfect encapsulations of teenage longing ever recorded. Beach Boys singer and all-round bad guy Mike Love hated the album and put pressure on Brian to return to the old formula of surfing and girls songs, but Brian, at the height of his powers, felt compelled to go on to do something even stronger. For the next six months he recorded over 90 hours of tape for one track, *Good Vibrations*. Brian felt that he had made the perfect three and a half minute pop song, but then disaster struck. Phil Spector had just finished recording The Ronettes' *Be My Baby*, and Brian heard it on the radio. It was even more perfect than *Good Vibrations* and it drove the Beach Boy insane. He would listen to the song for days on end, then howl profanities that God could subject him to such brilliance – by someone else. Determined to go one further, Brian teamed up with Van Dyke Parks to take a *musique concrete* approach to recording a new album, *Smile*. It was to be a"teenage symphony to God", but intense pressure from the other Beach Boys, escalating drug use, and the fact that The Beatles', who had heard early tapes of Smile sessions while visiting Wilson in LA had released the Smile-influenced *Revolver,* broke his will. Adventures with LSD a year or so before had already damaged the young composer: "I opened the Pandora's Box of my mind and saw things that scared the fucking daylights out of me, and I decided to hide." Now he went into lengthy decline. He burnt the tapes to one of the *Smile* songs, *Fire*, because he believed it had been responsible for a number of fires that had broken out in LA. He built a sandbox in his living room and stayed in bed for weeks. By the early Eighties he was so confused that he tried to chat up a girl at a party who turned out to be his own daughter. The block was finally chiselled away by old friend Van Dyke Parks, when in 1995 he asked Brian to collaborate on a new album, *Orange Crate Art*. In early 2000 Brian performed, for the first time and with a full orchestra, *Pet Sounds* in its entirety in Chicago. "I was real scared about doing it," he says today, "but then I realised that it's not good to be scared." Go, Brian.

My Bloody Valentine's Kevin Shields also had a hefty block. After the band's strange first singer David left to write gore novels, Shields took the reins, drafting in his girlfriend as lead singer and moving the sound from trashy feedbacked garage pop into ethereal indie psychedelia. "Ultimately, where we're all heading in music is a sort of integration of the reality of what it's all about in the end, and that's extremely psychedelic in its purest sense." After the success of the bands' '88 album *Isn't Anything*, the band went into the studio for two and a half years, during which time Creation's Alan McGee, who was putting up £200,000 for the record, was banned from the studio. One nervous breakdown later, McGee booted the band off Creation at around the time the album, *Loveless*, was released to rapturous reviews.

Rather than bask in the success of *Loveless*, Kevin Shields went mad. Island signed the band up for £500,000, and Shields responded by building a 16-foot fence around his house so that nobody could get in. He sent his sister to buy green barbed wire to put on the top of the wall, and told her: "You can't go on holiday until you buy some sandbags. I'll be needing them too." The band all left him, and he was content in the knowledge that nobody could penetrate his fortress. But as Alan McGee said to him, "Kevin, who would want to come in?" He went on to take a quarter of a million off EMI Publishing and another quarter of a million off Warner Brothers Of America, and is yet to produce a single piece of music that any of them have actually heard. He is, however, convinced that it's their fault and not his. "For me, everything hinges on one critical thing, and that's being in an inspired state of mind," says Shields now, still waiting for that state of mind to take over.

Perhaps Shields should take the Miles Davis approach to the creative block and just do things that are bad for him. In his biography Miles, the great jazz trumpeter of the 20th century, recounts how from 1975 to 1980 he didn't pick up his trumpet. Having been involved continuously in music since he was ten, and having produced some of the most groundbreaking, accomplished jazz albums of all time (*In A Silent Way* and *Sketches Of Spain* in the Sixties, *Bitches Brew* in the Seventies), Davis sank into degeneracy. "I just took a lot of cocaine (about $500 a day at one point) and fucked all the women I could get into my house. I was also addicted to pills, like Seconal and Percodan, and I was drinking a lot, Heinekens and cognac. Sometimes I would inject cocaine and heroin into my leg; it's called a speedball and it's what killed John Belushi."

Davis stopped going out entirely, and didn't leave his house for a solid six-month stretch. His only connection with the outside world was through television (on around the clock). After the maids stopped coming, his house became extremely squalid, with "clothes everywhere, dirty dishes in the sink, newspapers and magazines all over the floor, beer bottles and garbage and trash everywhere... filthy and real dark and gloomy, like a dungeon. The roaches had a field day." Food came by way of a young man, Eric Engles, who would buy fried chicken for Davis. Women came in for casual sex. Davis referred to the time as his "silent period".

Brian Wilson and Miles Davis are joint-winners of The Idler's Greatest Creative Block In Music award (although neither can match up to the great film director Terence Malick: a mammoth 21 years between 1978's Days Of Heaven and 1999's The Thin Red Line, during which period he became, amongst many other things, a Paris hairdresser). Kevin Shields, currently gigging with ageing rockers Primal Scream, does not exactly fall into the "must try harder" category, but he does have a few more years to put in. (Apparently he invented jungle music during his creative block, too.) Let them be an example to today's current hard-working but uninspired musicians (Stereophonics and Travis adopted a conventional career strategy to being in a band, and succeeded), who may not realise that although financial reward comes to those who toil, Inspiration – that fickle goddess – blesses the talented only when she feels like it. ☻

TRIPPED UP

**STEVE ROSE on the fascinating story of psychedelic rock star
Roky Erickson. Illustration by FERGADELIC**

f Robert Johnson sold his soul to the
devil in exchange for the blues, then
Roky Erickson sold his sanity for
psychedelia. And unlike most of his
contemporaries, he never came back for
a refund.

The guitarist and lead singer of The
Thirteenth Floor Elevators has earned his
place in music history as a member of the
world's first psychedelic rock band, but
boy has he paid the price. Although the
Elevators are still revered today, and are
cited as an influence by bands as diverse
as REM, ZZ Top, Television and Primal
Scream, Roky's personal story has been no
fairy tale; more like a real-life *One Flew
Over The Cuckoo's Nest* experience which
has left him with a tenuous grip on reality.
This being psychedelia, though, myth and
fact have become harder and harder to

separate over the years. Not only has the
prodigious drug intake of the time led to
muddled and conflicting memories from
those who were there (or think they were
there but can't quite remember); Erickson
himself rarely talks to the press, and when
he does, there's little chance of getting any
solid information out of him.

We do know that he was in the right
place at the right time for the birth of
psychedelia: not San Francisco, but Texas.
It was, and thanks to Governor Bush still
is, one of the most conservative states in
America, but being empty, wealthy and
close to Mexico, it was one of the few
places in the early Sixties with easy
access to mind-altering chemicals –
particularly marijuana, peyote and later
LSD, which was being tested at the
University of Texas at the same time as

Ken Kesey was developing a taste for it over in California. The popularity of these drugs, combined with the philosophies of Timothy Leary, Aldous Huxley, etc. sowed the seeds of psychedelic consciousness in Texas, which was later successfully exported, along with the music, to San Francisco's hippie scene. Janis Joplin was also around Texas at the time; she nearly joined the Elevators before pitching in with Big Brother and the Holding Company, and other bands like the Red Crayola, The Moving Sidewalks and The Clique were just starting out. Even as the Texan scene was taking hold, though, possession of a single joint could still result in a twenty-year prison sentence. In 1963, Chet Helms, manager of Big Brother And The Holding Company, was rounded up in Laredo as a suspect in JFK's assassination simply because he had shoulder-length hair. It was long hair, in fact, which started Roger Kynard Erickson (no-one ever called him Roger, he claims) on his rock'n'roll career. He was thrown out of his high school in Austin, Texas, for refusing to cut it, and armed with a musical education from his opera-singing, God-fearing mother, he graduated onto the burgeoning Texas music scene at the age of seventeen. In 1965, when Roky was already making an impression as lead guitarist in The Spades, he met Tommy Hall and they swiftly merged with another local band, The Lingsmen, to form The 13th Floor Elevators.

A part-time beat poet and a psychology major at the University of Texas (which is how he became acquainted with LSD), Tommy Hall was a good six years older than Roky and the others, and being up to

scratch on his Nietszche, Gurdjieff and Dylan, he took on the role of the band's chief lyricist and philosophical leader. Roky was sensitive, childlike and irresponsible. Tommy was authoritative and fatherly. On stage, though, Roky was the leader. His wailing, out-of-control vocals had only previously been heard coming from black singers like James Brown and Little Richard. Meanwhile Tommy played the jug; a staple of acoustic bluegrass bands which he miked up and made wibbly noises through, hence the random background vibrations which made the Elevators' sound so psychedelic. The fact that they were usually bombed out of their skulls while playing can only have helped cement their live reputation, even if Roky tended to forget the lyrics from time to time.

Signed to Leland (brother of Kenny) Rogers' new International Artists label, The Elevators' first single was a new version of Roky's old Spades number "You're Gonna Miss Me", which reached the national charts (number 55) and later became a garage staple thanks to its inclusion on the first Nuggets album. Soon after came their landmark album, *The Psychedelic Sounds Of...* It is difficult to imagine what it must have been like in 1965 to hear words like "After your trip, life opens up, you started doing what you want to do/And you find out that the world that you once knew/Gets what it has from you/No one can ever hurt you because you know more than you thought you knew/And you're looking at the world through brand new eyes/And no one can ever spoil the view." They are indistinguishable from many other amateurish attempts to describe drug experiences today, but at the time they were unlike anything else heard on a rock'n'roll record. The Beatles were still singing stuff like "Yesterday" and were some distance from *Revolver*, the Beach Boys had just started *Pet Sounds* and the Velvet Underground were only just getting their act together. So unless you were in on the scene at the time, you'd have had no idea what they meant.

The Elevators quickly attracted a devoted following, which in turn attracted the attention of the Texan authorities. Concerned by the outbreak of youth immorality in the Lone Star state, the police soon identified the band as Public Enemy Number One, and began a campaign of harassment. For a time the Elevators even had two tour buses, one for the cops to search and sabotage, and one for their real equipment. They were finally busted at Hall's apartment in early 1966 for possession of a substantial quantity of grass (not to mention long hair). Miraculously, the judge made an error while reading the evidence, and failed to realise just how much weed they had had. As a result they were released on probation. Several band members left at this time, so the Elevators regrouped and wisely decamped to California. Not only were the state's permissive drug laws better suited to their lifestyle, the emerging hippie scene loved them too. Members of The Grateful Dead and Jefferson Airplane remember seeing them at venues like Chet Helms' Avalon Ballroom and the Fillmore in San Francisco, alongside bands like The Charlatans and The Fugs. But

THE FACT THAT THEY WERE USUALLY BOMBED OUT OF THEIR SKULLS WHILE PLAYING CAN ONLY HAVE HELPED CEMENT THEIR LIVE REPUTATION, EVEN IF ROKY TENDED TO FORGET THE LYRICS FROM TIME TO TIME

STORIES OF WHAT HAPPENED NEXT VARY. THE POPULAR VERSION SAYS THAT, KNOWING HE WAS FACING A PROLONGED PRISON SENTENCE, ROKY CHOSE TO PLEAD INSANITY, AND PRETENDED THAT EXCESSIVE ACID CONSUMPTION HAD FRIED HIS BRAIN

unfortunately they went back in Texas in 1968, shortly after the release of *Easter Everywhere* (their second, and last, great album). Erickson was busted again, and this time the authorities were ready to come down hard.

Stories of what happened next vary. The popular version says that, knowing he was facing a prolonged prison sentence, Roky chose to plead insanity, and pretended that excessive acid consumption had fried his brain. In 1975 Roky said of the incident, "I was such a good actor, man. I had them all fooled; sayin' there were spots runnin' up and down the walls, beasts with big fangs everywhere – well, they believed me!" They believed him so well, they put him in Rusk State Mental Hospital, and when he claimed he was just pretending, no-one believed him any more. Clementine Hall, Tommy's wife and a powerful influence on the band (she wrote the lyrics to "Splash 1", and came up with the band's name), has a different version of events. She, Roky and Tommy had dropped some LSD, she says, and coming home, Roky asked to

be dropped at his mother's house. They suggested he crash at their place but he declined. "I don't know what happened after we dropped Roky off, but he either freaked out or his mother was appalled at the state he was in. Consequently his mother had him committed."

Another version of events, of course, says that there was no pretense, he really was going insane. His intake of LSD and speed had reached worrying levels (five trips a day, according to some), and many, including his record company, thought that a municipal healthcare facility really was the best place for him. Whatever happened, it made no difference. After three years of poring over lyrics and scoping out their performances, the Texas authorities had eliminated the greatest threat to the state's well-being. Roky was spirited away to Rusk for three years, where he was most likely subjected to electro-shock treatment and heavy doses of Thorazine. It was pretty much the end of the Elevators.

While in Rusk, Roky wrote songs (nearly 100, some of which were recorded by his mother on visits and have been released on CD), and some particularly messianic poetry (like "Jesus Is Not A Hallucinogenic Mushroom" and "Ye Are Not Crazy Man"), which eventually formed his first book *Openers*. He formed a band with fellow inmates and allegedly befriended Jimmy Wolcott, an Elevators fan who had murdered his family while high on glue. Outside, concerned friends made moves to secure his release, including a benefit concert organised by his brother, but by the time he came out, in 1972, putting the Elevators back together again proved virtually impossible. Aside from Roky's fragile state of mind, the other Elevators had also suffered at the hands of either the law or the drugs. Guitarist Stacy Sutherland had also been incarcerated for drugs at the same time as Roky. He came out a full-time junkie, and was shot to death by his wife in 1978. Tommy Hall, who had continued taking acid regularly, claimed to be receiving messages from God at fifteen-minute intervals.

Roky's musical career post-Elevators has tailed off to virtually nothing, and his life has fragmented into a series of disconnected incidents. He became obsessed with aliens, monster movies and religious conspiracy, as evinced by his first post-Elevators single, "Red Temple Prayer" (Two-Headed Dog), under the band name Bleib Alien ("blieb" being an anagram of bible). He later signed to CBS as Roky Erickson and the Aliens, and in 1982, signed a legal affidavit declaring that a Martian inhabited his body. He is also said to have developed a mail obsession, and was arrested again in 1989 for stealing his neighbours' mail. It was more a misunderstanding than a misdemeanor, although some of the mail was found taped to his walls.

Today Roky lives in a federally-subsidised house in a suburb of Austin, a diagnosed paranoid schizophrenic but not on any medication. He keeps several TVs and radios playing at the same time. Friends are still loyal to him, take him out to dinner, help him financially (they set up a trust fund for him Roky Erickson Trust Foundation #2 3216 Lafayette, Austin, TX 78722 AV. The Elevators never received a cent in royalties although *The Psychedelic Sounds Of...* has sold more than 140,000 copies), but there was a Roky tribute album, *Where The Pyramid Meets The Eye*, released in 1990.

Of the psychedelic pioneers of the Sixties, most of them either went one way or the other. They explored the edges of sanity too far and died young – Hendrix, Joplin, Morrison, Brian Jones – or they sobered up and became hard-headed music professionals – Starship, Genesis, Pink Floyd, the remaining Rolling Stones. Roky is one of the few still stranded in between. The notes of the Elevators' first album are full of ambitious talk about "the quest for pure sanity" and how man should "restructure his thinking and change his language so that his thoughts bear more relation to his life and his problems". The Elevators innocently set out to achieve and explore these things. And they lost everything. ☙

*www.myfreeoffice.com/kiloh//Roky.html
– the Roky Erickson Community*

FAIR ENOUGH

In this humdrum age, Jad Fair is the real thing — a pioneering musician from Half Japanese and a world-famous outsider artist. STEPHEN PASTEL pays tribute to the man of action

Action Man fetishists amongst the Idler readership may be excited to know of a special Jad Fair edition, moulded to commemorate Half Japanese's historic European tour of 1990. The Jad Fair Man Of Action series featured an impressively neutral Jad, like he really wasn't about to fall into a stupid trap and give something away; yet it was also an inquisitive Jad who seemed to be saying, "I need to know". There he was, laid out in quantity on the souvie-stall; multiple Jads, each kitted-out in a groovy individualised après-ski outfit and each with his own trademark glasses. Arriving in Amsterdam by jet with my friends, the other Pastels, Aggi and Katrina, this first encounter with Jad's entrepreneurial flair had gained our respect.

To us it was the most normal thing to go to Amsterdam to see this strange, wonderful group that went beyond simple cultdom, seeming more like exotic, quixotic pirates-in-reverse. And Half Japanese never played in the UK, like they thought we might be too square for them. That just didn't seem right, as it had been a UK label, Armageddon, who recognised that the original Half Japanese vision could not possibly be contained on two vinyl sides, and instead had donated a more reasonable triple-LP length for their debut, allowing Jad and his brother David a little

room to spread out and demonstrate their non-pro music skills. While Jad flailed away at his drum-kit like he was falling down the stairs, David grimly hung on in, battering out the rhythm to teenage-scuzz anthems like "Louie Louie" and "96 Tears", seemingly oblivious to the actual chord progressions. As they took it in turn to chant out their feelings about their lives, you can almost picture them egging each other on; a big guy with glasses and a skinny guy with glasses — indignant, confused and righteous. Back then I was an out-of-touch suburban kid coming to terms with my own life, and it was much later, in the mid Eighties, that I began to pick up Half Jap imports with titles like Charmed Life and Music To Strip By. By that time they'd evolved into a like-minded musical community with players like Mark Jickling and Don Fleming, inspired by and drawn into Jad and David's world. A more melodic out-thereness had evolved that was in places close to the first two Modern Lovers LPs. As I started to collect Half Japanese, the side-projects and Jad solo work, I was struck by how completely realised the whole idea was; the lyrics, the music, and the fabulous raw artwork.

Speaking to him after a sensational Half Japanese performance, it became clear that Jad had indeed identified a rival group that he was now intent on out-doing.

JAD FAIR

THE BEATLES WERE PHONEY IDOLS, HE CLAIMED, AND HALF JAPANESE WOULD SOON HAVE RECORDED MORE MUSIC THAN THEM

The Beatles were phoney idols, he claimed, and Half Japanese would soon have recorded more music than them; indeed had already issued more records. Jad had evidently circulated the rumour that Half Japanese were better even than The Beatles, and it was gaining credence. Even now, a respected US commentator like Byron Coley will call on simple empirical evidence to compare their respective merits, declaring Half Japanese the winners in each of these areas: Haircuts, Posters, Quality of Improvisation and Appreciation of Yoko Ono. But for Coley, the special quality of Half Japanese's music has little to do with its superiority to Beatles' music, having instead emerged "from an area so personally defined as to seem almost autistic". *The Wire*'s David Keenan is equally uncompromising: "purely in terms of mind-boggling what-the-fuckness, Half Japanese has blazed a unique trail. Hearing The Beatles makes me wanna dot a crotchet and fix my hair, but hearing Half Japanese I wanna scream while banging something."

Jad somehow knew that we were friends with a group that was being touted as "The Bellshill Beatles", Teenage Fanclub. In what he considered would be a stunning coup, he'd come to Glasgow and record with our massed ranks. I asked him if he had many new songs, and he replied

modestly, "around 100". Jad's sometime method of songwriting seems charmingly Idleresque. Asking him to teach us the first one, he told us to just start playing and he would join in. We looked around at each other a little baffled, but Jad's sense of optimism triumphed and we managed to cut quite a few spontaneous songs that we were all pleased with. We soon discovered that Jad's lack of preparation did not extend to his Scrabble playing where he knew how to bend every single rule, combining letters like x, y and z to form words that none of us had heard of. Years later when the *Idler* Music Editor came to Glasgow to interview The Pastels, Jad, upon learning that he also writes for the Guardian, mentally logged him as a potential high-scorer and co-opted him onto his team. I'm sure they won.

Over the years I've worried about Jad and his nomadic lifestyle; forever on the road, his catalogue all over the place and his best titles out of print. But this is a kind of chaos that suits a man of action with a million new musical projects, exhibitions, collaborations. Upcoming projects include a new Half Japanese LP, a Jad Fair-produced David Fair LP, a Teenage Fanclub collaboration and a new book of artwork. But the best news of all is that Jad just got married. ◉

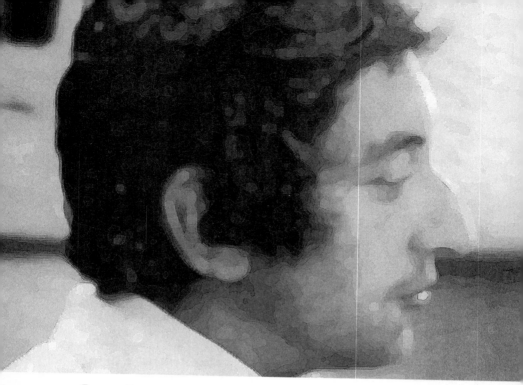

YÉ-YÉ

French pop is not renowned for its style or originality. But for three years in the Sixties, the yé-yé movement gave Gallic hipsters something to be proud of, says JEAN-EMMANUELLE DUBOIS

If there's one thing that brings together acts as diverse as April March, French pop poser Étienne Daho, his regular cohorts Saint Etienne, Sonic Youth, the Make Up and Pizzicato 5, it's their love of French yé-yé. The world of yé-yé is one of incredible sounds that pop devotees really owe it to themselves to explore. But though many of the sounds persist in all kinds of unusual covers and Jap reissues, the actual golden age of yé-yé sits between 1965 and 1968, just after the first stirrings of rock in France, an experience which could best be qualified as hit and miss. Yé-yé was so named as that's what

the French considered was being sung when long-haired beats would fill songs with "yeah yeah" once their supply of lyrics was over.

Where yé-yé as a genre comes into its own – what makes it better than just about any other non-English pop from the period – is when its creators would cross crude, questionable how's-yer-father propositions (à la Gainsbourg), with sweet, innocent youth (à la France Gall). And of course this would be one vain venture if we were to try and establish a panorama of the genre without mentioning one of its most important masterminds, the one, the only, Serge Gainsbourg. He was the first to understand that a French artist could do more than simply slavishly copy the Brits and the Yanks, the first to figure how to infuse his pop with a certain continental something. He managed this by giving his songs unusual themes, arrangements worthy of Phil Spector and moulding the French language inventively into something that could be adapted to pop rhythms, a feat it had often struggled with until then. Like the best yé-yé, his was a unique collision between jazz, French chanson, British Beat and psychedelic pop.

In 1967 Serge Gainsbourg, using arrangements by David Whitaker (whose CV includes everything from work for Marianne Faithfull to Led Zep), was evoking Swinging London. He did this not with the enthusiasm of a foolhardy, impressionable, acne-ridden, Johnny Foreigner teenager, the kind who'd go misty-eyed on hearing the words Carnaby Street, but instead as a cynical, middle-aged man out to get whatever bit of giggling jailbait he could. Hearing him, you know he wasn't for a minute taken in by Flower Power or any of its dizzy avatars. One minute he's telling of some teenage girl and her LSD experience ("Teenie Weenie Boppie/a pris du LSD/un sucre et la voici/au bord de la folie"), the next it's of a Rolling Stone drowning in the Thames ("que sont ces fleurs aux couleurs exquises/qui dérivent au fil du courant?/C'est Mick Jagger qui dans la tamise/s'est noyé dans ses beaux vêtements").

Before Gainsbourg put pen and melody to paper, who'd have dared mock – admittedly with a fair dose of elegance – Mick Jagger? After all, back then he was a gesticulating cypher for all that was Now and avant garde.

The number of ear-popping gems to be found amongst Gainsbourg's yé-yé period *oeuvre* is incredibly high, and some are still waiting in the back roads of France for all manner of record collecting folk to come and find them. (Of course, that's if the Japanese currently exporting the platters out of the country in industrial quantities don't get to them first. Then again, you'll still have the reissues to make do with.) And there are Gainsbourg songs to be found on discs other than those of the better known France Gall, Françoise Hardy or Brigitte Bardot. It's also worth hunting out for the man's songs lurking on discs by Michèle Arnaud, naff nightclub owner Régine, Godard muse Anna Karina, Nouvelle Vague stalwart Jean-Claude Brialy, Dominique Walter, Minouche Barelli (who lost out to Sandie Shaw in the 1967 Eurovision) or Zizi Jeanmaire.

The world of the yé-yé is a vast one, and constitutes an odd territory worthy of exploration. It would take one imposing tome to speak of all of those whose brief careers resulted in only one or two singles boasting lyrical daring and bizarre sounds rarely found in other non-French pop. But meanwhile, to get you started, a few ideas.

RECORDS FOR AN ASPIRING YÉ-YÉ:

Various: *Swinging Mademoiselle* volumes 1 & 2

Françoise Hardy: *If You Listen* covers album in English, and her superb new album *Clair Obscur* which includes a duet with her long-standing companion, Jacques Dutronc.

AND FOR YOUR NEO YÉ-YÉ NEEDS:

April March: *April in Paris* (Sympathy for the record industry)
Gainsbourgsion! (euro-visions)
Chrominance decoder (Tricatel)

THE SOUND OF THE SIXTIES

**One man's mission to construct an authentic 1967 recording studio by WILL HODGKINSON.
Illustration by WOODROW PHOENIX**

Liam Watson belongs in a comic strip from *Whizzer And Chips*. With his authentically pre-decimalisation pasty skin, bandy legs, protruding upper lip and overall mischievous demeanour, he looks like he should be shouting "Yaroo!" while being caned by Teach for putting laxatives in the fat kid's steam pudding. He dresses like a member of Sixties beat group The Dave Clark Five. No wonder then that he has put his life's work into creating a recording studio that, for all intents and purposes, could quite easily have existed in 1967.

Toerag Studios is Liam's brainchild. Hidden down a quiet Hackney street, it is a temple to the sound and philosophy of the original British Invasion bands led by The Beatles and The Stones. Recording equipment has been sourced from BBC storage rooms, Cumberland garden sheds and even Abbey Road clearouts, and the space is large enough for bands to take the old approach to recording, with all of the members playing together to create a live sound. Above the studio is Liam's office, and a storage loft that was constructed with the help of a notorious French sexual deviant. On minimum funds, Liam has set up an entire eight-track studio designed to create the immediacy of sound which made so many Sixties records so great – most records are made today in 24 or 48-track studios, which distance the sound of the album from the sound that the band would make playing live. The purpose of Toerag is not to create a living artefact, but to provide the circumstances for a band to record music that is as alive as possible. "The idea came to me and a friend, Josh Collins, who had recently left college and wanted to set up a workspace. I had this concept of setting up a vintage studio all with original equipment. We would give it a year, and if it was breaking even that was good enough, so that's what happened. It started when we found this Sixties mixing desk which was sitting in a shed in the back of a studio in the Lake District. Then we found an Abbey Road mixing desk – in 1982 EMI sold off all the Abbey Road equipment that they weren't using anymore, and a friend of ours had bought it but never used it. The Studer eight-track tape machine we bought off the BBC for £700, and it would have cost them £15,000 when they bought it in the Sixties."

Liam's main problem is that modern musicians are rarely proficient enough to record on eight-track. "Pop music is listened to on two speakers at home," explains Liam. "So at the end of the day, that has to be finished onto a two track format. But people are so stupid that they think, 'oh no, we can't do eight-track, what about the drums? We need a track each for all the different drums on there'. But here, I mix it while the drummer's playing. In 24-track, nothing is balanced as it goes down, it's all mixed later. The reason so many Sixties records sound good is because the band would work on the song until they got it right, then they'd put it down. An album like Revolver doesn't sound great because the studio they used had good quality valves, it sounds great because they were all playing together extremely well. They would lay that down on one track, then use the three other tracks to overdub with. These days people have too long to analyse it and get every last little bit polished, so there's an

urgency that is lost."

Liam is known for creating a Sixties sound, and is used predominantly by bands who want to go for that, but there's no reason why these supreme recording techniques couldn't be used by non-retro bands. "It's going to be live musician bands with guitars and drums, but they could be doing any kind of music. Sometimes I get managers of bigger bands or record companies phoning up because they've heard some recording I've done and they like it. Then they ask me how many tracks I've got, I say eight, and that's the end of the conversation. They don't even want to think about it. And I say, 'Hold on, you're calling me because you like the sound, well you know how I got that sound'. This Studer eight-track machine is the size of a refrigerator and sonically far superior to 24-track; you don't have to use noise reduction on it and its one-inch tape is far cleaner than two-inch 24-track tape, but people still think of eight-track as some home-recording device."

The studio is Liam's livelihood; it isn't a mere hobby. "I haven't got a choice about this, I don't know what I could do if I wasn't doing this. It's too late now." The amount of work that has gone into creating the studio is a milestone for the effort vs profit axis – on the side of effort. "All of the dimensions of the studio have been worked out following specific laws for acoustics, down to half an inch of the height, width and depth of the room. "

Toerag Studios make a defiant stand against the forces of modernism trampling over quality. "When did records start sounding a bit shitty? In the early Seventies, when sixteen-track came in. I'm compromising by having eight-track anyway, all the best records were made on four-track. But that's certainly not economically viable." ☙

Matthew De Abaitua writes short stories and is the presenter of *SF:UK* on Channel 4

Karl Abramovic is an illustrator based in LA. He can be found at 5332 Russell Ave. #408, Los Angeles, CA 90027. Phone/fax 323 464-0763 Mobile 323 697-0546

Steve Aylett is the author of several novels including *The Inflatable Volunteer* and *Slaughtermatic* and the short story collection *Toxicology* (Orion)

Babs Babylon is six foot tall and blonde

Mark Baines has drawn record sleeves for Two Dollar Guitar, Lung Leg and several others, edited the cartoon anthologies *Spooky Sounds Of Now* and *Cock-Eyed Comics* and currently runs the Salty Cellar club in Glasgow

Steve Beard is the author of the novel *Digital Leatherette* (Codex). A collection of his journalism, *Logic Bomb: Transmissions from the Edge of Style Culture* is published by Serpent's Tail

Bidisha's latest novel is *Too Fast To Live* (Duck Editions)

Hieronymous Bosch rocks

Jonathan Burton illustrates with scissors and sometimes pens

Adam Buxton is Adam from Adam and Joe

Bill Childish is an artist

JJ Connolly's novel *The Layer Cake* is published by Duck Editions

Joe Cornish is Joe from Adam and Joe

Andrew Copeman is a writer and performer

Brian Dean is editor of *Anxiety Culture* (anxietyculture.com)

Gareth Ellis is an internet consultant and writer

Jean-Emmanuelle Dubois is a French guy who writes for *Playboy* and other classy mags

Hannah Dyson draws anthropomorphic creatures and other beings

Fergadelic is an artist

Jon Fortgang is a freelance writer

Paul Hamilton runs the Peter Cook Appreciation Society, and edits *Publish And Bedazzled*, its fanzine

Joe Harrison does mainly erotic stuff

Gavin Hills was the most original journalist of his generation. He died in 1997. His collected journalism, *Bliss To Be Alive*, has been published by Penguin

Damien Hirst is an artist

Will Hodgkinson writes for the *Guardian*

Stewart Home's *Cunt* is published by the Do Not Press. *Confusion Incorporated: A Collection of Lies, Hoaxes and Hidden Truths* is published by Codex

Victoria Isherwood is an artist and writer

James Jarvis uses and endorses Pilot drawing implements

Dan Kieran is our webmaster

Nicholas Lezard has promised his wife he will finish his book on fun by Christmas

John Machon is a freelance illustrator

Mark Manning has two books out – *Crucify Me Again* (Codex) and *Get Your Cock Out* (Attack). He is still Zodiac Mondwarp occasionally. Visit him at www.zodiac-mindwarp.com

Edwin Marney is an illustrator who does work for dull computer, medical and business magazine

Simon McAuslane is a flâneur

Lorna Miller's *Bitch* is published by Slab-O-Concete. Her website is at www.lornamiller.com

David Mitchell is an artist

Jonathan Moberly is publishing publican at The Foundry and Ellipsis

Ben Moor is an actor, writer and comic

Michael Moorcock is one of the most prolific writers of his generation. He lives in Texas

John Moore is a jack of all trades

Jeff Noon's most recent novel is *Needle In The Groove*

Marcus Oakley is an illustrator who lives in Brixton and likes garibaldi biscuits

Stephen Pastel is a musician with the Pastels and operates the Geographic label with fellow Pastel Katrina Mitchell and Lawrence Bell of Domino

Woodrow Phoenix lives for crêpes and girls in nurses' hats

Vince Ray is a musician and illustrator

Tim Richardson is not sure how to describe himself

Gwyn Vaughn Roberts is a Cambridge-dweller

Steve Rose is film editor of the *Guardian Guide*

Greg Rowland plays keyboards and is on gregory@easynet.co.uk

Jock Scot is Jock Scot

Arthur Smith is a lovely man. He is writing a novel called *Pointless Hoax*

The League of Gentlemen are very funny

Louis Theroux is a journalist

Gwyn Vaughn Roberts lives in Cambridge

Walery can be found drawing people in Piccadilly Circus

Chris Watson is an illustrator whose site www.cwinc.co.uk is coming soon

Raymond Weekes's work has appeared in *New Eden* and *Time Out*. He's on raymondweekes@hotmail.com

Ged Wells is Insane. See him at www.insane.org.uk

Tony White is the *Idler*'s Lit Ed and author of three novels including, most recently, *Charlieunclenorfolktango* (Codex)